ROCKS FOR CROPS:
Agrominerals of sub-Saharan Africa.

Peter van Straaten

University of Guelph,
Guelph, Ontario
Canada

2002

Forewords

I am delighted to see the publishing of a book on a totally new subject, *Rocks for Crops: Agrominerals of sub-Saharan Africa*. It is seldom that geologists and agricultural scientists get together in such an effort. Sub-Sahara Africa is the only remaining region in the world where hundreds of millions of people go to bed hungry every night because of insufficient food production. Soil fertility depletion has been identified as the fundamental biophysical root cause for hunger in Africa. One of the most sensible ways of re-plenishing soil fertility is the use of available natural resources, and phosphate rocks are one attractive alternative for replenishing phosphorus in soils that have been depleted of this nutrient. Peter van Straaten's book, based on years of exploration and analysis, has identified a large number of small, indigenous phosphate deposits in 48 countries of sub-Sahara Africa. Many of these deposits are of sufficiently high quality to be used for direct application. The success of phosphate rock applications in the main farming areas of East Africa has helped increase crop yields by large amounts. When used in combination with leguminous tree fallows that fix atmospheric nitrogen, farmers are able to replenish the productivity of their soils using resources naturally available in Africa. This is a great contribution to overcoming hunger and opening the way for sustainable food production in Africa in ways that enhance their natural resource base.

Pedro A. Sanchez
Visiting Professor-ESPM
Center for Sustainable Resource Development
University of California, Berkeley, USA
Previously:
Director General
International Centre for Research in Agroforestry (ICRAF)
Nairobi, Kenya

It gives me great pleasure to write this preface for Professor van Straaten's book, *Rocks for Crops: Agrominerals of sub-Saharan Africa*. Developing countries, particularly those of sub-Saharan Africa, are facing a crisis of enormous proportions – their population has doubled twice since 1960, and per capita food production has declined over the same period, in spite of all of the developmental efforts over this period. At least part of the problem is declining soil fertility; since we are not replacing many of the chemical constituents that are required for agriculture, we are essentially mining the soil. Worldwide, billions of people suffer from malnutrition. We hear of the global crisis of 'food security,' a problem that in many regions is growing because of climate change related to the fact that we have changed the atmosphere of our planet.

What factors determine food security, food quality? First come the natural factors – soil quality, climate stability, water quality and quantity – and to these we may add modern agri-technology (e.g. tillage cultivation). We have growing problems related to soil erosion, over-irrigation, nutrient deficiencies, etc.

I was born on a farm near the Southern Alps of New Zealand. Our soils were rich, being derived in large part from volcanic rocks that formed the Alps along their great fault systems. These young soils were full of unweathered minerals capable of slowly releasing nutrients over a long period of time as they were broken down. Later I worked with colleagues in Brazil in many warm regions with heavy rainfall and no recent rock additives. These laterite soils were deficient in a host of components and have low bioproductivity. Such soils are common in many of the tropical and sub-tropical regions of the world, particularly those where food production is a problem. It is interesting to compare the low productivity of such regions with that of areas where the soils are derived from recent volcanism, such as Hawaii.

I remember the area of New Zealand where the sheep were dying for no obvious reasons – there was plenty of food. Then it was discovered that the soils were deficient in the element cobalt. It is well known that cobalt is needed for our immune systems. More recent data on this subject comes from a publication by W. Mertz, in *Science*, 1981, vol. 213, p. 1332, 'The Essential Trace Elements.' The list is very large. One need only look at recent vitamin pills (I, Cu, Mn, Cr, Mo, Zn....). Another example is provided by E.I. Stcifcl, *Science*, 996, vol. 272, where he showed that the process that accounts for much of natural nitrogen fixation in soils requires molybdenum. In many soils adding a trace of Mo would reduce the need for nitrogen fertilizers. And again, I return to Brazil where on a property in the hills near Rio de Janeiro, I once observed a region where trees had been planted several years before. Most of the soils came from granite but where there were basalts, the trees were ten times larger. All forms of life need a complex array of mineral nutrients and where the soils are poor and subsistence agriculture has been practiced for a long period of time, many of these nutrients are simply no longer in the soils.

This book provides a unique source of resource information on rocks and minerals that are available in sub-Saharan Africa for use in agriculture. This inventory is based on published and unpublished geological information of agrominerals from 48 countries in sub-Saharan Africa. The geological data base and the description of these vital resources is compiled in a systematic and thorough manner from a resource based point of view. But the author is not only a geologist. He provides us with valuable information on agricutural research conducted with some of the minerals and rocks locally available in sub-Saharan Africa. The book with its extensive and up-to-date references is an excellent starting point for integrated agricultural research and development work in sub-Saharan Africa, for soil scientists, geoscientists, engineers and extension officers. I congratulate Professor van Straaten, yes Rocks and Crops are related! The concept of agrogeology certainly needs more recognition and we must do more to foster trans-disciplinary research and development to tackle our environmental problems and address issues of food security. Soil remediation is critical to the global problem of food security.

There is a great and urgent need to quantify the relations between rocks, climate, soils and food security. And we need new approaches for soil remediation, not just the use of chemical fertilizers, which we know are often unavailable to the subsistence farmers of the developing world and which were designed as nutrient inputs for the highly-mechanized agriculture and soils of the developed world. And finally we must all ask ourselves the question, will we leave the planet in good order for those who will follow?

I very much liked a recent book published for schools by the British journal, *The Ecologist*. The book *Go M.A.D., Go Make a Difference*, is concerned with daily ways to save the planet. We must! And using the right 'rocks' on the right 'crops' certainly has the potential to make a real difference to food production where it is most needed – in the poorer countries of the developing world.

W.S. Fyfe
Professor Emeritus,
Dept. of Earth Sciences
University of Western Ontario
London, Ontario
Canada

Acknowledgements

This book is the follow-up result of a report commissioned by the United Nations Revolving Fund for Natural Resources Exploration (UNRFNRE) in 1999. My foremost thanks go to Mr. George Nooten, former Officer-in-Charge of the (now defunct) UNRFNRE, for his vision and encouragement to write this book. My sincere thanks are extended to Professor Pedro Sanchez, former Director General of the International Centre for Research in Agroforestry (ICRAF), now University of California, Berkeley, USA, and Dr. Bashir Jama (ICRAF Headquarters, Nairobi), who enthusiastically support the 'rocks for crops' approach and who were instrumental in getting financial support to publish this book.

There are many persons who assisted in sourcing primary geological literature as well as providing information on agricultural results. They include: Eng. Kavungo de Oliveira Marlon, Angola; Dr. G. Nziguheba, Catholic University of Leuven, Belgium; Dr. G. Chartry, Dr. Luc Tack and Dr. K. Theunissen, all from the Musée Royal de l'Afrique Centrale, Tervuren, Belgium; Dr. M. Hanon, Belgium; Mr. Sissay Abera, Canada; Dr. W. Chesworth, Dr. L. Evans and Mr. P. Smith of the University of Guelph, Canada; Dr. Calvin Pride, Canada; Mr. Derek Smith, Canada; Ms. M-C Ward from WGM, Canada; Ms. Karine Legér, Paris, France; Dr. J. Paul, Dr. D. Puhan, and Dr. A. Schmidt, all at the Geology Department, University of Göttingen, Germany; Mr. W. Schäfer, Germany; Dr. Thomas Schlüter, UNESCO, Nairobi, Kenya; Dr. André Bationo, Nairobi, Kenya; Dr. D. Friesen, Nairobi, Kenya; Mr. Kyaunguti and Mr. J. Mailu, ICRAF, Maseno, Kenya; Mr. Jeremiah Maroko, Mr. Peter (Vic) Mbugua, Mr. S. Ngoze, and Dr. P. Smithson, ICRAF, Nairobi, Kenya; Dr. T. Razakamanana, Toliari, Madagascar; Mr. L. Kalindekafe, Malawi; Dr. Amadou Niang, ICRAF, Bamako/Mali; Ms. Fatima Nomade and Mr. Geraldo Valoi, Mozambique; Dr. Saidou Koala, ICRISAT, Niamey, Niger; Dr. Roland Buresh, IRRI, Phillipines; Dr. Nellie Mutemeri and Dr. Paul Jourdan, MINTEK, South Africa; Mr. J. Tuhumwire and Mr. N. Wolukawu, Uganda; Dr. M. Abdelsalam, President Geological Society of Africa, Dallas, USA; Dr. A. Diop, Rodale Institute, USA; Dr. Moctar Touré (World Bank); Dr. R. Fernandes and Dr. O. Mapongo, Institute of Mining Research, University of Zimbabwe. Special thanks are extended to Professor Emeritus William (Bill) Fyfe, former Dean of Science, University of Western Ontario, Canada, and former President of the International Union of Geological Sciences (1992-1996) for valuable comments, advice and support. And also to the late Dr. G. Gabert of Germany, *asante sana*.

My gratitude is extended to Ms. Paula Cypas, University of Guelph, Canada, who meticulously drafted the first set of maps and Mr. Adam Reeb, student at the University of Guelph, who sourced and checked references as well as assisted with details of the text and maps. Thanks also go to Ms. Susan Robertson, University of Guelph, who gave the book its final touches and the index. My special thanks are extended to Mr. Steven Sadura, University of Guelph, who was the solid 'anchor' for this project, never tired of reworking information and finally putting the text and drawings together. His editorial assistance is gratefully acknowledged. Finally, I am very thankful to my wife 'Twiga' Ellen, and our sons, Oliver Tembo and Jos Kibo for their encouragement and patience.

The International Centre for Research in Agroforestry (ICRAF), now re-named into World Agroforestry Centre, and the Rockefeller Foundation supported the publication of this book. Joint field work with researchers of ICRAF was inspirational and provided me with an excellent trans-disciplinary experience.

To the Rockefeller Foundation I am very thankful for financing the production of this book. In particular, I wish to acklowledge the support by Dr. J. Lynam, Rockefeller Foundation, Nairobi.

Scientists in nationally and internationally supported projects have collected most of the data presented in this book. Sources of information include also data from agrogeological projects in sub-Saharan Africa supported by the International Development Research Centre (IDRC), and the University of Guelph.

Table of Contents

List of Abbreviations

Å	1 Ångstrom = 10^{-10} m
Al	Aluminum
As	Arsenic
B	Boron
BRGM	Bureau de Recherches Géologiques Minières
Ca	Calcium
Cd	Cadmium
CEC	Cation exchange capacity
Cl	Chlorine
Co	Cobalt
COFAN	Companhia de Fosfatos de Angola
CSPT	Compagnie Sénégalaise des Phosphates de Taiba
Cu	Copper
DAP	Di-ammonium phosphate
DGSM	Department of Geological Surveys and Mines (Uganda)
DMGH	Direcion des Mines de la Géologie et des Hydrocarbons (Benin)
DRC	Democratic Republic of Congo (formerly Zaire)
EIGS	Ethiopian Institute of Geological Surveys
F	Fluorine
FAO	Food and Agriculture Organization of the United Nations
Fe	Iron
FMP	Fused Magnesium Phosphate
GDP	Gross Domestic Product
GFSA	Goldfields of South Africa
GTZ	German Technical Cooperation
H	Hydrogen
ha	Hectare
ICRAF	International Centre for Research in Agroforestry
ICRISAT	International Crops Research Institute for Semi-Arid Tropics
ICS	Industrie Chimiques du Sénégal
IDC	Industrial Development Corporation (South Africa)
IDRC	International Development Research Centre
IFDC	International Fertilizer Development Center
K	Potassium
KARI	Kenya Agricultural Research Institute
LREE	Light rare earth elements
MAP	Mono-ammonium phosphate

MCP	Monocalcium phosphate
Mg	Magnesium
MINDECO	Mineral Development Corporation (Zambia)
MINEX	Mineral Exploration (Zambia)
Mo	Molybdenum
MPR	Mussoorie phosphate rock (India)
N	Nitrogen
NAC solubility	Neutral ammonium citrate solubility
O	Oxygen
OTP	Office Togolaise des Phosphates
P	Phosphorus
PAPR	Partially acidulated phosphate rock
PMC Ltd.	Palaborwa Mining Company Ltd. (South Africa)
ppm	Parts per million
PR	Phosphate rock
RAE	Relative agronomic effectiveness
REE	Rare earth elements
RMRDC	Raw Materials Research and Development Council (Nigeria)
RUDIS	Yugoslav Mining Association
S	Sulphur
SEM	Scanning electron microscope
SOTOMA	Société Togolaise de Marbrerie et Matériaux
SSP	Single superphosphate
SSPT	Société Sénégalaise des Phosphates de Taiba
STAMICO	State Mining Company (Tanzania)
TSP	Triple superphosphate
UNDP	United Nations Development Programme
UNRFNRE	United Nations Revolving Fund for Natural Resources Exploration
VOD	Vermiculite Operations Department of PMC Ltd. (South Africa)
XRD	X-ray diffraction
XRF	X-ray fluorescence
Zn	Zinc

Part 1. Rocks for Crops

1.   Introduction.

A productive and sustainable agricultural system is fundamental to the well being of a nation and a cornerstone of its development. In most of sub-Saharan Africa, more than 50% of the population rely on agriculture for their livelihood, which generally contributes more than 30% of the Gross Domestic Product (GDP). Agriculture is the major source of income, employment, food security and survival for the majority of the population. While agricultural production is steadily increasing in sub-Saharan Africa, the population is growing faster than food production. The result is a net decline in per-capita food production, which contributes to increased food deficits and poverty. A high proportion of African farmers are resource-poor in terms of capital, land, labour and livestock and about one-half of the population is classified as 'absolute poor' with per capita incomes of less than US $1 per day. Life expectancy in parts of Africa is very low. For example, in Guinea-Bissau, Madagascar, Malawi, Rwanda, Sierra Leone, Uganda, and Zambia, life expectancies at birth are less than 42 years. As well, sub-Saharan Africa has the highest proportion of undernourished children in the world.

The rural population in most of sub-Saharan Africa relies on soils and rain for life-supporting agricultural production. Soils are the basis for survival, food security, and employment, but in much of Africa the soils are over-exploited. For soil fertility to be sustainable, exported soil nutrients must equal imported soil nutrients. But in large areas of Africa more soil nutrients are exported than replenished. As a consequence, soils are 'mined' (Van der Pol 1993). In addition, large areas have not been protected from erosion and soils have been washed away from farmers' fields. Over the last few decades, soil productivity has steadily declined. The annual soil depletion rate in sub-Saharan Africa, 22 kg of nitrogen (N), 2.5 kg of phosphorus (P) and 15 kg of potassium (K) per hectare of cultivated land per year, is equivalent to US $4 billion in fertilizer (Sanchez 2002). This decreasing soil quality is regarded by many scientists as the fundamental biophysical cause for the downward trend of food production in sub-Saharan Africa (Sanchez *et al.* 1997; Sanchez 2002).

The need for sustaining agricultural productivity over a long period of time calls for effective resource management practices including sound soil, water and nutrient management. To meet the food challenges that face sub-Saharan Africa, major efforts must to be made at all levels of society; individual, communal, national and international. The well-being of future generations is increasingly linked with sustainable development and food security, and access for all to sufficient and nutritious food is the key to poverty reduction.

To increase soil productivity, food production and food security, farmers have to not only increase soil nutrient concentrations but also improve the structure of the soil, and reduce soil losses. The utilization of manures and other local nutrient inputs is one of the strategies of effective resource management. Use of imported water-soluble fertilizers is another management practice that can replenish soil nutrients. However, the use of these externally-produced nutrient inputs by resource-poor farmers is constrained by high costs (Sanchez 2002), and poor availability. In addition, macro-economic policy changes in the 1990s resulted in 'structural adjustment programs' with subsequent liberalization of crop and input prices, abolition of commercial fertilizer subsidies and other measures. In reality, these policies resulted in reduced use of imported water-soluble fertilizers. Regional fertilizer use per hectare is extremely low in sub-Saharan Africa. On average less than 5 kg of water-soluble mineral fertilizers per hectare are applied to food crops in sub-Saharan Africa (Quiñones *et al.* 1997), which are the lowest application rates in the world.

The need to reduce poverty, increase food security and protect the environment requires substantially more and broader efforts and innovation than simply the improvement of soil quality and food production. Sanchez and Leakey (1997) point out three important requirements to increase per capita agricultural production for smallholder farmers, including enabling policies and improved infrastructural environment (including access to education and health facilities, credits, inputs, markets and extension services), reversal of soil fertility depletion, as well as intensification and diversification of land use with high-value products.

Most soils related research and development efforts (including this one) focus on technical issues. But non-technical factors (mainly social, economic and political) are important as well. The situation on farms is complex and simple resource-based 'fixes' are rare to find and apply. The addition of soil nutrients should be seen as only one of the building blocks of integrated locally adapted soil fertility management.

Agricultural nutrient inputs include manures, fertilizers, and geological resources ('agrominerals') with the potential to enhance soil productivity. Agrominerals are naturally occurring geological materials in both unprocessed and processed forms that can be used in crop production systems to enhance soil productivity. Agrominerals include geological materials that contain one or more recognized plant nutrients and so-called 'rock fertilizers' (Benetti 1983; Appleton 1990), sometimes called 'petrofertilizers' (Mathers 1994; Leonardos *et al.* 1987, 2000), which are ground rocks of different compositions.

The term 'agromineral' is used here in a very broad sense. It includes naturally occurring nutrient-providing rocks and minerals such as phosphate rocks, nitrogen and potassium salts, as well as other nutrient-providing rocks. It also includes 'soil amendments' including agricultural limestone and dolomite, and various ground silicate rocks. Some of these natural geological resources are only moderately soluble in the short term but can release their nutrient content into the soil over long periods of time as 'slow-release' nutrient inputs. Agrominerals also include rocks and minerals that improve the physical status of soils. For example, perlite is used to enhance aeration in artificial growth media in greenhouses, vermiculite and zeolite are minerals able to store and release nutrients and moisture slowly, and volcanic scoria and pumice and other rocks are used as 'rock mulch' to reduce evaporation.

Conventional, chemically processed 'industrial' fertilizers are largely water-soluble and contain high and immediately available nutrient concentrations. Except for some nitrogen-based fertilizers, almost all of them are chemically processed rocks. They are derived from geological materials and have been chemically modified. In contrast, agrominerals are commonly only physically modified, by crushing and grinding. There are however some 'hybrid' rock and mineral modification techniques that use various amounts of chemicals in combination with agrominerals; for example, partially acidulated phosphate rocks (PAPR) or phosphate rocks mixed with acidulating triple superphosphates (TSP).

To date, national and international earth science institutions have mainly compiled mineral resource data for metals, with less emphasis being extended to industrial minerals. One exception is the internationally supported program to compile geological data on the phosphate resources of the world (Notholt *et al.* 1989). Another is the account of limestone resources in Africa, compiled by Bosse *et al.* (1996). In general, however, data on agromineral resources are scattered, and a comprehensive overview of all geological nutrient assets that could enhance crop production in sub-Saharan Africa is necessary.

The purpose of this book is twofold: firstly, to summarize the potential role that rocks and minerals can play in sustaining and enhancing soil productivity and biomass production, and secondly to provide an inventory of known agromineral resources, on a country-by-country basis, for 48 countries in Africa south of the Sahara.

2.   Agrominerals and farming.

With the exception of nitrogen, all plant nutrient resources for farming systems are of geological provenance. In natural systems, nitrogen is 'harvested' from the air by legumes or through N-fixing organisms and recycled in the soil. Other nutrients critical for plant growth, like P and K, Ca, Mg, S and micronutrients are supplied by geological resources – rocks. Weathering of these rocks, as well as organic inputs, atmospheric deposition, and re-sedimentation of soil materials eroded from upper slopes, supplies most of the nutrients essential for plant growth.

Under natural climatic conditions the physical breakup, chemical weathering and release rate of nutrients from minerals is not fast enough to provide nutrients for annual crop production. In the past, soils were given rest periods to recover and naturally replenish after periods of cultivation and harvesting. But these fallow periods have been shortened in recent years or even abandoned due to increasing pressure on the land base. These days, the soil is given no rest. Continuous cultivation, however, requires continuous replenishment of soil nutrients. It has been widely recognized that the removal of nutrients from soils through repeated harvesting, leaching, gaseous and losses and runoff and erosion is too high to retain enough soil nutrients in the soil for sustained crop production. The result is that soils are 'mined.' Van der Pol (1992), Stoorvogel *et al.* (1993), Smaling *et al.* (1993, 1997), and Smaling (1995) presented nutrient balances of the cultivated land base in various parts of sub-Saharan Africa. The calculations of nutrient 'stocks' and 'flows' indicate that sub-Saharan Africa is losing 4.4 million tonnes of N, 500,000 tonnes of P, and 3 million tonnes of K every year through nutrient depletion.

To correct the imbalance between soil nutrient exports and imports it is necessary to replenish nutrients that have been removed or lost. If not replenished, soil fertility will decrease and result in continuous loss of capacity to support plant growth. This will have dire consequences and lead to increased food insecurity and poverty.

To sustain crop production, soils need replenishment of nutrients through inputs such as manures, water-soluble fertilizers or some other alternative inputs. Although most smallholder farmers in Africa appreciate the value of water-soluble fertilizers, they can rarely afford them. Often, if fertilizers are available, farmers are unable to apply them at recommended rates and at the appropriate time. Fertilizer imports have been hampered in many parts of the developing world by the scarcity of foreign exchange, political problems, civil wars, transport problems, and other challenges. In addition, farmers often get low prices for their agricultural products, leaving them with little or no incentive to increase crop production.

In many parts of Africa, farmers depend on local resources and natural processes to replenish soil fertility, and instead of spending their savings on expensive, mainly imported water-soluble fertilizers, they resort to alternative ways of accessing vital plant nutrient resources. They utilize organic materials like manure and plant material, for example. In parts of sub-Saharan Africa, replenishment strategies for nitrogen have been successful though improved fallow and crop-fallow rotation practices (Sanchez *et al.* 1997; Sanchez and Jama 2000). But these organic resources generally have low nutrient contents, especially phosphorus, and they are bulky. To substantially increase the inflow of new nutrients other than the ones provided by organic matter, farmers could add locally available agromineral resources. Some agrominerals occur naturally in concentrations and forms that can be used as alternative fertilizers or soil amendments. 'Reactive' sedimentary phosphate rock (PR), potash, gypsum, dolomite, limestone, and various other minerals fall in this category. In other cases, mineral resources do not occur in a form that is directly available to crops and must be modified physically, chemically and biologically to become effective nutrient sources for soils and crops. For other agromineral resources, such as ground silicate rocks, large quantities of rock material are needed to be agronomically effective (Roschnik *et al.* 1967; Gillman 1980; Gillman *et al.* 2000; Harley and Gilkes 2000).

Due to substantial cuts in external aid and fertilizer subsidies, many developing countries rely more and more on their own nutrient resources and it is important to know the indigenous agromineral resources available to support a viable and sustainable rural agricultural economy.

The development process must be viewed as a long-term goal. Short- and medium-term solutions like the import of fertilizers can have positive short-term impacts on food security, but this is only a partial solution to national independence from foreign agricultural inputs. The disruption of fertilizer supplies by economic, political and other pressures can seriously impede the development and livelihood of rural inhabitants. It is therefore imperative to live and work within these limitations and not proceed as if these constraints do not exist (Pride and van Straaten 1993).

3. Agrogeology, an emerging trans-disciplinary science.

The use of rocks and minerals as low-cost, locally available geological nutrient resources for agricultural development is not new. It has been tested over centuries. Agricultural research with finely ground and chemically unprocessed rocks and minerals, based on the concept of 'bread from stones,' started in the 19th century by Missoux (1853/54), Hensel (1890, 1894) and others. A period of conceptual and practical work on rocks for agricultural development re-started with Keller (1948), Keller *et al.* (1963) followed by the research of Fyfe and co-workers (Fyfe 1981, 1987, 1989, 2000; Fyfe *et al.* 1983; Leonardos *et al.* 1987, 2000) and Chesworth and co-workers (Chesworth 1982, 1987, 1993; Chesworth *et al.* 1983, 1985; van Straaten 1987; van Straaten and Chesworth 1985; van Straaten and Pride 1993). In the early 1980s the first trans-disciplinary 'agrogeology' project receiving major funding was the Tanzania-Canada agrogeology project, financed by the International Development Research Centre (Chesworth *et al.* 1985, 1989).

Agrogeology is broadly defined as 'geology in the service of agriculture,' a study of geological processes that influence the distribution and formation of soils, and the application of geological materials in farming and forestry systems as means of maintaining and enhancing soil productivity for increased social, economic and environmental benefits (Chesworth and van Straaten 1993; van Straaten and Fernandes 1995). This trans-disciplinary approach combines the knowledge of soil scientists and farmers with that of geologists and process engineers. Soil scientists define the soil limitations and needs, geologists find, delineate and characterize the geological raw materials that address those needs and process engineers contribute by concentrating the agrominerals and transforming them into more plant available forms. Processing technology is to be kept at an appropriate level to reflect the size, grade, location and end use of the raw material. A close liaison between geologists, process engineers and soil scientists must be kept throughout the exploration, development process and testing, as is the active participation of extension officers and farmers. In the agrogeological approach, communication, consultations and interactions between the different stakeholders are crucial. Farmers and other beneficiaries should be closely involved in agromineral utilization projects from the early phases of design to implementation, to modification and finally to the enjoyment of the benefits. They will utilize these agromineral materials to sustain food and fibre production for the benefit of their families, their communities and society as a whole.

Farmers have adapted their production systems over periods of time lasting much longer than a scientific experiment, and have often preserved indigenous knowledge of soils. This knowledge of soil productivity is often passed on from generation to generation orally. Traditional management systems often exhibit considerable elements of sustainability. These agricultural management systems are commonly adapted to their specific environment and climate, they rely on local resources, they are small-scale and decentralized, and in many cases they tend to conserve the natural resource base. To improve on the effectiveness of these systems, the option of using locally available geological nutrient resources needs to be tested. The option to use locally available geological materials must fit into the existing socio-cultural system to be successful.

4. Enhancing soil productivity with agrominerals.

Many of the problems of tropical agriculture originate in the nature of soils (Sanchez 1976). Tropical soils commonly have inherently low fertilities. They have been exposed to long periods of weathering, which results in highly depleted soils with low organic matter, low cation exchange capacities, and an overall low inherent fertility. Common tropical soils, such as oxisols and ultisols, are acid, and have low N and P status. Over-cropping and/or inappropriate use of fertilizers can accentuate the soil related problems and can result in poor soil productivity and low crop yields.

Existing agromineral resource inventories have been compiled in many countries, but have concentrated mainly on large deposits. There are however many more deposits in the world that have not been developed, most of them being of medium to small size.

The best known agrominerals are:

- saltpeter, the only naturally occurring nitrate mineral that occurs in sizable deposits,
- phosphate rocks (PRs) with apatite as the principle phosphate mineral,
- guano minerals, complex P- and N-bearing compounds,
- potash, mainly sylvite (KCl), and complex K-bearing salts,
- K-silicates, such as K-micas, glauconites, and K-bearing volcanic rocks and K-zeolites,
- sulphur, sulphides (e.g. pyrite) and sulphates (e.g. gypsum),
- calcium and magnesium carbonates,
- various silicate minerals and rocks used to conserve nutrients (e.g. zeolite) or used to conserve soil moisture (e.g. scoria and pumice).

Rocks and minerals are used in crop production systems for several purposes, among them:

- improving soil fertility,
- correcting the pH of soil,
- conserving nutrients and water.

At present, the main nutrient limiting factors in sub-Saharan Africa soils are nitrogen (N) and phosphorus (P). While nitrogen can be introduced to the soil through various organic inputs, including manures, plant and tree prunings, and leguminous mulches, there is no equivalent process to nitrogen fixation for the introduction of P into the farming system. Phosphorus can be supplied in small amounts through organic residues and by-products, but the amount is generally insufficient to meet crop demand (Palm 1995; Sanchez and Palm 1996). Phosphorus must be added to the depleted soils in a concentrated form, either as P-containing fertilizers or locally available phosphate rocks.

4.1 Phosphate rocks

Most of the world's phosphate fertilizers are produced from phosphate rock (PR) resources and almost all of these resources contain some form of the mineral apatite. There are many PR deposits and occurrences in sub-Saharan Africa. Detailed accounts of these resources are described in the second part of this book in the country profiles. To furnish a general overview of known phosphate resources, general maps with the distribution of known sedimentary and igneous and metamorphic P resources are provided in Figures 1.1. and 1.2.

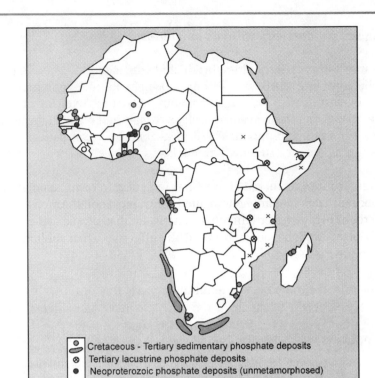

Figure 1.1: Distribution of known sedimentary phosphate rock deposits in sub-Saharan Africa.

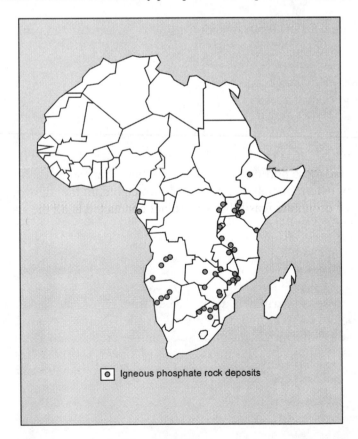

Figure 1.2: Distribution of known igneous and metamorphic phosphate rock deposits in sub-Saharan Africa.

4.1.1 Factors affecting agronomic performance of phosphate rocks

Soil acidity with associated Al toxicity, as well as P and Ca deficiencies, are common growth-limiting factors in highly leached tropical soils. Typically, low crop yields occur on strongly nutrient depleted acid oxisols and ultisols. To overcome the specific P nutrient deficiency in soils, various forms of P are applied. Inorganic P sources applied to the soils range from processed phosphate rocks (P-fertilizers) to ground phosphate rocks and slightly modified forms of phosphate rock. The use of commercial P-fertilizers, initially designed for soils in the northern hemisphere (Leonardos *et al.* 1987), is often not cost effective on these strongly depleted weathered soils of the tropics, as the phosphate ions are easily 'sorbed' by aluminum and iron oxide minerals. It has long been recognized that major efforts are needed to develop phosphate fertilizers that are better suited for tropical soils. Among the alternative P-sources are local phosphate rock (PR) resources, but this route is not that simple and easy. Not all of the PR resources are readily plant-available and agronomically effective when applied directly to the soils. The effectiveness of PR-resources varies and is influenced by various factors. The main factors that affect the agronomic effectiveness of PRs in soils are outlined below.

4.1.2 Rock factors

Types of phosphate rocks

Phosphate rock (PR) is a globally accepted but imprecise term describing any naturally occurring geological material that contains one or more phosphate minerals suitable for commercial use. The term comprises both the unprocessed phosphate ore as well as the concentrated phosphate products (Notholt and Highley 1986). In agricultural circles phosphate rocks are also called rock phosphates.

The various phosphate minerals present in PR have diverse origins and chemical and physical properties. The phosphorus content or grade of phosphate rocks is commonly reported as phosphorus pentoxide (P_2O_5). The principal phosphate minerals in PR are Ca-phosphates, mainly apatites. Pure fluor-apatite contains 42% P_2O_5, and francolite, the carbonate-substituted form of apatite, may contain 34% P_2O_5.

The differentiation of the terms 'resources' and 'reserves' is based on degree of geological assurance and the economic feasibility of extraction and processing. 'Resource' is the less specific term, and is defined as the concentrations of naturally occurring solid, liquid or gaseous materials in or on the Earth's crust in such form that economic extraction of a commodity is regarded as feasible, either currently or at some future time. Reserves are those portions of the resource base that can be economically and legally extracted at the time of determination, i.e. currently extractable. In the following, the less strict term 'resource' is used since economic feasibilities were not conducted at all the sites, and the reliability and interpretation of geological and economic data vary.

Five major types of phosphate resources are being mined in the world:

- marine phosphate deposits,
- igneous phosphate deposits,
- metamorphic deposits,
- biogenic deposits,
- phosphate deposits as a result of weathering.

Approximately 75% of the world's phosphate resources are won from sedimentary, marine phosphate rock deposits, 15-20% from igneous and weathered deposits, and only 1-2% from biogenic resources, largely bird and bat guano accumulations.

Different types of phosphate rocks have widely differing mineralogical, chemical and textural characteristics. While there are more than 200 known phosphate minerals, the main mineral group of phosphates is the group of apatites. Calcium-phosphates of the apatite group are mainly found in primary environments (in sedimentary, metamorphic and igneous rocks) but also in weathering environments. Other phosphates include minerals of the crandallite group, as well as variscite and strengite, which are Fe- and Al-containing phosphates principally found in secondary weathering environments.

Phosphate minerals occurring in the primary environment include:

- Fluor-apatite ($Ca_{10}(PO_4)_6F_2$), found mainly in igneous and metamorphic environments, for example, in carbonatites, and mica-pyroxenites,
- Hydroxy-apatite ($Ca_{10}(PO_4)_6(OH)_2$), found in igneous, metamorphic environments but also in biogenic deposits, e.g. in bone deposits,
- Carbonate-hydroxy-apatites ($Ca_{10}(PO_4,CO_3)_6(OH)_2$), found mainly on islands and in caves, as part of bird and bat excrements, guano,
- Francolite ($Ca_{10-x-y}Na_xMg_y(PO_4)_{6-z}(CO_3)_zF_{0.4z}F_2$). This complex, carbonate-substituted apatite is found mainly in marine environments, and, to a much smaller extent, also in weathering environments, for instance over carbonatites.

Methods used to identify and characterize these minerals include X-ray diffraction (XRD), X-ray fluorescence (XRF), scanning electron microscopy (SEM), infra-red methods, microprobe analysis, microscopic identification and measurement of refractive indices, and chemical analyses.

Parameters reported in many phosphate characterization studies include:

- unit-cell a-dimension (a-value), a crystallographic expression of the composition of the apatite composition. The a-cell dimension is expressed in Ångstrom ($1 \text{ Å} = 10^{-10} \text{ m}$),
- refractive index,
- solubility data based on chemical extraction methods, e.g. neutral ammonium citrate solubility (NAC) (Chien and Hammond 1978; MacKay et al. 1984),
- PO_4/CO_3 ratio as a measure of carbonate substitution in phosphate minerals,
- surface area (expressed in $m^2 g^{-1}$) indicating potential reactivity (Wilson and Ellis 1984).

Reactivity of phosphate rocks

Naturally occurring phosphate rocks (PRs) differ widely in their mineralogy and chemistry. The chemical reactivity or solubility of phosphate rocks is a measure of the PR's ability to release P for plant uptake. Reactivity is defined by Rajan et al. (1996) as 'the combination of PR properties that determines the rate of dissolution of the PR in a given soil under given field conditions.' The reactivity of sedimentary phosphate rocks is relatively high compared to those of igneous and metamorphic origin. The fundamental difference lies in the crystal chemistry of apatite, specifically the degree of isomorphous substitution of phosphate by carbonate. It has been shown that the solubility of carbonate substituted phosphate rocks is higher than the solubility of pure fluor-apatite with little or no carbonate-substitution (Chien and Hammond 1978). Increasing carbonate substitution in the phosphate rock increases the ease of breakdown of the structure of the apatite thereby releasing P to the soil solution under acidic conditions. The chemical and mineralogical features are key factors in determining the reactivity and subsequent agronomic effectiveness of a given phosphate rock.

The crystal-chemical composition of apatites can be analyzed by several methods, including X-ray diffraction (XRD) analyses. The XRD patterns of apatites provide an array of peaks that are typical for the crystal-composition of the apatite. Slight shifts in the peak positions and intensities indicate shifts in the crystal chemistry of the mineral. Changes in composition of the mineral can be determined by specific crystallographic parameters, for example the unit-cells of the crystallographic a-axis. Early work by Smith and Lehr (1966) and McClellan and Lehr (1969) established the relationship between changes in the apatite crystal chemistry, specifically substitution in the apatite, and the so-called unit-cell a-values. Briefly, apatites with a-values between 9.370 and 9.420 Å (Ångstrom) are not francolites but belong to a series of fluor- to hydroxy-apatites. Typical crystallographic and optical properties for francolites and fluor-apatites to hydroxy-apatites are given below. It should be noted that the unit-cell a-values of francolites change with the degree of carbonate substitution. Francolites with the highest carbonate substitution have unit-cell a-values of 9.320, francolites with the lowest carbonate substitution have unit-cell a-values of 9.369 (Van Kauwenbergh 1995). There is a clear relationship between carbonate substitution and the unit-cell a-values in sedimentary francolites and solubility: The lower the unit-cell a-value the higher the 'reactivity' and solubility. For example, the Tilemsi phosphate rock (Tilemsi PR) from Mali with a unit-cell a-value of 9.331 has a high 'reactivity,' while the Hahotoe PR from Togo has a unit-cell a-value of 9.354 and a relatively low reactivity. The lower the unit-cell a-value the better the francolite is suited for direct application in acid soils.

Low solubility fluor-apatites have unit-cell a-values of around 9.370, and hydroxy-apatites have a-cell parameters around 9.420. Details of the relationships between the a-cell parameters and the various substitutions in the crystal-chemistry of apatites is documented in Smith and Lehr (1966), McClellan and Lehr (1969), Van Kauwenbergh and McClellan (1990), and Van Kauwenbergh (1995).

Apart from the crystal-chemical characteristics analyzed by XRD, there are other rock factors that influence the effectiveness of phosphate rock (PR) application to soils. Some of these factors are inter-related.

The main factors are:

- mineralogy and chemistry of PR,
- reactivity/solubility of PR,
- grain size and surface area,
- chemical and physical status of the soil, especially pH, moisture holding capacity, P and Ca status, and P-fixing capacity of the soil,
- type of crops and their nutrient requirements,
- management practices including method and time of application, and liming.

The raw materials used for commercial phosphate fertilizer production are mainly of sedimentary, igneous and biogenic origin. The most extensive of these PR resources are mined and processed in large-scale operations in North Africa (Morocco and Tunisia), the United States, Jordan, Russia, China and other countries. The phosphate rocks are concentrated and then chemically processed with sulphuric and phosphoric acid into soluble phosphate fertilizers such as single superphosphates (SSP), and triple superphosphates (TSP), as well as mono-ammonium phosphates (MAP) and di-ammonium phosphates (DAP).

There are many phosphate deposits in the world that have not yet been found or developed, most of which are medium to small size. Small PR deposits are common and exist in almost every region of the world. Sheldon (1987) contends that 'small phosphate rock deposits are one to two orders of magnitude more abundant than the large commercial ones but are mostly undiscovered.' Considerable information exists on the geology and mineralogy of the large phosphate deposits. Reasons for not developing more of the smaller, locally available resources vary from unfavourable geographic locations to uneconomic agronomic returns to lack of processing technologies, and other reasons.

Phosphate rocks with high relative reactivity are best suited for direct application to acid soils with low Ca and P concentrations. Examples of high to medium 'reactive' phosphate rock resources that do not need any further modification, apart from fine grinding, are those of Mali (Tilemsi PR), Tanzania (Minjingu PR), Nigeria (Sokoto) and Niger (Tahoua PR), and, if confirmed, the ones from Cabinda in Angola, and the Republic of Congo (Holle PR).

There is no generally accepted classification system for grading phosphate rocks for direct application. Many scientists rate the phosphate rock quality according to their mineralogical, chemical properties. Apart from crystallographic parameters such as the unit-cell a-values, there are other important mineralogical and physical parameters that influence the solubility of minerals, such as their surface area, measured in $m^2 g^{-1}$. With regard to chemical solubility, Hammond and Leon (1983) proposed a system of four solubility rankings (high, medium, low, and very low) largely based on laboratory work analyzing phosphate rock solubilities in extraction media. A widely accepted method is that of measuring phosphate rocks on their neutral ammonium citrate solubility. To illustrate the inherent chemical and mineralogical differences of phosphate rock concentrates from sub-Saharan phosphate deposits the crystallographic-mineralogical a-cell parameters and chemical data on neutral ammonium solubility, as well as specific surface area of phosphate rock concentrates from sub-Saharan Africa are summarized in tables 1.1 and 1.2.

Table 1.1: Crystallographic parameters and chemical solubility of various phosphate rock concentrates of sub-Saharan Africa.

	a-cell (in Å)	Neutral ammonium citrate solubility (% of total P_2O_5).
Bikilal (Ethiopia)	9.394	
Busumbu (Uganda)		2.3
Cabinda (Angola)		4.5
Chilembwe (Zambia)		1.0
Dorowa (Zimbabwe)		0.8
Hahotoe (Togo)	9.354	1.3 - 3.1
Holle (Congo Rep.)	9.3247	
Kodjari (Burkina Faso)	9.355	2.3
Kurun (Sudan)		4.5
Langebaan (South Africa)	9.364	
Matam (Senegal)		4.5
Matongo (Burundi)		1.6
Mekrou (Benin)		1.9
Minjingu (Tanzania)		5.6-12.9
Panda (Tanzania)	9.387	
Parc W (Niger)	9.354	1.4-2.8
Rangwa (Kenya)	9.380	
Sokoto (Nigeria)	9.353	3.1-3.9
Sukulu (Uganda)		1.6
Tahoua (Niger)	9.351	1.9-3.6
Taiba (Senegal)	9.354	3.1
Tilemsi (Mali)	9.331	4.2
Tundulu (Malawi)	9.357	1.6

Sources: McClellan and Notholt 1986, and various other sources.

Table 1.2: Specific surface area of selected phosphate rocks of sub-Saharan Africa.

	Specific Surface Area $(m^2 g^{-1})$
Arly (Burkina Faso)	3.7
Hahotoe (Togo)	7.1
Kodjari (Burkina Faso)	7.1
Tahoua (Niger)	14.7
Taiba (Senegal)	5.4
Tilemsi (Mali)	26.4

Source: Truong and Montange 1998.

From the above data it can be seen that several phosphate rocks have relatively high inherent neutral ammonium citrate solubilities and reactivities while other PRs are relatively unreactive and require some form of modification to become agronomically more effective.

Apart from the composition and reactivity of the phosphate rocks there are other mineralogical, physical and chemical factors that can affect the apparent solubility of the phosphates. They include impurities such as calcite, dolomite and gypsum.

Sedimentary phosphates commonly have a higher specific surface area than igneous fluor-apatites (Table 1.2). In general, the PRs with the highest specific surface areas also have the highest citrate solubilities. These mineralogical factors provide prognostic information on the agronomic effectiveness of the phosphate rocks. As an example, the agronomic effectiveness of low carbonate-substituted and low specific surface area Togo PR is clearly inferior to the highly carbonate-substituted, high specific surface area Tilemsi PR from Mali. One way to increase the surface area is by grinding, which creates fresh surfaces that positively affect solubilities.

4.1.3 Soil factors

There are specific soil properties that influence the dissolution of apatite minerals in the phosphate rocks. They are:

- pH,
- CEC,
- Ca concentration,
- P concentration,
- P sorption capacity,
- organic matter content.

The dissolution of PR is enhanced in low pH soils following the equation of figure 1.3:

Figure 1.3: Simplified equation of apatite dissolution:

$$Ca_{10}(PO_4)_6F_2 + 12H^+ \Leftrightarrow 10\,Ca^{2+} + 6H_2PO_4^- + 2F^-$$

The driving and 'pushing' force for the dissolution of apatites is the neutralizing reaction between proton (H^+) ion concentrations and the apatites in PRs. The reaction is driven from left to right by increasing the H^+ ion concentrations (protonation/acidulation) in the soil. Many studies have shown that acid soils and acid generating processes, as well as inorganic and organic acids, all contribute to enhanced PR dissolution at low pH. The conditions of low pH, low exchangeable Ca and low P concentrations are common in many tropical, weathered soils. Acid soils are more conducive to PR dissolution than Ca^{2+} rich alkaline soils (Hammond *et al.* 1986b).

The law of mass action also indicates that apatite dissolution will be enhanced by decreasing the activity of Ca^{2+} or the P-species respectively. By decreasing the Ca^{2+} and/or P concentrations, the reaction will be 'pulled' from left to right. Since the goal is to enhance the P concentration in soils, a useful way to pull the dissolution reaction from left to right is by decreasing calcium ion concentrations in the soil solution.

Soil P-sorption capacities also effect the dissolution of PR. High P-sorbing soils such as oxisols and ultisols enhance the dissolution of PRs by reducing the P concentration in the immediate surrounding of the PR (Smyth and Sanchez 1982; Cabala-Rosand and Wild 1982a; Syers and MacKay 1986). Slow-release P-desorption from these soils might become important in the long term, 'turning a liability into an asset' (Sanchez *et al.* 1997).

Volcanic soils with the principal mineral allophane on the other hand are ultimate sinks of P with very low release rates. Field data from South America indicate that directly applied finely ground low reactivity PRs were more effective on soils with low P-sorption capacity than on volcanic soils (andisols) with high P-sorption capacity in comparison to TSP (Hammond *et al.* 1986a; Chien and Menon 1995).

Another factor that is closely related to the Ca status of soils is the soil cation exchange capacity (CEC), which in turn is commonly related to soil texture. Sandy soils with low CEC, for example, do not provide substantial Ca-sinks, hence the dissolution is slowed and the agronomic effectiveness reduced (Kanabo and Gilkes 1988).

The influence of organic matter on the dissolution of PR is related to the formation of Ca and organic matter complexes. By reducing Ca activity in the solution (Ca-sink) the phosphate rock dissolution will be increased. Hence, the higher the organic matter content in the soil the better the dissolution of the PR.

4.1.4 Crop factors

Crops vary in their ability to use P from PR sources mainly because the mobilizing capacity of P from various PRs varies with crop species.

The best known plants with relatively high P-mobilizing capacities are:

- Buckwheat (*Fagopyrum esculentum*),
- White sweet clover (*Melilotus albus*),
- Kale, or rape (*Brassica napus*),
- White Lupins (*Lupinus albus*),
- Cabbage (*Brassica oleracea*),
- Pigeon pea (*Cajanus cajan*).

Other legumes and some crops of the *Cruciferae* family are also effective in enhancing PR solubilization (Fried 1953; Khasawneh and Doll 1978; Flach *et al.* 1987; van Diest 1991). These plants enhance P solubilization from inorganic P sources by the excretion of organic acids from their roots. For example the roots of the leguminous pigeon pea (*Cajanus cajan*) release piscidic acid that can complex iron to enhance the availability of iron-bound phosphorus (Ae *et al.* 1990). Subsequent crops or intercropped sorghum for example can thus benefit from the increased availability of phosphorus. Other plants, like buckwheat (*Fagopyrum esculentum*) can enhance P uptake through high uptake of Ca (Fried 1953; van Ray and van Diest 1979; Flach *et al.* 1987; van Diest 1991). By lowering the concentration of Ca ions, the dissolution of apatite is enhanced. Acidification of the rhizosphere will also result in an increase in the rate of dissolution of apatite in the PR. P-deficient rapeseed plants (*Brassica napus*) acidify parts of their rhizosphere by exuding malic and citric acids (Hoffland *et al.* 1989a,b; Hoffland 1992) and can thus access the P pool of poorly soluble PR sources. The dissolution and uptake mechanisms include root exudation of various other acids and the formation of extensive fine root hairs, as well as uptake through mycorrhizae (Leyval and Berthelin 1989).

An example of P transfer from insoluble PR sources into biomass is shown by the tropical legume, cover and fodder crop *Pueraria javanica* (de Swart and van Diest 1987). With a small starter P application (priming effect) the solubilization of PR from Tilemsi (Mali) proceeded rapidly enough to supply sufficient P to the young *Pueraria* plant to start nodulation and N-fixation. The ensuing acidification of the rhizosphere resulted in further PR solubilization (de Swart and van Diest 1987).

4.1.5 Management factors.

Management practices, such as method of placement, timing of application and lime application can influence the effectiveness of PR or water-soluble P-fertilizer (Hellums 1991; Chien and Menon 1995).

The placement of PR in soils influences the rate of P release from PR. Studies in many parts of the world have shown that the method of broadcasting and incorporating the PR in the soil increases the effectiveness of PR. Banding of PR is less effective (Khasawneh and Doll 1978; Sale and Mokwunye 1993; Chien and Menon 1995).

Timing the application of PRs is important for their effective use. Cabalda-Rosand and Wild (1982a) demonstrated that the effectiveness of low soluble PR was enhanced when applied directly on acid soils well in advance of crop planting. It was expected that early application of PR would allow some time for dissolution to begin. However, when applied to high P-sorbing soils the effectiveness was actually reduced when the PR was applied too early (Hammond *et al.* 1986b).

Liming is a management option to increase pH and reduce exchangeable Al^{3+} concentration, especially for crops that are sensitive to Al. However, when increasing the pH through liming, the PR dissolution is decreased due to increased Ca concentration (the common ion effect).

The effect of pH on P sorption in weathered environments has shown different results. Some authors report decreasing P-sorption with increased pH, others report increasing sorption of P in soils that have been limed. Khasawneh and Doll (1978) compared the effects of $CaCO_3$ and $SrCO_3$ in order to separate the effects of soil pH from that of exchangeable Ca. They showed that plant yield was less depressed with $SrCO_3$ than with $CaCO_3$, attributing the reduced PR dissolution to the combined effect of pH and exchangeable Ca. This demonstrates that lime rates should be chosen with great care as to avoid adverse effects on PR dissolution rates in acid soils.

The primary reason for increasing the soil pH through liming is to reduce the aluminum toxicity to plant roots. Increasing the pH decreases the supply of H^+ ions and, on calcareous soils, increases the supply of exchangeable Ca^{2+} which, through the common ion effect, will decrease the dissolution of PR. Thus, liming will on the one hand reduce aluminum toxicity but on the other hand reduce the dissolution of PR. A practical approach to overcome the two contrasting effects is to apply the PR well in advance of the application of liming materials, as long as the P-sorption capacity of the soil is not high (Sanchez and Salinas 1981). The rates of lime application should be relatively low so as not to reduce PR dissolution.

4.1.6 Guidelines for PR use in direct application.

Decisions to use PR directly without chemical modification of the PR should be based on several factors, including PR factors, plant factors and soil factors.

The PR factor is largely dependent on the nature and reactivity of the PR. Francolitic ores from sedimentary PR deposits with high carbonate substitution and corresponding high neutral ammonium solubilities are more suitable than fluor-apatites with low substitutions and low reactivities. To assess the suitability of direct application PRs it is also crucial to know the form and concentration of impurities of the PRs. For example, minerals like calcite and dolomite can inhibit the release of P from the PR ore. PRs with accompanying carbonates or groundmass are less effective than PRs with silicates.

In the literature usually only occurrences of high-grade phosphate rocks are reported, as they could be used for the production of high-analysis phosphate fertilizers. However, even phosphates at a considerably lower grade can be very useful if they occur close to P-deficient soils, or can be upgraded or modified by simple methods. Practical factors like ease of extraction (mining) and processing of agrominerals play a role as well as transport, distribution and availability parameters. If the phosphates are low-grade, easy to mine and easy to modify then they might be useful on close-by, P-deficient soils. Obviously, the economic aspects of using low-grade phosphates in relation to their effectiveness must be assessed on a case-by-case basis.

Another factor that has to be taken into account when deciding on the use of a certain PR for direct application is the soil factor. Most suitable soils for the direct application of PR are acid soils with low exchangeable Ca and low P concentrations. The more acid the soil, the faster the dissolution. The effectiveness of P release from PRs will decrease as the soil pH increases. Also the P-sorption of the soils plays a major role in the effectiveness of PR dissolution. As pointed out before, high P-sorption soils like oxisols and ultisols enhance the dissolution of PR (Smyth and Sanchez 1982) while the initial effect of PR application on high P-sorbing volcanic soils (andisols) with allophane minerals is generally negative. At least initially the dissolved P may become unavailable to plants (Hammond *et al.* 1986a, 1986b). However, the residual P effect of PR application increases with time on these volcanic soils (Hammond *et al.* 1986b).

The effectiveness of extracting phosphorus from the soil depends also on plant species and P uptake kinetics. While fast growing food crops commonly require relatively rapid release of P, perennial crops, pasture and trees require PRs with slow-release and residual effects. But among the food crops there are also significant differences in P demand. In addition, some plants are able to increase the solubilization of P from PR through excretion of organic acids from their roots or through high uptake of Ca^{2+}. These crops include several legumes and crops from the *Cruciferae* family. Crops like rapeseed (*Brassica napus*) are able to increase the solubilization, even from less reactive PR sources (Mnkeni *et al.* 2000; Weil 2000). Some of the sedimentary PRs from Africa, for example from Mali (Tilemsi), Senegal (Matam), Nigeria (Sokoto), Angola and Congo, as well as the biogenic phosphates from Tanzania (Minjingu) and guano-derived phosphates have relatively high inherent reactivities and are suitable for direct application for most crops. For perennial crops like tea, sugar cane, and plantation and tree crops, less reactive PR sources can be utilized with good agronomic efficiencies.

It should be stressed that PRs commonly have long-term residual effects and contribute to recapitalization of P in soils. However, if directly applied, many PRs are not able to produce the desired short-term outcome. They must be modified before application to optimize the P utilization under the local conditions. There are several alternative options of PR modification other than industrial acidulation.

Table 1.3: Agronomic potential of PRs for direct application.

Suitability depending on mineralogy of PR	Suitability depending on soil characteristics Suitable soil = Soil pH < 5.5, low exchangeable Ca, and low P concentrations
Reactivity ranking (after Hammond and Leon 1983)	
High (NAC solubility: > 5.9)	most annual and perennial crops
Medium - high (NAC solubility: 3.4-5.9)	low P demanding crops; perennial crops like sugar cane, plantation crops plants with high P-mobilizing capacities, including various leguminous crops, and plants, like rape and cabbage.
Low (NAC solubility < 3.4)	various perennial crops, e.g. tea, as well as trees, and some plants, like rape and cabbage.

4.1.7 Alternative options for PR utilization

Roots take up P from the soil solution. Many of the PR resources in the world are inherently low in their reactivity and are not likely to release sufficient P into the soil solution to be agronomically effective, at least not in the short term. Because of inherent chemical and mineralogical properties, many of these PRs are not suitable for direct application for high P-requiring annual crops. These phosphates have to be modified to become more plant available.

The breakdown of apatite can be achieved through various processes. The main industrial process used to solubilize apatite in PR and to get P into a soluble form is through acidulation, for example with sulphuric or phosphoric acid. While the resultant products are in general very effective, the production of superphosphates (SSP and TSP) as well as ammonium phosphates (MAP, DAP) require high capital investments, advanced technology and trained personnel. These conditions are sensitive to available capital, technology, location and infrastructure.

Sulphuric acid for the production of superphosphates is usually produced from elemental sulphur, or sulphur-bearing minerals like pyrite (FeS_2). In much of sub-Saharan Africa industrial acidulation or even partial acidulation for breaking down the phosphate minerals and making phosphorus more available is constrained by the lack of local sources of sulphur, or inadequate infrastructure to allow for economical transport of sulphur or sulphuric or phosphoric acid, or for lack of capital.

The search for alternative ways to enhance the breakdown of PR into plant-available P forms has led to an array of PR modification techniques. Over the last few decades, various innovative techniques to enhance PR solubility have been investigated, including modification techniques like partial acidulation, heap leaching, thermal treatment, mechanical activation, as well as modification through biological processes. Although there are several options open to process PR into a form that is more plant available, the options for small-scale farmers are limited. Practical alternative methods and technologies of PR modification have to be developed for the farm level. Alternative processing techniques of PR need to be screened as to their suitabilities and acceptance in the local environment. Some of the known modification techniques are presented below.

Partial acidulation.

The technique of partial acidulation of phosphate rocks (PAPR) requires only a portion of the theoretical (stoechiometric) quantity of acid required for the conversion of insoluble phosphate minerals into water-soluble monocalcium phosphate monohydrate (MCP). In the preparation of PAPR the proportion of acid used to prepare PAPR relative to the quantity of acid required for full acidulation is expressed as 'percent PAPR.' When used with sulphuric acid, the resultant product will also provide some sulphur to the soil. The technology provides a portion of the P in a readily available form and the remainder in a form that should enhance the residual value (Hammond *et al.* 1986b).

Partial acidulation has been tested with phosphate rock from Togo, Zimbabwe, Zambia, Uganda, Tanzania, Burkina Faso and Niger.

The technology is most effective when using PR material that is low in iron and aluminum oxides (Hammond *et al.* 1989, Chien and Hammond 1989). Bationo *et al.* (1990) showed that the $Fe_2O_3 + Al_2O_3$ content played a major role in the effectiveness of partially acidulated sedimentary PRs of Niger. They demonstrated that the partially acidulated, Fe+Al-rich Tahoua PR with an initial higher reactivity than Parc West PR was less effective than the Fe+Al-poor, unreactive Parc West PR. This was consistent with the findings of Hammond *et al.* (1989) who showed that the $Fe_2O_3 + Al_2O_3$ content of PR significantly influences the agronomic effectiveness of PAPR. Another example of partial acidulation with an unreactive, in this case igneous phosphate rock, is that of Butegwa *et al.* (1996). They tested the agronomic effectiveness of unacidulated and partially acidulated phosphate rocks from Sukulu Hill in eastern Uganda in greenhouse experiments. Blending and partial acidulation of Sukulu PR concentrate with a low Fe + Al-oxide content and TSP at a ratio of 50:50 was clearly more effective than blending and partial acidulation with TSP (50:50) with the Fe and Al-oxide rich raw Sukulu phosphate rock.

Research in many parts of the world has shown that the partial acidulation technique can be successful and effective with relatively unreactive PR materials with low Fe+Al oxide content. An advantage of the method is the robustness of the technology. It can be adapted to local circumstances. Low-tech solutions with the application of appropriate technology have been successfully tested in Zambia, where a local cement mixer was used for the blending and partial acidulation of Chilembwe PR (Borsch 1993). A major drawback of this technique is the unavailability of inexpensive local sulphuric or phosphoric acid.

Acidulation through heap leaching

Another form of acidulation is heap leaching, a technique described by Habashi (1989, 1994). This technology requires low-carbonate or carbonate-free phosphate ores piled in heaps with an impermeable liner at the bottom. Nitric acid at 20% or 10% hydrochloric acid is percolated through the heap. The phosphate minerals dissolve during the acid's passage through the heap. The phosphate-bearing solution is collected at the bottom and can be treated further to remove potentially harmful uranium, radium as well as lanthanides (Habashi 1994).

In Zambia, an initial laboratory leach test (with 1% sulphuric acid) was conducted with phosphate-rich and Fe-rich residual soils from Nkombwa Hill. The leachate was neutralized with dolomite and dried. The resultant extract contained 15% P_2O_5, O.7% Fe, 11% Ca, 6.7% Mg and 7% SO_4 (Borsch 1988).

Thermal treatment

Thermal treatment of PR includes three types of processes: calcination, sintering and fusion. Calcination is a process that breaks down carbonates and drives off CO_2. No entry of oxygen is required for this process. Sintering is agglomeration of small particles to form larger ones without reaching the melting point. Fusion is heating minerals, ores, concentrates and other inorganic matter above the melting point. PRs that have low citrate solubility (e.g. igneous fluor-apatites) are heated to high temperatures, to below the melting point (sintering), or to above the melting point (fusion).

The best-known thermal phosphates are Rhenania phosphates and Fused Magnesium Phosphates (FMP). The Rhenania process entails mixing soda ash (Na_2CO_3) with PR and silica and subjecting it, in the presence of steam, to temperatures between 1,100 and 1,200°C. The resultant sodium-silicophosphates are then quenched with water and ground to a fine powder. Rhenania phosphates have high solubilities and are suitable for tropical soils. The Rhenania phosphates have been as effective or even more effective than superphosphates in high P-sorbing soils of Brazil, in ultisols of Nigeria (Obigbesan and Kuhn 1974) and high P-sorbing soils of Ethiopia and Congo (Werner 1969). Rhenania phosphates were produced in western Kenya in the 1950s using PR from Busumbu in Uganda and soda ash from Lake Magadi (Mathers 1994).

Rhenania phosphates contain silicate components, which can compete with phosphate ions for adsorption sites. Additionally, these materials are alkaline in reaction and can be used as liming material in acid soils. The main disadvantages of Rhenania phosphates are their high costs of production, their reliance on the availability of soda ash and large amounts of water for quenching.

Fused Magnesium Phosphates (FMP) are formed by mixing PR sources (usually of low citrate solubility) with Mg sources such as olivine or serpentine. The mix is then fused in a furnace at about 1500-1600°C. Fused Magnesium Phosphates have been successfully field tested in many countries including Brazil (Cekinski and da Silva 1998) and Zambia (Goma *et al.* 1991). FMP produced in Zambia using locally available serpentine as the Mg source proved agronomically as effective as superphosphate on the acid P-deficient soils of northern Zambia (Goma *et al.* 1991). The disadvantages of this method are similar to those of Rhenania phosphates: large amounts of cheap electricity and large quantities of water for quenching are required.

Both types of heat treatment result in a phosphate product that is relatively effective in tropical soils and both techniques can be applied at various scales. Formal feasibility studies are required to further assess the agronomic effectiveness and practicality of these methods and products in other countries.

Another type of thermal phosphate is calcined Al-phosphate. In this process, Al-phosphates (crandallite, wavellite, millisite) are calcined at temperatures of about 550°C. The calcined product contains 32% P_2O_5 and has a high solubility (citrate solubility >12%). An example of calcined Al-phosphates is Thies in Senegal. This product is marketed under the trade name 'Phospal,' for animal feed use it is marketed under the trade name 'Polyphos.' Field test data with calcined Al-phosphates have shown positive results on neutral to alkaline soils. Since the solubilities of calcined Al-phosphates increase with increasing soil pH they have a high potential for P-deficient high pH soils. Experiments conducted by the International Fertilizer Development Center (IFDC) between 1996 and 1998 have shown that thermally treated Al-phosphates (from the Christmas Islands) are 83-93% as effective as TSP for flooded rice under alkaline soil conditions (IFDC report 1998).

Basic slag is another thermally produced phosphate-rich material (see below, section 4.10) widely used in Europe. A byproduct of the steel industry, it has also proven highly effective on tropical soils, mainly in South America (Sanchez and Uehara 1980).

The advantage of all these processes is that low reactive PRs or Al-phosphates that would otherwise be ineffective when applied directly to the soils can be used. The products (after thermal treatment) could be used for direct application, especially in high P-sorbing soils. Appropriate heat generating technologies exist that can be utilized at various scales. A simple technology for potential use in thermal transformation is, for example, the circulating fluidized bed reactor, tested with aluminum phosphates in Brazil (Guardani *et al.* 1989).

Blending techniques

A practice to enhance the agronomic effectiveness of low reactive PRs is blending PR with water-soluble phosphates, commonly TSP. Chien *et al.* (1987) showed that small amounts of water-soluble phosphates act as a starter dose for the plants until P from the PR becomes available to the plants. This initial starter dose of water-soluble P will stimulate root development. The denser root system will then increasingly utilize the remaining PR (Chien *et al.* 1996). This technique, with various blending ratios, has shown promise in many agronomic tests in sub-Saharan Africa (Chien *et al.* 1987, 1996; Govere *et al.* 1995; van Straaten and Fernandes 1995; Mnkeni *et al.* 2000).

In practice, the technique employs either compacting the water-soluble P source (e.g. TSP) with PR on a dry base, or pelletizing the mix in a rotary pelletizer. In the process, not only PR and TSP can be mixed but several more water-soluble components can be added, for example, urea and KCl (Chien *et al.* 1987, Chien and Menon 1995), making these blends multinutrient fertilizers. Compaction techniques have low capital and energy requirements and can be carried out in units of various scales (Lupin and Le 1983). Also, low capital and energy requirements are needed for pelletizing techniques. A small compactor and a low-tech rotary pelletizer using blended materials has been tested successfully in Zimbabwe (van Straaten and Fernandes 1995).

In Uganda, unreactive Sukulu phosphate rock concentrate and Sukulu raw phosphate mixed and compacted with TSP at a ratio 50:50 (with 5% urea as binder) had higher citrate solubilities of P and dry matter yields than partially acidulated Sukulu PRs (Sukulu PAPR), acidulated with the same 50:50 ratio (Butegwa *et al.* 1996). The relative agronomic effectiveness of compacted Sukulu PR concentrate + TSP as well as compacted raw Sukulu PR + TSP had RAE values of 94.4% and 89.7% respectively. PAPR from the Sukulu PR concentrate had a RAE value of 54.8% (Butegwa *et al.* 1996). These data suggest that blending and compaction can improve the effectiveness of low reactive PRs like Sukulu PR (Uganda) or Togo PR or Kodjari PR (Burkina Faso) and could be used as effective substitutes for soluble P sources.

In Zimbabwe, products from blending PR + TSP have shown promising agronomic responses (Govere *et al.*1995; van Straaten and Fernandes 1995). The PR used was the unreactive Dorowa PR concentrate or materials from 'wasted' PR fines (van Straaten and Fernandes 1995). Similar techniques using low reactive Busumbu PR from eastern Uganda plus small amounts of TSP as a starter dose have been tested in western Kenya (Smithson *et al.* 2001).

The technique was also applied in Tanzania where low reactive Panda PR blended with TSP and compacted was agronomically tested by Mnkeni *et al.* (2000). While Panda PR was ineffective when applied alone, the mixture of Panda PR plus TSP or its compacted product increased wheat, maize, and soybean yields and P uptake significantly (Mnkeni *et al.* 2000).

Ion exchange

Another method to increase P availability from PRs to plants is through the process of ion exchange. This alternative process is based on the principle that ions released during the dissolution of PR, especially Ca^{2+}, can be sequestered by zeolites, which in turn furthers the dissolution of the PR (Lai and Eberl 1986; Chesworth *et al.* 1987).

A simplified reaction of the systems is: $PR + NH_4^+$-zeolite $\Leftrightarrow$ Ca-zeolite $+ NH_4^+ + H_2PO_4^-$. For this reaction to take place, zeolites have to be charged with NH_4^+ and then reacted with PR. The NH_4^+-charged zeolite will act as Ca^{2+} sink during the exchange, thereby releasing NH_4^+ and taking up Ca^{2+} ions. This will lower the activity of Ca^{2+} in the solution and more PR will dissolve (Lai and Eberl 1986). Laboratory experiments with NH_4^+-zeolite and PR with 2:1 and 5:1 ratios of NH_4^+-zeolite to PR on non-calcareous soils indicate a good potential for this system.

Mnkeni et al. (1994) showed in an experiment with untreated zeolite (phillipsite) of the Mapogoro deposit in southwest Tanzania and PRs from Minjingu and Panda that the breakdown of the reactive Minjingu PR could be enhanced, but not the unreactive Panda PR. However, the quantities of zeolite used in the experiments were prohibitively high. In order to make the system more effective and less costly, the authors suggest devising methods similar to the ones used by Lai and Eberl (1986), for example using NH_4^+ charged zeolites as exchangers.

Mechanical activation

Gock and Jacob (1984) proposed another way of processing low reactive PRs. They tested a new type of rotary-chamber vibrating mill for mechanically 'activating' sedimentary phosphate rock from Egypt. This dry milling technique not only reduces the grain size of the PR considerably, it opens up defect sites in phosphate minerals and subsequently changes the solubility parameters of the PR as a function of milling time. X-ray diffraction and infra-red data supported by citrate solubility tests over time provide evidence for mineralogical changes that enhance solubility of the PR (Gock and Jacob 1984).

Citric acid tests of mechanically activated Togo PR showed increasing solubilities with increased energy inputs for grinding (Gock and Jacob 1984). Mechanically activated Kodjari PR from Burkina Faso was tested in greenhouse experiments and resulted in significantly higher yields (Kantor et al. 1990).

Organic solubilization:

The use of organic resources plays an important role in the dissolution of phosphate rocks. There are many factors that influence the transition from inorganic PR to organic P pools and finally to the plants. Of special importance is the role of organic materials in enhancing the availability of P from medium to low reactive PRs. The principal processes in biological solubilization of PRs are acidulation and chelation of Ca^{2+}.

Increased solubilization of PR has been reported from exposure to phosphate-solubilizing microorganisms. Research focused on the isolation of PR solubilizing microorganisms (Sperber 1958; Kucey 1983, 1987; Asea et al. 1988; Cerezine et al. 1988; Nahas et al. 1990; Vassilev et al. 1995; Nahas 1996; Bojinova et al. 1997; Mba 1997; Goenadi et al. 2000; Narsian and Patel 2000; Sahu and Jana 2000). Most effective in dissolving relatively unreactive PRs are Aspergillus niger (Cerezine et al. 1988; Nahas et al. 1990; Sassi et al. 1991; Vassilev et al. 1995; Bojinova et al. 1997), Penicillium bilaji (Kucey 1987; Asea et al. 1988) and Pseudomonas cepacia (Nahas 1996). These microorganisms have been consistently identified as good PR-solubilizing microorganisms. In general, fungi are more effective in producing acids to dissolve PRs than bacteria (Nahas 1996).

So far, most of the research has been conducted under laboratory conditions and few data are available from field experiments. The interaction of the introduced microbial populations with microorganisms already present in the soil will determine the survival rate of the introduced PR-dissolving micro-organisms and therefore their potential practical application.

Aspergillus niger produces organic acids, including citric, oxalic and gluconic acids that increase PR dissolution (Cerezine et al. 1988; Bojinova et al. 1997). The production of organic acids and the subsequent dissolution of PR can be enhanced by providing suitable substrates for the growth of acid-producing microbial populations. Banik (1983) showed that glucose was a good carbon source for microorganisms to enhance PR dissolution. Other substrates that provided carbon sources for microorganisms were sugar wastes such as vinasse, a residue of alcohol production from sugar cane (Cerezine *et al.* 1988; Nahas *et al.* 1990), and sugar-beet waste (Vassilev *et al.* 1995). Nahas *et al.* (1990) used vinasse as a substrate to enhance the dissolution of unreactive fluor-apatite by acids produced by *Aspergillus niger* under laboratory conditions. It was found that after 13 days, about 73% of the PR was dissolved. There was also a high production of mycelial mass, a source of organic matter that contains nutrients other from phosphorus (Nahas *et al.* 1990).

The acidulation of phosphate rocks by organic acids produced during fermentation of agricultural residues provides a great opportunity and challenge. There are many bioconversion processes known using agricultural wastes as substrates for acid-producing microorganisms. There is a good potential for those agricultural operations that produce organic acids during fermentation to utilize these acids for the production of acidulated or partially acidulated PRs on a local scale. The industrial production of oxalic acid, one of the most effective organic acid for the dissolution of PR, has been documented from sugar cane wastes (Mane *et al.* 1988). The production of citric acid using banana extracts has been demonstrated by Sassi *et al.* (1991). The bioconversion of natural phosphates into organo-mineral fertilizers is a promising technology that should be tested on farms that produce large amounts of organic 'waste,' for example pineapple, banana, or sugar cane plantations. It could be a technology that increases the effectiveness of indigenous PR resources without importing expensive acidulating reagents.

An *in-situ* method that can increase PR solubilization through acid root exudation and organic acids has been documented by Hinsinger and Gilkes (1996) in Australia, Mnkeni *et al.* (2000) with two phosphate rocks from Tanzania, Bekele *et al.* (1983), Bekele and Hofner (1993) with Ethiopian phosphate rocks, and Kpomblekou and Tabatabai (1994) with phosphate rocks from West Africa.

Other methods that involve organic acid producing residues and/or Ca^{2+} sorbing organic matter include the 'waste' product and coir dust, a solid organic residue obtained after the extraction of coconut fibres from coconut husks. Coir dust is discarded in numerous coconut processing operations. Recently, however, these 'wastes' are being reworked and exported to Europe and North America where they are used in potting media in greenhouses. Coir dust is largely made up of lignine, cellulose and hemicellulose with low Ca and low Fe concentrations. It has a pH of 5.5 - 6.0, high surface area and high cation exchange capacity. When unreactive PR from Sri Lanka (Eppawela PR) was added to coir dust the rate of PR dissolution increased significantly (Pereira 1995). The causes for the enhanced PR dissolution are not entirely clear but are thought to be related to the low exchangeable Ca concentration in the coir dust, which could act as a sink for Ca^{2+} ions and thus enhance the dissolution of PR.

The positive role of mycorrhizae in P-acquisition is largely restricted to P-deficient soils whereby mycorrhizae extend the root system and explore more soil volume for P and other nutrients. There are conflicting reports as to whether mycorrhizae will actually increase the release of P from PRs. Encouraging results have been reported, for example, by Cabala-Rosand and Wild (1982b) in Brazil.

Phospho-composting

Decomposing organic matter generally produces organic acids that can enhance PR dissolution. Microorganisms in the compost pile require P nutrition for growth. In the process inorganic P is converted into the organic form of P. Upon death and decomposition this organic P pool is converted to plant available P, but calcium chelation by organic functional groups or anions supplied during composting can also contribute to PR dissolution (Singh and Amberger 1990).

While the protonation effect is important for the dissolution of PR (Sagoe *et al.* 1998b), in some cases it may not be the dominant factor. Sagoe *et al.* (1998a) demonstrated in incubation studies that protonation accounted for only 13-38% of the amount released from PR sources while Ca^{2+} removal from soil solution by organic acids accounted for the largest proportion of P released. The concentration of Ca^{2+} ions in the compost pile is thus important. Mixing PR with organic matter with high levels of Ca^{2+} can inhibit the release of P from PR, due to the common ion effect driving the reaction of PR dissolution (Fig. 1.3) from right to left instead from left to right (Smithson 1999).

Composting systems with PR additions have been studied in many countries with different composts and different PR sources (Bangar *et al.* 1985; Ikerra *et al.* 1994; Lompo 1993; Mathur *et al.* 1986; Singh and Amberger 1990, 1991, 1998; Singh *et al.* 1983; van den Berghe 1996; Tian and Kolawole 1999; Odongo 2002; Oshier 2002). Experimental data of phospho-composting with sedimentary PRs have shown generally increased solubility of these P resources and that it is an effective way to increase PR dissolution. The results of experiments on the dissolution of less reactive igneous phosphates through composting are less consistent. Mathur *et al.* (1986) demonstrated increased P release from composted igneous phosphates from Canada, and van den Berghe (1996) illustrated enhanced P release from composting igneous Matongo PR from Burundi in the presence of urea. Odongo (2002) showed that composted feces with relatively unreactive Busumbu PR supported statistically significant P uptake and yield of maize on strongly P-sorbing soils of Kenya. Chirenje (1996) and Oshier (2002) provide data showing that composting of unmodified unreactive igneous PRs from Zimbabwe and Uganda with both manure and leaves were essentially ineffective on sandy soils of Zimbabwe and eastern Uganda respectively.

Unreactive phosphate rock from Dorowa, Zimbabwe, incorporated and mixed with cattle manure within cattle pens and in-situ composted, is currently being tested on P-deficient soils of central Zimbabwe (Dr. R. Fernandes, University of Zimbabwe, pers. comm. 2002).

Other PR dissolution methods

Other PR dissolution methods with various acid producing materials include mixing of pyrite with PRs and burying PR in low pH peat.

The oxidation of pyrite produces acid solutions that theoretically can enhance PR dissolution. In a laboratory study Lowell and Weil (1995) incubated pyrite with different African phosphate rocks in several ratios and measured the resultant pH and P concentrations in the leachates. Soluble P measured in the leachate was greatest in pyrite - PR mixtures with Togo PR and Sukulu PR from Uganda. Soluble P released from pyrite-unreactive Togo PR and Sukulu PR (from Uganda) mixes was clearly higher than P released from Tundulu PR (Malawi) and Minjingu PR (Tanzania), which were negligible (Lowell and Weil 1995). When a mix of pyrite and Mussorie PR from India was incorporated into decomposing cattle manure, the agronomic effectiveness of the P- and S-enriched manure was enhanced as testified by increased yields of mustard (Gupta *et al.* 1988).

Dahanayake *et al.* (1991) tested the effect that high-sulphur peat had on the solubility of the sparingly soluble local PR from Sri Lanka. The PR was buried in the low-pH sulphate-rich zone of local peats for several weeks and showed gradual increase in P-release over time (Dahanayake *et al.* 1991).

Tests on PR dissolution with other acids include the work by Tennakone *et al.* (1988), who used hydrochloric acid. The reaction product was mixed with ammonium sulfate to produce a non-hygroscopic superphosphate.

Green manure and PR

While phospho-composting is a biological transformation process that is practiced in confined composting spaces, the application of green manure is practiced by incorporating organic matter directly into the soil without prior collection and decomposition. Research has been carried out in various countries in an attempt to increase PR dissolution by incorporating green leaf manure together with the PR. In western Kenya reactive Minjingu PR from Tanzania and unreactive Busumbu PR from Uganda were incorporated into the soil along with various green manures. The system is very complex and so are the results. Field results from western Kenya indicate increased yield when combining Minjingu PR with *Tithonia diversifolia* biomass (Sanchez *et al.* 1997; Nziguheba 2001). One of the explanations for the increased agronomic effectiveness of PR + *Thithonia diversifolia* is related to the role of organic anions that compete with phosphate ions for adsorption sites in the soils (Nziguheba 2001).

Investigations in Burkina Faso indicate that under certain conditions, green manure of legume crops, cowpea (*Vigna ungiculata*) and crotolaria (*Crotolaria retusa*) plus relatively low reactive PR from Burkina Faso (Kodjari PR) is suitable as a preceding crop treatment for maize (Muleba 1999; Muleba and Coulibaly 1999).

Biological superphosphate

Biological superphosphate ('biosuper') is produced by dry mixing and co-granulating finely ground PR (95% < 150 μm) with finely ground sulphur (< 150 μm) at a ratio of 5:1 by weight and inoculating it with *Thiobacillus spp.* bacteria (Swaby 1975; Rajan 1982, 1983, 1987a; Schofield *et al.* 1981). The reaction in the soil is similar to PR dissolution with sulphuric acid in a P-fertilizer factory. The sulphur in the granule is oxidized in the soil to sulphuric acid, which in turn acidulates the PR *in-situ*. Best results were obtained with reactive PRs (Rajan 1982). Various pot and field studies confirmed the high agronomic effectiveness of this type of P-S fertilizer. In comparative studies 'biosuper' performed as well as SSP and provided additional S to the soils. The most promising soils for this kind of fertilizer are S-deficient soils with a pH > 5.8, which is too high for straight PR applications (Rajan 1982).

So far, no experiments have been carried out in sub-Saharan Africa with biological superphosphate. This is at least in part due to a shortage of easily available sulphur sources in large parts of Africa.

Affordable phosphate rock-N fertilizer-seed packages for smallholder farmers

A practical, inexpensive 'fertilizer + seed' packet has been developed for smallholder farmers in Kenya by a group of researchers and practicioners (Woomer *et al.* 1998; Okalebo *et al.* 2001). This fertility-restoring mix of locally available reactive phosphate rock (Minjingu PR), urea and N-fixing legume seeds contributes to nutrient replenishment, and has been designed, and agronomically and economically tested on P-deficient acid soils in Western Kenya. The low-cost locally packaged product consists of 2 kg reactive phosphate rock, 0.2 kg imported urea, 0.13 kg seed of a N-fixing legume (e.g. beans), rhizobial inoculant, seed adhesive (gum arabic) and lime pellets. It has been scientifically tested on 52 farms and is distributed by local NGOs and retailers in Western Kenya. The package is designed to ameliorate low pH, low fertility patches of 25-30 m^2 with P-deficient soils at low pH. With a retail price of less than US $0.80 per package and a gross agronomic benefit, it represents an example for a successful 'low-cost fertilizer + seed' kit for the small-holder farming community. Similar technologies could easily be implemented in other countries of sub-Saharan Africa with reactive phosphate rock deposits, for example, Mali, Senegal, Congo, Angola, and Tanzania.

4.2   Liming materials

Widespread soil acidity is a common soil-related constraint to crop production in many parts of the world including sub-Saharan Africa. High leaching rates, unfavourable parent materials and, in some rare cases, the continuous application of acidifying chemical fertilizers such as ammonium-sulphates are largely responsible for high soil acidity. However, the main constraint for crop production in highly acidic soils is not so much the high amount of H^+ but the increased concentration of highly toxic Al^{3+} at low pH, and low exchangeable Ca^{2+} levels (Sale and Mokwunye 1993).

Agricultural liming materials are those whose Ca and Mg compounds are capable of neutralizing soil acidity. Liming materials such as limestones, dolomites and calcined and slaked limestones (lime) are used to raise the pH of acid soils, provide Ca-ions, and decrease Al-toxicity. Finely ground limestone and dolomite resources have been applied to acid soils for centuries and are still being applied in many countries of the world. There are several types of limestones: sedimentary bedded or massive limestone, dolomitic limestone, calcitic dolomite and dolomite. Marble is the term used for metamorphosed limestone or dolomite. Calcretes are carbonates formed by in-situ cementation of pre-existing material, and by precipitated calcium carbonate in near-surface environments. When dolomite is dominant in the calcretes it is called dolocrete. Calcretes can be earthy and soft, or form highly indurated hard crusts. Travertine, another form of calcium carbonate, is formed by rapid chemical precipitation from surface or groundwater, or by evaporation around natural springs. Travertine can be hard and compact, layered and banded, or porous and spongy. 'Tufa' is the name for a soft, spongy and porous variety of travertine. Marl is soft $CaCO_3$ mixed with various amounts of clay and organic matter. It is found mainly in swampy areas and in reservoirs, and in certain sedimentary successions.

Traditionally, liming materials are evaluated according to their neutralizing value (measured by titration) and fineness (measured as particle size distribution), and in a combined form, the 'agricultural index.' Typical ground limestone has a neutralizing value of 100%, dolomite 106% and agricultural hydrated lime, after energy intensive calcination, 136%. Other ways of assessing the expected performance of liming materials is by surface area, chemical composition and solubility. While the fineness is expressed as particle size distribution of ground and sized material, the surface area is expressed as the total surface area of the liming material. The surface area does not necessarily correlate with the particle size analysis as internal pores, cracks and irregular surfaces largely increase the surface area. Only in very finely ground materials, surface area and particle size show strong correlation (Conyers *et al.* 1996). Liming materials from coral limestone and 'earthy limestones' often contain aragonite as form of $CaCO_3$, which is slightly more soluble than calcite. Dolomite is less soluble than calcite.

The application of limestone/dolomite as 'agricultural lime' is of benefit to the farmer where costs of production and transport are relatively low. Dolomite or limestone resources developed close to actively cultivated acid soils will be able to raise the pH of acid soils, creating favourable conditions for increased crop production. The mineralogical reactivity and chemical solubility and the kinetics of dissolution of liming materials play major roles in determining their agronomic effectiveness.

Some farmers utilize fast acting 'quicklime' as primary liming material for acid soil. Quicklime is a product of calcination ('lime burning') of limestone between 900 and 1200 °C. The calcination process requires considerable energy (often from fuel wood), thus increasing the energy costs for the production of liming material for agricultural purposes. When choosing to use agricultural limestone or dolomite instead of calcined lime, the rocks are mined, and crushed and finely ground only. Certainly these are energy intensive processes as well, but are often the only processes needed to get an effective agricultural limestone product.

The quality and processes for the production of agricultural 'liming materials' have to be assessed critically. Carbonate rocks are typically assessed by professionals who look for cement grade limestones, by 'cement geologists.' More than 3-5% MgO is detrimental for the production of cement, but for agricultural application the Mg-component could be beneficial.

Farmers often prefer sedimentary limestones and coral limestones over more crystalline metamorphosed limestones and marbles. Unless the marbles are very finely ground the efficacy of the much finer and more porous sedimentary limestones is usually higher than the crystalline limestones. Reducing the grain size of limestones through fine grinding increases their agricultural efficacy.

The size of limestone and dolomite mining operations for agricultural lime production vary from country to country, but range from several thousand tonnes per month to small operations with only a few tonnes per cropping season. In cases of application to soils with low buffering capacities it is often not advisable to calcine the limestone/dolomite but to use them directly. While calcined and hydrated limes are more soluble, they are caustic and will 'burn' the roots of emerging plants if applied shortly before seeding or too close to the seeds. The application of uncalcined limestones also saves wood, the main energy source for such calcining operations.

The application rate of lime or limestone/dolomite depends largely on the pH, the Al^{3+} concentration and buffering capacities of soils, but is generally in the range of 2-4 tonnes per hectare. Since large quantities of liming materials are required per unit of land and since these materials are low-value high-bulk products, it is of utmost importance to find local sources to keep transportation costs reasonably low.

As the mineralogical and chemical parameters of liming materials vary strongly from place to place it is important to assess these parameters along with soil testing prior to application.

Alternative liming materials to be considered include wood ash, and several industrial byproducts such as slag and fly ash. Wood ash (Ohno and Erich 1990) and industrial byproducts (see chapter 4.10) have liming properties but can also provide other nutrients, for example, modest amounts of P and Ca.

Termite mounds, known for their naturally enhanced soil fertility, also have some liming properties. They are used in some parts of sub-Saharan Africa as soil amendments to increase the pH, provide additional soil organic matter and free $CaCO_3$ (Watson 1977; Moormann and Kang 1978; Nyamapfene 1986).

Like other industrial minerals, there are some important technical, economic and environmental considerations for mining of limestone/dolomite that have to be addressed. They include location, form of deposit (bedded/layered or massive, inclined or horizontal), nature and thickness of the interbedded rock materials, as well as chemical and physical characteristics. It is also important to determine the amount of overburden that has to be removed. It is critical to find energy resources for mining and calcination that are the least environmentally harmful and to determine low-cost, adapted beneficiation techniques (drying/crushing/grinding/physical concentration) suitable for the specific site. More energy efficient kilns can reduce wood consumption. Spiropoulous (1991) reported an example of the effectiveness of improved vertical-shaft kilns adapted to suit the specific conditions in Malawi. Lime is applied to the soils in different forms, but mostly it is broadcasted and later incorporated into the soil. Another method of making optimal use of agricultural lime is the application of lime in lime seed pellets (Pijnenborg and Lie 1990). Small amounts of lime are coated together with rhizobia species onto wet seeds to create evenly coated lime pellets. The pellets were field tested and showed early root development on legumes, as well as increased nodulation of various legume species (Pijnenborg and Lie 1990).

The case of liming materials illustrates the great advantage of the active cooperation between soil scientists, geologists and process engineers. Soil scientists outline the areas with high soil acidity which require liming materials and geologists search for agricultural limestone and dolomite resources close to the acid soils. Even if the carbonate resources are only of small extent and not of the quality required for cement manufacture, they may be suitable for improving the local acid soils.

The success stories of the use of liming materials in Rwanda (Yamoah *et al.* 1992) and Brazil (Sanchez and Salinas 1981; Goedert 1983) demonstrate that even small locally produced limestones and liming materials can be used to increase crop production on acid soils. Locally available carbonate resources such as calcitic and dolomitic marbles, carbonatites, sedimentary marine and lacustrine limestones, and secondary limestones (calcretes) are relatively common in many countries of sub-Saharan Africa and are well suited for small-scale mining and processing. Many more small limestone resources should be mined and, with some advice from agricultural extension personnel, applied on many more acid soils of the tropics.

4.3 Sulphur and pyrite

Sulphur is essential to all plants, especially for the synthesis of proteins. Sulphur deficiencies in soils are becoming more and more apparent in recent years, especially in areas far away from the sea and from industry. These sulphur deficiencies are partially due to depletion of S through heavy crop removals, intensive cropping and lack of organic matter recycling but also due to the expanding use of S-free fertilizers such as TSP, MAP, DAP, and urea.

Sulphur and pyrite (FeS_2) are naturally occurring minerals that can provide sulphur to plants, but in oxidizing environments they can also produce acids to lower the pH. Crops with a high demand for S include sugar cane, protein-rich leguminous crops like lucerne and clover, oil crops such as rapeseed, mustard, and cruciferous plants like cabbage and cauliflower.

Sulphur as elemental sulphur is found in relatively small amounts in many volcanic areas but also as part of sedimentary gypsum- ($CaSO_4 \cdot 2H_2O$) and anhydrite-($CaSO_4$) bearing sequences. Sulphur is abundant or even over-abundant in many countries as a byproduct of the refining of sulphide ores and of treating sour gas wells. Pyrite and marcasite (both FeS_2) occur in many sedimentary successions in varying purity, and as a minor constituent in hard coal deposits. 'Coal pyrites' are by-products of the upgrading and purification of hard coals. Pyrite is also the main sulphide mineral, occurring together with many base metals. It is often discarded together with low grade metal-containing rocks and wastes on mine tailings.

Elemental sulphur applied to alkaline soils for pH reduction is not a very common practice because high amounts of S are required to be effective. Sulphur applied in combination with phosphate rock has been tested to achieve *in-situ* phosphate solubilization and increase supplies of P and S to soils and plants (Swaby 1975; Rajan 1983, 1987a; Loganathan *et al.* 1994). When S and PRs are mixed together and applied to the soil, the sulphur oxidizes, forming sulphuric acid which in turn assists in the dissolution of phosphate rock. The actual rate of P release can be controlled to a great extent by the amount of S used. Sulphur mixed with phosphate rocks and inoculated with the sulphur oxidizing bacteria *Thiobacillus ssp,* has been tested in many soils and proved as effective as superphosphates (Logonathan *et al.* 1994), particularly as slow-release P and S fertilizer. 'Biosuper,' as this blend is called, is very effective in many tropical soils and is superior to single superphosphate in areas that receive more than 635 mm of rain (Swaby 1975). Under these conditions it can be used as controlled P and S fertilizer for pastures and long-term agricultural and horticultural crops.

The iron sulphide mineral pyrite has not been widely regarded as a promising agromineral because of its common association with potentially toxic metal impurities. But in some parts of the world, for example, India, pyrite is widely used as an S (and Fe) fertilizer (Tiwari *et al.* 1985). Agricultural pyrite from Amjore (Bihar) of sedimentary origin contains 22-30% S and is used successfully on calcareous soils of northern Bihar State as a S and Fe fertilizer for production of chickpeas, peas and lentils (Tiwari *et al.* 1985).

Another use of pyrite is to reclaim alkaline sodic soils. Pyrite has been tested as a soil amendment to reclaim sodic and calcareous soils by reducing the pH and improving soil structure (Banath and Holland 1976; Dubey and Mondal 1993). In many experiments, pyrite applied to alkaline sodic soils was however outperformed by another sulphur-bearing mineral – gypsum. Gupta *et al.* (1988) incorporated pyrites and

Mussoorie phosphate rock (MPR) from India in decomposing cattle manure and tested the effectiveness of the P- and S-enriched manure in pot trials. The level of available P for mustard can be increased by decomposition of MPR in organic manure in the presence of acidifying pyrite.

Pyrites from mill tailings have also been tested as an inexpensive material to correct Fe deficiencies in calcareous soils (Barrau and Berg 1977). Depending on the particle size of the pyrite and susceptibility to oxidation, pyrites can serve as a continuous slow release Fe source on sodic and Fe-deficient soils (Vlek and Lindsay 1978).

Few experiments with pyrites have been carried out in Africa. Among them is the experiment by Lowell and Weil (1995), who tested pyrite as a means of enhancing phosphorus availability from phosphate rock in a laboratory study. Pyrite and various African phosphate rocks in several ratios were incubated and the soluble P and pH was measured in the leachates. Soluble P measured in the leachate was greatest in Pyrite-PR mixtures with Togo PR and the Sukulu PR from Uganda. Soluble P released from pyrites mixed with phosphate rocks from Tundulu in Malawi and Minjingu in Tanzania was virtually zero (Lowell and Weil 1995).

4.4   Gypsum

Another useful agromineral is gypsum, the most commonly applied soil amendment for the reclamation of sodium affected soils (Shainberg *et al.* 1989). 'Black alkaline soils' are soils with excessive quantities of sodium adsorbed to clay minerals. They are characterized by surface crusting and formation of physically impermeable, hard-setting soils. The processes of hard setting and crusting can be overcome by spreading gypsum over the surface. Gypsum improves black alkali soils by providing soluble calcium, which replaces the sodium adsorbed on the clay minerals. Results from field experiments in many parts of the world showed that gypsum applied at several tonnes per hectare decreases the sodium adsorption ratio, physically improves the infiltration rate and significantly increases yields. Naturally occurring gypsum can be used for this purpose but an industrial by-product from the phosphate fertilizer industry, phospho-gypsum, is also very effective in improving the soils' physical properties.

Gypsum, applied at the surface or subsoil, is reported to reduce phytotoxicity in acid soils (Alva and Sumner 1989; Sumner 1995). The mechanism for this reduction is the downward movement of soluble calcium and the subsequent exchange with aluminum in the subsoil (McRay and Sumner 1990; Sumner 1995).

High-analysis fertilizers like urea, di-ammonium phosphate (DAP), or Triple superphosphate (TSP) have economic advantages because of savings in transport, storage and handling but they have a major set-back as they do not include sulphur. This vital soil nutrient is needed in many soils of Africa, including soils in West Africa (Friesen 1991) and Malawi (Weil and Mughogo 2000). Field trials at many sites in semi-arid and sub-humid West Africa have shown the agronomic effectiveness of elemental sulphur or sulphates, such as gypsum or phosphogypsum. Friesen (1991) demonstrated that the S deficiencies in the region could be corrected at relatively low cost.

Studies in Brazil, South Africa and the United States have found that gypsum significantly increases yields when applied at rates between 1 and 10 tonnes per hectare. In most cases the yield responses were related to Ca and S nutrition. Groundnuts (*Arachis hypogaea*) have high requirements for Ca (McNeil 1987; Alva *et al.* 1989; Caires and Rosolem 1991) but also for other elements, such as S and P, B and other trace elements. Without sufficient Ca, pod development will be curtailed leading to empty pods or poorly formed seeds. Calcium is most critical for pod development between 15 and 35 days after the pegs reach the soil. Gypsum is used in groundnut production schemes as it provides both Ca and S (Walker 1975).

The main gypsum deposits in sub-Saharan Africa are associated with Mesozoic to Recent sediments and evaporative crusts. They are found in many coastal basins and in various localities in continental basins in

West-Central Africa and the Rift valleys. Gypsum as by-product from the phosphate industry (phospho-gypsum) is found in large amounts in Senegal and Zimbabwe.

4.5   Natural K-minerals and rocks

The most commonly used form of K input in agriculture is potassium salts (potash) These naturally occurring K fertilizers are mainly obtained from sedimentary potash (K-salt) deposits providing minerals such as sylvite (KCl) or complex K-Mg chlorides and sulphates. These K-fertilizers are water soluble and are consequently favoured as fast acting K- and K-Mg fertilizers.

The main source of K for plants growing under natural conditions comes from the weathering of K minerals and organic K-sources such as composts and plant residues. The most important K minerals are K-feldspar, leucite, K-micas such as biotite, phlogopite, and glauconite, and clays such as illite. K-rich silicate rocks with relatively fast weathering characteristics are leucite-bearing volcanics.

Potassium occurs in feldspars in very weathering-resistant framework lattice positions (Sanz-Scovino and Rowell 1988). The potassium ion is not easily released and is therefore not easily plant available. In contrast, the minerals of the mica and micaceous clay group have sheet silicate structure. Here, K occupies the interlayer position and Mg and Fe^{2+} in the octahedral positions. Laboratory studies by Schnitzer and Kodama (1976) and Tan (1980) showed that naturally occurring humic compounds can extract a large percentage of K, Mg, Fe, and smaller amounts of Si and Al from the crystal structure of biotite and phlogopite but not from muscovite. Biotite, the tri-octahedral more iron-rich mica, is less stable with acid treatment than phlogopite (Schnitzer and Kodama 1976; Feigenbaum et al. 1981). The consequence is that K can be easily and quickly released from both biotite and phlogopite. In contrast, the release of K from muscovite and K-feldspar is too slow to be of much agronomic use.

Mica minerals such as phlogopite and biotite contain considerable amounts of K_2O (usually > 10%), MgO (5-22%) and Fe (5-20%). Most of these nutrients are part of the silicate structure, in a form not readily available to plants and animals. Their release has been studied in fundamental soil and mineral research in laboratory studies (Rausel-Colom 1965; Schnitzer and Kodama 1976; Tan 1980; Feigenbaum et al. 1981; Kodama et al. 1983; Song and Huang 1988; and others). Weerasuriya et al. (1993) conducted experiments with scrap grade phlogopite from a Sri Lankan mica processing centre. The researchers treated phlogopite with various acids and reported that up to 65% of the K and Mg contained in the phlogopite could be recovered. In greenhouse experiments they demonstrated that acidulated phlogopite chips at an application rate of 200 kg ha^{-1} gave significantly higher yields of rice as compared to the control with KCl (Weerasuriya et al. 1993).

The release of K from phlogopite and biotite through the actions of rhizosphere microflora has been studied by many scientist including Berthelin et al. (1991), Hinsinger and Jaillard (1993), and Hinsinger et al. (1993). Electron-microscopic and x-ray studies prove that the roots of rape (Brassica rapus) and ryegrass can transform phlogopite into vermiculite, releasing K and Mg to the plants. Roots and rhizospheres of plants are active biological weathering agents that transform micas and release K and other cations.

Glauconite is a hydrous iron potassium mica with the chemical formula $3X_2(Fe^{3+},$ $Fe^{2+},Y)_6(Si_4O_{10})(OH)_4 \cdot nH_2O$, whereby X is K^+, Na^+, or Ca^{2+} and Y is Al or Mg. Glauconites occur commonly in 'glauconitic greensands' as unconsolidated sandy, silty and clayey sediments of marine, near-shore sediments with slow rates of sedimentation. Clean glauconites contain up to 11% K_2O, while glauconite-rich 'greensands' contain commonly 5-9% K_2O. Glauconites are often spatially associated with sedimentary phosphate accumulations.

Glauconitic greensands can be used, in large application rates, as slow-release, low-grade K soil amendments with cation exchange capacities around 20 cmol$^+$ kg^{-1}. They have been used in large amounts in the 19th century in the United States and are still produced in the US in low tonnages, but mainly for water purification purposes. In the 1860s the annual production of greensands from New Jersey were almost 1 million tonnes. In 1960 glauconite production for agricultural purposes was only 3,750 tons (New Jersey Geological Survey, cited in Markewicz and Lodding 1983). In current agricultural land management practices higher-grade K sources have largely displaced agricultural use of greensands. The use of glauconitic greensands should only be considered when the glauconite content is > 70-80% glauconite, and for crops that require slow-release potassium resources, for example, coconuts, bananas, oil palm.

Leucite ($K(AlSi_2O_6)$) and nepheline ($KNa_3(AlSiO_4)_4$) as well as kalsilite ($K(AlSiO_4)$) are feldspathoids found in various rock types, specifically silica undersaturated volcanics and other alkaline rock suites. Large areas of East Africa's volcanic provinces are covered with volcanics that contain leucite, nepheline and in rare cases kalsilite. Also, alkaline complexes with nepheline-bearing rock suites are well described in parts of sub-Saharan Africa, mostly in eastern and southern Africa, associated with rift structures (Black *et al.* 1985). No use of nepheline- or leucite-rich rock materials has been reported, although Mathers (1994) mentioned the potential of these K-rich rock types as 'petrofertilizers.' Bioleaching experiments using leucite concentrate and the microorganisms *Penicillium expansum* and *Aspergillus niger* showed that between 21% and 27% of the potassium contained in the leucite mineral could be leached by microbial means (Rossi 1978).

Environmental and economic considerations are the driving forces in the move from highly reactive, soluble fertilizers towards the use of slow release fertilizers. The presently used K-fertilizers are not only soluble and easily available, they are also easily leachable nutrient sources, especially in sandy soils with little clay and organic matter. Many of these soluble K sources traded as K-fertilizers, for instance 'muriate of potash' – KCl, are salts, which can pose problems to salt-sensitive crops.

Novel approaches are needed to 'unlock' K from the silicate structure of these minerals in order to render K more available for plant and animal nutrition. Similar to long-term slow release natural fertilizers like rock phosphates, the two micas biotite and phlogopite, as well as some of the feldspathoids (for example, leucite) will gradually release K and Mg nutrients, but to be practical for agriculture and horticulture, the release rate might have to be speeded up. Some potassium-demanding crops like bananas, coconut trees, and rubber and oil palm plantations may benefit from the slow release of K from these minerals and rocks.

4.6   Micronutrients

Eight of the seventeen elements that are essential for plant growth are micronutrients. On soils with micronutrient deficiencies, the application of small amounts of these nutrients can greatly enhance crop production. The micronutrients are: Boron (B), chlorine (Cl), cobalt (Co), copper (Cu), iron (Fe), manganese (Mn), molybdenum (Mo), and zinc (Zn). The term micronutrient does not imply that these elements occur in 'micro' amounts in rocks and soils. Two of the eight micronutrients, Fe and Mn, are among the most abundant elements in the earth's crust. The other six elements occur in concentrations of less than 0.1%, they are 'trace elements.' The term micronutrients only means that these elements are required in very small amounts by plants. In addition, there are other elements that are, in small amounts, helpful but not essential for the growth of certain plants, such as silicon (Si), vanadium (V), nickel (Ni) and sodium (Na). Small amounts of other elements, including chromium (Cr), tin (Sn), iodine (I), and fluorine (F) are essential for animal growth.

While the micronutrients are required in small amounts, they may be harmful when added to the soil in high amounts. There is a small 'window' of concentration of these elements where plant growth is optimal. Taking molybdenum as an example, it can be shown that the addition of 35-70 g Mo ha^{-1} to specific soils will be beneficial to soils and plants. However, if applied at rates exceeding 3 kg Mo ha^{-1} some plants may show toxicity signs. In addition, at these high rates the concentration in the forage may become toxic to animals consuming these plants. It is important to know the original concentration of micronutrients in the soils and add only as much of the micronutrient as is beneficial to plants and foraging animals.

The replenishment of micronutrients through fertilizers or other amendments is still in its infancy in many tropical countries. In most fertilizer applications, only the macronutrients are applied although cropping, erosion and leaching also remove micronutrients from the soils. Some of the nutrients 'lost' through harvesting, erosion or leaching are replenished by the return of organic residues, through farmyard manure and other organic matter.

The availability of micronutrients is influenced not only by the total amount of micronutrients but also by soil factors such as pH, soil texture, organic matter content, moisture, oxidation/reduction condition and others. The most obvious relationship is between total micronutrient concentration and parent material.

Micronutrients in soils of sub-Saharan Africa

Few accounts have been published of the micronutrient status of soils in sub-Saharan Africa (Schutte 1954; Sillanpaeae 1982; Kang and Osiname 1985). Ironically, large numbers of soil samples from sub-Saharan Africa have been analyzed on their 'trace element' contents. These soils data outlining metallic trace element concentrations have been collected by geologists and geochemists from national geological surveys, international organizations and private exploration companies. Exploration geochemists commonly use trace element soil survey data as indicators to higher metal concentration and metal deposits. By and large, however, these trace element data compiled by geochemists have not been shared among the scientists of the two principle disciplines of agrogeology, geology and agriculture.

In sub-Saharan Africa, micronutrient deficiencies or toxicities were first recognized in areas where cash crops were grown. Only in the last few decades has more emphasis been given to the micronutrient status of soils for other crops. Kang and Osiname (1985) provide examples of common micronutrient deficiencies in sub-Saharan Africa. The worldwide study by Sillanpacac (1982) provided data on micronutrient concentrations in selected soils of Africa. It illustrated that copper, zinc and molybdenum deficiencies are common in many coarse textured, acid soils of Ethiopia, Ghana, Malawi, Nigeria, Sierra Leone, Tanzania, and Zambia.

Boron deficiencies have been reported mainly from research on cash crop oil palm and cotton-growing areas in West and East Africa (Kang and Osiname 1985), and response to boron fertilization has been reported in forestry research. A statistically significant reduction of incidence of die-back of eucalyptus species was achieved through boron application (Kadeba 1990). In Zimbabwe, colemanite and borate fertilizers were applied on cotton and sunflower and were equally effective when incorporated in NPK fertilizers (Rowell and Grant 1975).

Few systematic studies have been undertaken to determine the distribution of chlorine in soils of sub-Saharan Africa, although a preliminary survey of savanna soils of Nigeria indicates that about eighty percent of these soils may be chlorine deficient (Raji and Jimba 1999).

Cobalt is required by nitrogen-fixing microorganisms. It is an essential element for N-fixing legumes. In animal health, the lack of cobalt in forage plants can lead to muscular 'wasting' and death in ruminants. In New Zealand this deficiency-induced disease is called 'bush-sickness;' in Australia it is the 'coast disease' or 'wasting disease,' and in Kenya it is called 'Nakuruitis' (McDowell 1992). Cobalt deficiencies in grazing ruminants can be prevented or cured by treating pastures with 'cobaltized' fertilizers, or through oral application of heavy pellets (bullets) made of cobalt oxide and iron (McDowell 1992).

Copper deficiencies are common in many coarse textured acid soils in sub-Saharan Africa. Deficiencies of copper have influenced the growth of wheat on soils derived from volcanic ash and pumice in Kenya and Tanzania (Nyandat and Ochieng 1976; Kamasho and Singh 1982) and copper deficiencies are also reported from peat and muck soils in various countries.

Iron deficiencies are rare in sub-Saharan soils due to the large pools of iron in weathered soils. However, areas that have been subjected to bush fires showed iron-deficiencies. Burning resulted in increased soil pH and thereby reduced the plant-availability of iron. The ferrous form is the preferred form of Fe for micronutrient use. Ferric oxides like magnetite are not suitable as micronutrient source. Sources to successfully overcome iron deficiencies in high pH soils include Fe-chelates and organic materials, such as manure. Pyrite-enriched manure proved a good source for iron on alkaline soils (Bangar *et al.* 1985). Barak *et al.* (1983) successfully used finely ground basalt and volcanic tuff from a local quarrying operation that contain several percent Fe as Fe (II to remedy chlorosis of groundnuts (*Arachis hypogaea*) in calcareous soils.

Although <u>manganese</u> deficiencies are rare in sub-Saharan Africa, high plant-available Mn can cause toxicities, especially in acid soils. Increasing soil pH through liming can prevent Mn toxicities. In parts of the world where Mn is deficient in soils, Mn sulfates, Mn carbonates or MnO have been applied successfully (Mordtvedt 1985).

<u>Molybdenum</u>, essential for nitrogen fixation through symbiotic microorganisms, is critical for many leguminous crops. Molybdenum deficiencies have been identified in some groundnut growing areas of Senegal, northern Ghana, and northern Nigeria (references in Kang and Osiname 1985). Martin and Fourier (1965) describe the positive effects of Mo application on sandy aeolian sands of West Africa leading to improved groundnut yields, nodulation and nitrogen fixation. Mo deficiencies and related problems can be expected in many parts of Africa, especially for legumes that have high Mo requirements like soybeans and groundnuts. Molybdenum deficiencies have also been observed on acid soils of Zimbabwe where maize is grown.

In contrast to deficiencies there are also Mo toxicities, especially in parts of the world with high-molybdenum parent materials and poorly drained alkaline soils. Cases of molybdenosis (molybdenum toxicity), a disease in ruminants (stiffness of legs, loss of hair) feeding on forage containing more than 10 to 20 mg Mo kg^{-1}, have been reported from North America and from Kenya (McDowell 1992).

Low <u>zinc</u> concentrations have been found to reduce maize yields in several parts of Africa, for example in Nigeria (Osiname *et al.* 1973), Zimbabwe, and Zambia (Banda and Singh 1989). Zinc deficiencies are also quite common with the cultivation of rice (Kanwar and Youngdahl 1985). There is growing evidence that Zn becomes gradually deficient in parts of Nigeria's savanna, especially in areas under continuous cultivation and phosphate fertilization (Lombin 1983; Agbenin 1998). Zinc is commonly supplied to crops as manufactured zinc sulfate fertilizers, but slowly dissolving zinc oxide has also been used successfully on wheat in South Africa (Dietricksen and Laker, cited in Mortvedt 1985).

<u>Micronutrient resources</u>

Natural abundances of micronutrients are closely linked to rock types. For example, igneous ultramafic and mafic rocks (pyroxenites, basalts) contain generally higher amounts of Cu, Co, Fe, and Mn than silica-rich granites. Several sediments are enriched in micronutrients; for example black shales contain elevated concentrations of boron and other trace elements. In general, basalts and shales are rock types with abundant micronutrient elements.

The highest concentrations of micronutrient elements found in rock-forming minerals.

- Boron occurs in tourmaline, in clay minerals and evaporate salts (borax, colemanite, kernite, ulexite) in desert playas,
- Chlorine is the primary component of common salt, halite (NaCl), and sylvite (KCl),
- Cobalt is common, in small amounts, in ferromagnesian silicates substituting for Fe, or associated with Mn oxides, or in sulfides, carbonates, and in marine Mn-nodules,
- Copper is a component in the sulfides chalcopyrite ($CuFeS_2$), bornite ($Cu_5 FeS_4$), chalcocite (Cu_2S), or occurs as carbonates (malachite $Cu_2(OH)_2CO_3$ or azurite $Cu_3(OH)_2(CO_3)_2$),

- Iron occurs as constituent of certain silicates, and is the main metal compound in the Fe-oxides hematite, magnetite, goethite/limonite, as well as in the sulfides (mainly pyrite FeS_2),
- Manganese occurs mainly as oxides (pyrolysite MnO_2, hausmannite Mn_3O_4, manganite $MnOOH$), and less abundantly, as Mn-carbonates and in Mn-silicates,
- Molybdenum occurs as sulfide (MoS_2), and more rarely as molybdite (MoO_3) or as powellite ($CaMoO_4$) in hydrothermal veins,
- Zinc occurs as sulfide ZnS, carbonate (smithsonite $ZnCO_3$) or, in small amounts, in magnetite and silicate.

Most micronutrient element resources are of geological origin, derived either from primary ore or as a by-product. While some of the borates and chlorides can be concentrated and processed simply by dissolution in hot water (borax, halite, sylvite) or calcination (for colemanite), most micronutrient resources have to be processed by hydrometallurgical or pyrometallurgical processes to get them into a soluble form.

Commercial micronutrient fertilizers are generally manufactured as by-products or intermediate products of metal mining and processing industries. There are only a few large mineral deposits of micronutrients in sub-Saharan Africa, mainly iron oxide deposits and manganese oxide deposits, as well as copper/cobalt and zinc sulphide deposits. Only a few boron and molybdenum occurrences are known in sub-Saharan Africa. However, it should be kept in mind that only small amounts (traces) of these elements are needed to correct deficiencies. One kg of molybdenite (MoS_2), for example, contains about 600 g Mo. Obviously, molybdate would have to be subjected to an oxidizing environment to get it into a plant available form. But, on a total Mo basis, the 600 g of molybdenum would be enough to provide additional molybdenum to 10-20 hectares at a rate of 30-60 g total Mo per hectare. Currently, molybdenum fertilizers are sodium and ammonium molybdates that are either applied with commercial fertilizers or applied in the form of treated seeds.

Many of the existing mining and processing of metal deposits produce micronutrient-rich 'wastes,' which should be investigated on their suitability to remedy local micronutrient deficiencies. Examples for cobalt-rich 'wastes' include the 'waste-pyrites' at Kilembe mine in Uganda with 1% Co and many old mine tailings in the Democratic Republic of Congo. These materials need careful geochemical screening before testing on land to avoid introducing toxic elements to the soils.

Since only small amounts of nutrients are necessary to overcome micronutrient deficiencies it will be useful to test the application of organic wastes, which are commonly high in micronutrients, or to apply trace element rich rock wastes, for example quarry fines from basalt or 'black granite' (dolerite) operations. The mean micronutrient concentration (in mg kg^{-1}) of basaltic rocks are: B = 5; Cl = 60; Co = 50; Cu = 100; Fe = 86,000; Mn = 2,200; Mo = 1; and Zn = 100. Micronutrient concentrations in common shales are, in mg kg^{-1}: B = 100; Cl = 180; Co = 20; Cu = 50; Mn = 850; Mo = 3; and Zn = 100 (Levinson 1974). Organic-rich 'black shales' contain much higher concentrations of micronutrients. In fact the average Mo content of black shale is 70 mg Mo kg^{-1} (Ure and Berrow 1982). Disadvantages of using these rock materials are the large amounts needed to provide the micronutrients in the field, the availability of these resources close to the area where they are needed, and the value-to-cost ratio.

4.7   Ground silicate rocks

Silicate minerals and rocks contain most of the nutrients that plants require for growth and development. Ground silicate rocks have been investigated for their potential to provide these nutrients to plants in various soil environments. The application of ground silicate rocks to highly weathered, low fertility, acid soils has been proposed as alternative to conventional fertilization with water-soluble fertilizers in areas where fertilizers are not available or in organic agriculture (Leonardos *et al.* 1987, 2000; Von Fragstein *et al.* 1988; Coroneos *et al.* 1996). The effects of applying large tonnages of ground silicate rocks as byproducts of the quarrying industry are part of an alternative sustainable strategy to 'remineralize' or 'recapitalize' degraded soils (Von Fragstein et al. 1988; Leonardos et al. 1987, 2000).

Most research on nutrient release from rock-forming minerals has focused on dissolution mechanisms, dissolution rates, pathways and processes of primary minerals in soils. While the mineralogical and geochemical processes involved in the dissolution of various rock-forming minerals have been well covered, pathways and reactions in complex soil systems are less well understood. They include physical, chemical, mineralogical and biochemical factors and interactions that control the processes at the interface between the minerals, solutions, air and organisms in soils. In a comprehensive paper, Harley and Gilkes (2000) reviewed the various factors, which influence the release of plant nutrients from silicate rock powders.

In laboratory studies Blum et al. (1989a,b) investigated 5 different silicate rock powders available in Austria for their suitability for agricultural application. They showed that under laboratory conditions the release rate of nutrients from these ground rocks was very low. Ground silicate rocks contain a high proportion of elements that have no importance for plant nutrition. However, Blum et al. (1989b) concede that certain smectite-rich volcanic ashes could increase the cation exchange capacity of poor soils, for example of forest soils, but that their use in conventional agriculture under temperate climatic conditions would be not suitable. Von Fragstein et al. (1988) carried out similar tests, analyzing 32 different ground rock samples for their water and HCl extractable cations, trace micronutrients and pH. The highest cation release rates were from phonolitic rocks followed by basaltic rock types. Granite powder released the least amounts of cations regardless of extraction method. In water extracts, the pH of all samples was alkaline with ground phonolitic rocks reaching a pH of > 10, basalts pH 8-10, and granites pH 7-10. Von Fragstein et al. (1988) question the effectiveness of applying only small amounts of ground silicate rock (1 t ha^{-1} per year) and provide some figures on the high costs for the farmers for the various ground silicate rocks. It is apparent that large volumes are required to provide sufficient nutrients for sustainable growth of crops and trees.

So far, most investigations were carried out under laboratory conditions. In addition, experiments with rocks and minerals as potential nutrient supplying materials come mainly from temperate environments and only few investigations have been carried out under tropical conditions.

Investigations in temperate climates include the work of Bakken et al. (1997, 2000), who studied the fertilizing value of various K-bearing rocks and tailings on grasslands in Norway. The results of these trials under field conditions show that considerable parts of the K bound in biotite concentrate (from the feldspar production in Lillesand, Norway) and from nepheline in alkaline complexes and epidote schist is plant available. However, only 30% of the K added as ground silicate rocks was taken up by plants as compared to 70% from KCl. The weathering rate of the rock and mineral products was regarded as too slow to replenish the native pool of plant-available K within a three-year period with five harvests. The potassium held in potassium feldspar was almost unavailable to the grass plants (Bakken et al. 2000).

There are various mechanisms that can provide potassium from minerals to crops. For example, potassium can be released from phlogopite by biologically induced transformations (Berthelin et al. 1991; Hinsinger et al. 1993). The root zone of plants has proved a very active medium and habitat for microorganisms that enhance weathering and mineral concentration. In recent years the importance of biochemical processes at the root surface, and the role of microorganisms in the process of mineral weathering has been highlighted by Berthelin et al. (1991), Hinsinger et al. (1993) and Hinsinger (1998). Some minerals are more suitable for chemical and biological weathering than others and the release rates of nutrients from rock-forming minerals to roots and crops differ with differing physico-chemical and biological environments. In addition, weathering rates and kinetics in temperate climates are different from those in tropical and sub-tropical climates.

But not only the release of macronutrients from rocks and minerals has been studied. In field studies, Barak *et al.* (1983) demonstrated the effectiveness of finely ground basalt and basaltic tuff in micronutrient (Fe) fertilization of peanuts grown in calcareous soils.

While there are several studies in North America, Europe and Australia on the potential use of rock fertilizers, only very few studies and experiments have been published on rock-forming silicate minerals as soil amendments for agriculture and forestry in tropical soil environments. The few experiments that are reported indicate only the potential of ground rocks with high cation contents in tropical soils. Available data indicate that some of these minerals and rocks can be used as slow-release nutrient-supplying materials for crops in degraded tropical soils for agriculture and forestry (Roschnik *et al.* 1967; Leonardos *et al.* 1987, 2000; Gillman *et al.* 2000).

Leonardos *et al.* (1987) provided positive results of three greenhouse and field trials from lateritic soils in Brazil with beans (*Phaseolus vulgaris* L) and napier grass (*Pennisetum purpureum*). The potential of applying ground silicate rocks for tree fertilization purposes in the tropics is illustrated by the positive results of the initial experiments by Leonardos *et al.*(1987).

Studies by Gillman (1980) and Gillman *et al.* (2000) illustrate the positive effects of the application of large amounts of ground basaltic rocks on weathered soils of tropical Australia. The application of large quantities of ground basaltic rock raised pH, increased cation exchange capacities, and enhanced cation levels in soils.

In sub-Saharan Africa only few results of trials with crushed rock have been published. Among them are the results of greenhouse and field experiments from Zimbabwe and Mauritius. In Zimbabwe, Roschnik *et al.* (1967) tested finely ground basaltic rocks in strongly weathered Kalahari sands in glasshouse experiments. High application rates (5-40 tonnes per acre) showed exponential growth increase in total yield of two slow-growing legumes. The yield increase of sunflowers grown on Kalahari soils following treatment with 5-40 tons per acre of finely ground basalt showed a linear response curve (Roschnik *et al.* 1967). Increased yields of sugar cane are reported from systematic field trials in Mauritius (d'Hotman de Villiers 1961). Here, significant yield responses of sugar cane to the application of large doses (up to 180 tonnes per hectare) of ground basalt have been reported.

More research using ground silicate wastes from rock crushing operations for soil amelioration on acid strongly weathered tropical soils is necessary to validate positive results from greenhouse and field experiments. Also, the combination of ground rocks with soluble fertilizers and organic residues should be assessed. More laboratory, greenhouse and field studies need to be conducted with rocks and minerals with high cation concentrations and relatively high weathering potential, like feldspathoids, and mafic, ultrapotassic and potassic volcanic rocks. It is also important to better understand which soils and which plants may promote the dissolution of rock powders. These experiments must be carried out over a long time period in order to assess their long-term effect.

As with phosphate rocks, it is important to study inorganic-organic interactions and transformations using locally available organic materials in combination with rock and mineral materials. In addition, it is important to conduct economic and ecological studies as well in order to evaluate the practicality and sustainability of these systems.

Extensive parts of sub-Saharan Africa are covered with large volumes of relatively young basaltic and potassic/ultrapotassic volcanics and other potentially suitable silicate rocks. Young volcanic rocks are mainly found in rift valley environments in east and southern Africa, as well as in parts of West Africa. The challenge is to explore these and other suitable rock materials as potential 'petrofertilizers' and assess their agronomic potential for perennial crops and trees.

4.8   Natural zeolites

Zeolites are a group of naturally occurring framework alumino-silicates with high cation exchange capacities, high adsorption and hydration-dehydration properties. About fifty different species of this mineral group have been identified, but only eight zeolite minerals make up the major part of volcano-sedimentary deposits: analcime, chabazite, clinoptilolite-heulandite, erionite, ferrierite, laumontite, mordenite and phillipsite. The structure of each of these minerals is different but they all have large open 'channels' in the crystal structure that provide a large void space for the adsorption and exchange of cations. The internal surface area of these channels can reach as much as several hundred square meters per gram of zeolite, making zeolites extremely effective ion exchangers (Mumpton 1984). Other useful chemical and physical properties include:

*   high void volume (up to 50%),
*   low density (2.1-2.2 g cm^{-3}),
*   excellent molecular sieve properties,
*   high cation exchange capacity (CEC): 150-250 cmol$^+$ kg^{-1},
*   cation selectivity, specifically for cations like ammonium, potassium, cesium, etc.

Relatively pure zeolite deposits have been discovered in over 50 countries, most of the major deposits being in or close to volcanic areas. Most geologists agree that many deposits have yet to be discovered especially in less investigated volcanic areas of the world. Initial geological investigations in Ethiopia have shown that extensive deposits (several million tonnes) of relatively pure natural zeolites exist in the Rift Valley of East Africa. Other zeolite deposits are known from Kenya and Tanzania.

Zeolites are increasingly being used in aquaculture, agriculture, horticulture, chemical industry, construction, waste management and for domestic uses (Clifton 1987; Mumpton 1984; Parham 1989). In the agricultural/horticultural field zeolites are used as:

*   as animal feed additives,
*   as soil and compost additives,
*   as carriers of pesticides and herbicides,
*   as potting media.

Zeolites are useful in agriculture because of their large porosity, their high cation exchange capacity and their selectivity for ammonium and potassium cations. They can be used both as carriers of nutrients and as a medium to free nutrients. The main use of zeolites in agriculture is, however, for nitrogen capture, storage and slow release. It has been shown that zeolites, with their specific selectivity for ammonium (NH_4^+), can take up this specific cation from either farmyard manure, composts or ammonium-bearing fertilizers, thereby reducing losses of nitrogen to the environment. Ammonium-charged zeolites have also been tested successfully for their ability to increase the solubilization of phosphate minerals (Lai and Eberl 1986; Chesworth et al. 1987), leading to improved phosphorus uptake and yields for sudangrass (Barbarick et al. 1990). Eberl and Lai (1992) developed urea-impregnated zeolite chips, which can be used as slow release nitrogen fertilizers. In Cuba, zeolites have also been successfully used as potting media in horticulture ('zeoponics'), where nutrient-charged zeolites together with other mineral phases provide the plants with substrate and nutrients for growth.

But the performance of natural zeolites must be assessed critically. There are about 50 different species of zeolites, each having a different chemical composition and structure. While most zeolites are beneficial in improving animal and plant growth, there are cases where zeolites do not perform effectively. For example, it has been demonstrated that certain zeolites with sodium as the main exchangeable cation can actually decrease rather than increase plant growth and yield (Barbarick and Pirela 1984). Also, the zeolite erionite can be harmful to health when inhaled by animals and humans (Suzuki and Kohyama 1988). This demonstrates the importance of good mineralogical and chemical characterization of zeolites and an intelligent selection of zeolites to suit their application.

4.9   Moisture storing rocks

The productivity of soils is not increased through nutrients alone. Other limiting factors such as lack of moisture can seriously limit crop production anywhere precipitation is limited. If there is not sufficient precipitation during the growing season, a crop either needs irrigation or must rely on moisture reserves stored before the time of planting. Mulching is a soil management technique to reduce high evaporation rates. Most mulches are organic materials, but inorganic materials like plastic films are also applied successfully. Another much cheaper mulching material is rock. The effectiveness of rock mulches in reducing evaporative losses is well illustrated in the Canary Islands, where volcanic scoria and pumice, even sand, have been applied for centuries in vegetable and crop farming (Chesworth *et al.* 1983; Caldas and Tejedor Salguero 1987). Results from an IDRC-supported agrogeology project in Ethiopia show that the soil moisture content can be conserved considerably by mulching with a 3-5 cm thick layer of volcanic scoria. The mulch helped bridge the soil moisture gap between the irregularly occurring rains (Woldeab *et al.* 1994).

Scoria is used in Saudi Arabia as support medium for trees outside the Geological Survey headquarters. Combined with an innovative subsurface drip irrigation system, the use of scoria proved to be highly effective for conserving water. This system required only about 10% of the water used with normal soils (Habib *et al.* 2001).

4.10 Wastes from selected mineral-based industries

There are several 'wastes' from mining and mineral-related industries that may be useful for low-input agriculture. They include:

- waste from incomplete calcining in lime operations,
- calcium carbonate wastes from cement and other industries using $CaCO_3$,
- tailings from diamond mining from kimberlites,
- wastes from 'black granite' operations,
- waste from phosphate mining,
- wastes from phosphate processing,
- pyrite wastes,
- wastes from steel production, such as basic slag, and calciumsilicate slag,
- wastes from coal burning operations, for example fly ash, bottom ash, the by-products of fluidized-bed combustion and materials from flue gas desulphurization scrubbers.

Some of the 'wastes' or 'byproducts' disposed of by mineral-based industries should be considered as a potential 'resource' for various crop production systems. Examples of 'waste utilization' for agricultural purposes are the use of incompletely calcined limestones or carbonates, or 'dust' from the cement industry as liming materials. Other already ground up and reprocessed 'dumps' include the tailings fines from kimberlite operations. These resources, characterized by rapidly weathering olivine-rich rocks and other Mg-rich rocks, are potential liming materials and local Mg sources, for example, for pastures.

Also the 'wastes' from phosphate mining operations, for example, phosphate fines, need agronomic testing. The International Fertilizer Development Center (IFDC) tested the phosphate fines of Togo for use as direct application P-fertilizer and the Zimbabwe-Canada agrogeology project currently investigates the use of phosphate fines and vermiculite-rich tailings in agriculture in communal lands in Zimbabwe. Phospho-gypsum should be tested as a soil amendment on sodic soils and for groundnut fertilization.

Mine tailings containing biotite have been tested as slow-release K fertilizers on pasture in Norway (Bakken *et al.* 1997, 2000). Calcium silicate slags, also by-products of the steel industry, have shown considerable yield increases for sugar cane, specifically on low-Si soils (Ayres 1966; Anderson *et al.*

1991). Magnesium-containing fluidized bed combustion byproducts have proved to be effective liming materials with a high effectiveness to ameliorate subsoil Al phytotoxicity (Stehouwer *et al.* 1999). Pyrites and pyritic mill tailings with low heavy metal contents have also been tested as inexpensive Fe-sources for sodic and Fe-deficient soils.

Basic slag is a known P resource that is widely used in European agriculture. Basic slag is a byproduct from the steel industry, either from the basic Bessemer or the basic open-hearth process (Waggaman 1952), has been used in a ground form as a phosphatic fertilizer and liming material since the late 1800s. In recent years, the steel industry in many countries has been using different steel making processes and different ores, thus making P-rich basic slag less available. In the early days of steel making, basic slag was a 'waste' of steel production from highly phosphatic iron ores. A process was developed that completely removed phosphorus from pig iron, resulting in high-grade structurally sound steel, and the byproduct, basic slag (Waggaman 1952). In the late 1800s it was discovered that ground basic slag had considerable fertilizing value. In Europe, basic slag was used extensively as fertilizer and liming material. Before World War II, basic slag supplied about 70% of the phosphate used for fertilizing purposes in Germany, and substantial amounts were used in Belgium, France, and Britain. In 1970/71 about one third of the phosphate used by German farmers was in the form of basic slag (Fleischel 1972). Basic slag was also widely used in Brazil (Sanchez and Uehara 1980).

The composition of basic slag varies from one steel producer to another, depending largely on the iron source material used in the process. In general, basic slags are composed of mainly calcium silico-phosphates and some iron silico-phosphates (Waggaman 1952), and significant amounts of iron, and smaller amounts of Si, Mg, and Mn. Basic slag contains between 11 and 23% P_2O_5, 38-59% CaO and 2-8% MgO. It also contains small amounts of Al, V, and S, as well as trace amounts of copper (100-200 mg kg^{-1}), molybdenum (5-40 mg kg^{-1}), zinc (10-30 mg kg^{-1}) and cobalt (2-9 mg kg^{-1}).

The fertilizer value of basic slag has been evaluated over the decades under a wide range of climatic and soil conditions, as well as on different crops, grasses and trees. As expected, the agronomic effectiveness of basic slag as a fertilizing and liming material differs from crop to crop and from soil to soil. Successful applications of basic slag are reported from fertilizing potatoes, sugar beet, fodder beet and various cereals (ryegrass, rape, maize) in temperate climates. In comparison to water-soluble phosphate fertilizer, the effectiveness of basic slag was inferior in crops that need readily available P like carrots, lettuce, or broccoli (Mattingley 1968). Basic slag has also been used as P-fertilizer and liming material for grassland on acid soils in many countries, including New Zealand (Lynch and Davies 1964), Germany (Fleischel 1972) and Brazil (Sanchez and Uehara 1980). Basic slag has proved effective in forest soils as a liming material and fertilizer, providing P, Ca and Mg (Mayer-Krapoll 1969; Vandre *et al.* 1991; Belcacem *et al.* 1992). Addition of basic slag improved growth and health of trees, especially on poor sandy soils.

Past 'waste utilization' practices usually centred around application of solitary products. A new concept is that of combining or co-utilizing byproducts. An example is coal fly ash in combination with biosolids, such as sewage sludge and poultry manure (Schumann and Sumner 2000). Large amounts of fly ash and sewage sludges are currently applied for forest fertilization in India and large afforestation projects using fly-ash and biosolids are planned in India and China (Dr. M. Powell, pers. comm. 2002). This concept of blending and co-utilization could easily be expanded into other areas of 'waste' utilization for agriculture and forestry, for example, blending selected mine wastes with sewage sludge.

5. Agrominerals in greenhouses and plant nurseries.

Greenhouse production of vegetables and flowers, mainly for the overseas market, is developing rapidly in parts of sub-Saharan Africa. For the growth and packaging of plants and flowers the industry requires growth media and light-weight sterile packaging media. Tree nurseries are common in most countries, but the use of growing media other than soil is still very limited in sub-Saharan Africa. In the world there are millions of plants grown in shallow-drained container soils each year. Constructed growth media are used in containers and pots, on sportsfields and restricted landscapes, for example, on rooftop gardens, on courtyards, patios, etc.

Constructed growth media offer several advantages over conventional soil mixes: They are homogenous, disease- and insect-free and light weight. Fertilization and water use can be carefully controlled. Constructed growth media provide anchorage for plant roots, good aeration, and water-holding capacities, and the flow of fertilizers can be easily regulated. Among the common ingredients of soil-less mixtures are peat, perlite, and vermiculite. They can be used as soil amendments and growing media in greenhouse operations and tree nurseries. Growth media in greenhouses generally include mixes of lightweight bulky and sterile mineral materials like perlite, vermiculite and peat.

5.1   Perlite

Perlite is the term for unprocessed and processed forms of a volcanic glassy material. The 'crude' unprocessed perlite is a meta-stable, amorphous, silica-rich volcanic rock of rhyolitic to rhyodacitic composition, usually of Tertiary age or younger. The transparent light gray to glassy black rock has pearl-like lustre and exhibits numerous concentric cracks resembling an onion skin in appearance. Crude perlite is chemically inert, has a pH of about 7, a specific gravity of 2.2 to 2.4 g cm^{-3}, and contains 2-5% combined water. When the mineral is rapidly heated above 1000° C in special furnaces, the rock melts and then expands up to 20 times its original volume by the vaporization of the trapped moisture. It is this mass of white, glassy foam that forms commercial 'perlite,' a porous, light-weight, sterile, physically stable silicate with good thermal insulation properties, and a neutral pH. Expanded perlite has a low bulk density (for example bulk density of coarse perlite is 0.1 g cm^{-3}) but has virtually no cation exchange properties. Perlite is a resilient rock material that does not deteriorate in potting mixes and soils.

Perlite has been used successfully in many applications as a component of various growing media for a variety of horticultural crops and flowers. In recent years it is increasingly being used in commercial plant growing and hydroponic operations, and in special perlite 'bag systems,' for example, for the production of tomatoes and cucumbers (Wilson 1985). Coarse 'horticultural perlite' is used as part of potting mixes for tree and horticultural plant seedlings. In these applications this resilient material is especially valued for its good aeration and drainage properties. In addition, finely ground white perlite powder sprinkled onto the surface of seedblocks aids early plant growth due to its high brightness and reflectance of light onto the underside of leaves of the growing seedlings.

Crude perlite has been described from a number of volcanic regions in sub-Saharan Africa, including Djibouti, Mozambique and South Africa. Only in South Africa is perlite commercially mined. There is however a great potential of finding perlites in other volcanic regions of Africa, including Ethiopia, Kenya, Tanzania, and other areas with young silica-rich volcanism, such as along the Western Rift, and on various volcanic islands in which obsidians and rhyolitic tuffs are reported.

5.2   Pumice

Pumice is a naturally occurring light-coloured, cellular, frothy, chemically inert and physically resilient volcanic rock, similar to the artificially expanded perlite. It forms as result of violent expansion of dissolved gases in a viscous, silicic-rich lava such as rhyolite or rhyodacite. It is found in large consolidated and unconsolidated deposits close to the volcanic vents from which it was ejected. Like perlite, pumice has sealed internal pores, making it a very light-weight material. In fact, most pumice blocks can float on water.

Pumice resources are exploited for many purposes, mainly for the building industry, for the abrasive industry and the stonewashing of jeans, and only a minor amount is used for soil amending purposes (McMichael 1990). Pumice produced for horticultural purposes is won from unconsolidated deposits solely by crushing and sizing. Environmentally, the production of pumice is more 'friendly' than that of perlite or vermiculite as it does not require high-energy inputs for thermal expansion. Nature has already completed this process during the formation of pumice.

In many unconsolidated deposits sizing is the only processing technology required, thus making it a very inexpensive soil amendment and growth medium. Differences with perlite are mainly related to the range of pore sizes, shape and independent particle size. Investigations by Noland *et al.* (1992) showed that pumice has similar physico-chemical properties to those of perlite and can thus be used as an inexpensive substitute for perlite in greenhouses and plant nurseries.

Unconsolidated pumice deposits have been described in several countries in sub-Saharan Africa with Tertiary to younger silicic volcanism. Countries in which sizeable pumice deposits have been described include the countries along the Eastern and Western Rift; for example, Ethiopia, Djibouti, Kenya, Uganda, and Tanzania. It is not known whether pumice is used anywhere in sub-Saharan Africa for soil amending purposes or in container-based cropping systems, in greenhouses or in plant nurseries.

5.3 Vermiculite

In its crude form vermiculite is a laminar hydrated ferromagnesian sheet silicate mineral that resembles mica. It is found in various geological environments, the main occurrences being associated with surficially altered carbonatites and pyroxenites.

When subjected to high temperatures (> 900° C), particles of vermiculite exfoliate by expanding at right angles to the cleavage of the mineral. The exfoliation of vermiculite is the result of mechanical separation of the layers by the rapid conversion of contained water to steam. It is this exfoliated low-density vermiculite that is known in the building and horticultural industry for its excellent properties of insulation and fire resistance, good absorption and cation exchange capacities. In greenhouse applications this light-weight mineral has good water retention and high cation exchange capacities (50-150 cmol kg^{-1}). Vermiculite is widely used in container mixes, but also for seed germination, transplanting of trees and other plants, as a carrier of pesticides and fertilizers, and in feed additives for poultry, cattle and other animals.

Vermiculites have been discovered in various geological environments in sub-Saharan Africa. Most potential vermiculite accumulations are found in surficially altered carbonatites and ultramafic bodies; for example, in Kenya, Malawi, South Africa, Uganda, Zimbabwe. To date, most of the vermiculite is exported from the above countries and little has been consumed locally.

5.4 Peat

Peat is a unique natural organic material that is found in marshes, bogs, swamp systems and low-lying coastal areas where organic matter has accumulated under reducing conditions. Peat deposits are found not only in the northern hemisphere, but also in vast areas of the tropics. Peat is valued for its physical and chemical properties. It has high water-holding capacities, high cation exchange capacities (100-150 cmol kg^{-1}), high porosity, low density and low heat conductivity. It has by itself only very low nutritional status but can be used as a fertilizer carrier. Other uses include peat as a clean media for oil spills, a filtering agent in sewage treatment plants, for chemical and pharmaceutical purposes and as an energy source.

In potting soils it is valued for its light weight, good aeration and water holding qualities. Northern peat commonly has a low pH and has been used as a medium in phospho-composting systems (Mathur *et al.* 1986). A high sulphur peat found in the coastal region of Sri Lanka has been selected as a low pH medium to enhance phosphate rock dissolution (Dahanayake *et al.* 1991).

Peat deposits in sub-Saharan Africa are found in high altitude swampy areas of Rwanda and Burundi, and in many low lying coastal swamp areas, for example, in Benin, Congo, Mauritania, Senegal.

There are serious environmental concerns related to the extraction of peat deposits in many parts of the world, because swamp areas are natural carbon sinks and wetlands of high ecological value.

6. Agrominerals and rocks for forestry, plantation crops and pasture

6.1 Applications of agrominerals in forestry

In sub-Saharan Africa, more forests are destroyed through human intervention than are regrown. So far, afforestation efforts have concentrated almost exclusively on plantation forestry with the aim of producing tree products for industrial purposes for export. This results in large amounts of nutrients being harvested and exported. Soils under managed plantation forests in Nigeria showed significant declines in organic carbon, N, P, K, Ca and Mg (Kadeba 1998). Examples from other parts of the tropics indicate that logging and other exports of biomass from natural tropical rainforests can cause serious depletion of nutrients (Nykvist 1998). Sustainable forestry is not possible without replenishing these losses. So far, however, forest management practices in large parts of the world do not include fertilization, largely because of lack of immediate responses in tree production and high costs.

Forestry studies in North America, Europe and countries along the Pacific indicate that some of the tree decline is due to changes in tree nutrition. While the tree decline and die-back in Europe is largely related to industrial and agricultural air pollution and subsequent nutrient losses (especially Mg), the die-back in the Pacific area is largely related to soil nutrient stress (Mueller-Dombois 1991). At a limited scale, tree fertilization and liming has been practiced in forests affected either by acid rains and/or those with nutritional disorders related to high atmospheric nitrogen loads (Wilmot *et al.* 1996). Several naturally occurring minerals have been tested as soil amendments in forests of Central Europe. One way of correcting the pollution damages to Europe's conifer forests is the application of kieserite (Mg-sulfate), and/or dolomite (Huettl 1990). In fact, liming forest soils is a widely practiced form of correcting deficiencies in forests of northern Europe (Huettl and Zoettl 1993). In New Zealand, where Mg deficiencies have damaged large plantation forests of *Pinus radiata*, the application of calcined magnesite (MgO) has resulted in a significant increase in soil exchangeable Mg (Mitchell *et al.* 1999).

Other agrominerals, for example, phosphate rocks from carbonatite operations, have been used with success in central Brazil for plantation forestry with *Eucalyptus* (Cerqueia *et al.* 1982, quoted in Appleton 1994). Simpson (1998) describes the widespread application of biogenic Nauru phosphate rock to pine plantations in south-east Queensland, Australia. In the early 1950s Nauru PR was applied by hand, but this was superseded in the 1970s by aerial nutrient spraying with TSP. The rate of application was 50 kg PR ha^{-1}. In Brazil, the application of 2 kg basaltic rock into the planthole of *Eucalyptus* species in lateritic soils resulted in higher height and standard diameter than the application of 170 g of NPK (5-10-2) per hole over a six year period (Leonardos *et al.* 1987). The application of 2 kg of limestone with NPK also showed good responses.

So far, little work on replenishing tree nutrients in the form of fertilizers or agrominerals has been carried out in sub-Saharan Africa. For trees with high values grown in farmers fields, the use of local slow-release phosphate rocks in combination with locally available N and K organic resources (e.g. the prolific shrub *Tithonia diversifolia*) should be tested. As trees are long-term crops, the use of slow-release, cation-rich ground silicate rocks (petrofertilizers) in combination with locally available organic N sources should be tested agronomically in long-term trials.

6.2 Application of agrominerals in perennial plantation crops

The management of plantation crops like bananas, coconut, coffee, cacao, oil palm, pineapple, rubber, sugar cane and tea, as well as floricultural operations, requires considerable financial, technical and material inputs. Plantation schemes are for the most part export oriented, and run by large overseas or national companies. Plantation crops require considerable external inputs such as fertilizers, as well as efficient pest, disease and weed control. There are many social, environmental and market-related economic problems and vulnerabilities associated with the growing and managing these kinds of monocultures.

Imported fertilizers form the commonly used soil inputs in plantation systems. While there have been considerable efforts to formulate site-specific, highly effective soluble nutrient inputs for various plantation crops, there is increasing interest in less soluble, slow-release and maintenance-type nutrient inputs as well.

The nutrient requirements of plantation crops differ. While some require mainly N inputs, there are some perennial plantation crops for which slow-release agromineral inputs are suitable and in use. The main agrominerals involved are phosphate rocks, Mg-containing rocks and liming materials. In particular, the application of phosphate rock on tea, rubber, oil palm, and to a lesser degree sugar cane, seem to have positive value-to-cost ratios (van Kauwenbergh and Hellums 1995).

Cacao

Cacao is grown in many tropical countries approximately 15° North and South of the equator at altitudes not higher than 650 metres. Cacao is grown in plantations and/or interspersed with other crops and trees, largely under shade. The effectiveness of reactive phosphate rock as a P source for cacao has been demonstrated in Malaysia. PR is used in cacao nurseries during pre-planting along with ground Mg-limestone, and in the planthole on acid P deficient soils. In the past, mainly PR imported from the Christmas Islands was applied in the cacao plantations of Malaysia, although in recent years other PRs have also been imported. Recent data show that the imported North Carolina PR was as effective as TSP (Yusdar and Hanafi 2001). Although West Africa (Ghana, Nigeria, Côte d'Ivoire, Cameroon) is the major supplier of cacao in the world, no data on the utilization of phosphate rocks, local or imported, or dolomite in cacao plantations are available.

Oil palm

The production of edible oil from oil palm plantations plays a major role in the economy of many tropical countries. In Malaysia, the world's leading producer of palm oil, some 3.46 million hectares are covered with oil palm plantations and oil palm growing areas. In sub-Saharan Africa large oil palm plantations are found in West Africa.

Since 1929 long-term experiments comparing various PRs in comparison with soluble P fertilizers have been conducted in Malaysia (Zin *et al.* 2001). The research included studies of P effectiveness in various stages of growth, from the seedling stage to mature oil palm stands. The results of intensive research on the effects of PR treatments on various soils show that soluble P fertilizers are more effective at the seedling stage, but that most PRs are as effective as soluble P sources for mature oil palm production (Zin *et al.* 2001). Limestone and dolomite as well as ground PR (at a rate of 1 tonne per hectare) are applied to the soils for leguminous cover crops between the oil palms in the immature growth phase (Zin *et al.* 2001). The application of K as a major nutrient for oil palm production is important, as is the use of Mg sources. Magnesium nutrition of oil palms in plantations is commonly covered by the application of kieserite (Mg-sulfate) and dolomite. It is not known whether any of the PRs of sub-Saharan Africa have been tested in West Africa's oil palm plantations.

Rubber

Rubber is grown in equatorial lowlands of tropical Asia, Africa and South America below 200 m altitudes. Rubber exports provide a large contribution to the national revenue of countries like Malaysia, where rubber plantations occupy about 1.4 million hectares.

While water-soluble P fertilizers are clearly more effective in the seedling stage, the application of 2 kg PR per tree over a six year period has been an effective P source for rubber tree growth. With the application of 2 kg of relatively unreactive PR from the Christmas Islands, the trees could be tapped 22 months earlier than the control trees (de Geus 1973). In Indonesia, where about half of the rubber is produced by smallholder farmers/foresters in 'jungle rubber' systems, the application of 1 tonne of PR per hectare resulted in significantly enhanced growth and brought forward the start of rubber harvesting by 1 or 2 years (Penot *et al.* 1998). The greatest response of PR is in the establishment phase. In addition, the application of PR will also stimulate the growth of cover crops.

Magnesium deficiencies are widespread in rubber plantations of southeast Asia and West Africa. Mg fertilizers are applied in the form of MgO (calcined magnesite) in rubber plantations in southern China (Michalk and Zhi-Kai 1992). From sub-Saharan Africa there are few data on PR utilization on rubber plantations available. Newly planted rubber trees in Ghana use 90 g phosphate rock in the planting hole (de Geus 1973). Kieserite and dolomite are used as the Mg component. Leguminous cover crops of *Pueraria phaseoloides* provide some of the nitrogen requirements during the maturing phase of rubber tree growth.

Sugar cane

Sugar cane is grown in most tropical and subtropical countries and requires an ample water supply. While N is the prime nutrient required, no good response to N fertilization can be obtained without sufficient P and K. Phosphorus can be supplied in various forms, including phosphate rock. Recent research on acid, P-deficient soils of south China illustrates the effects of various phosphate rocks on sugar cane production (Huang *et al.* 2001). The application of the reactive North Carolina PR showed good residual effects when applied at the highest rates of application (125 - 250 kg P ha^{-1}). In comparison, the Moroccan phosphates were less effective, and the PR originating from China was the least effective of those tested (Huang *et al.* 2001).

Sugar cane soils, low in silicon, have responded economically to the application of calcium silicate slags (Ayres 1966; Anderson *et al.* 1991). In Mauritius, large applications of ground basalt increased sugar cane yields (D'Hotman de Villiers 1961). The application of large tonnages of ground rock is made possible by the close proximity of industries in which the crushed rock is a by-product.

Another agromineral required by the sugar cane industry is lime, used in the processing of the sugar juice. The resulting large amounts of 'sugary lime-wastes' have good fertilizing properties but are often discarded.

Tea

Tea is mostly grown on strongly weathered acid soils. It is commonly cultivated at high altitudes in the humid and sub-humid tropics where annual rainfall exceeds 1,500 mm. While tea plants require significant N applications, the needs for P are small. Phosphorus acquisition by roots is enhanced via higher rhizosphere acidification, root exudation and mycorrhizal association (Zoysa *et al.* 1999). Tea can be fertilized effectively with low cost phosphate rocks. Examples of PR applications are mainly from India and Sri Lanka (de Geus 1973; Sivasubramanian *et al.* 1981). In sub-Saharan Africa, local PR sources have only been tested in a few places, notably in Malawi (Appleton 1994), where field data from tea plots in the Thyolo area showed positive responses after two years of application of Tundulu PR (Appleton 1994).

Organic wastes from plantation crops.

Plantation crops commonly produce large amounts of organic residues and some of these 'wastes' could be used to enhance the performance of agrominerals. For example, research in Brazil has shown that residues from the sugar industry can be used as substrate for growing microorganisms that partially solubilize unreactive phosphate rock (Cerezine *et al.* 1988). The utilization of sugary wastes from sugar cane and pineapple operations should be investigated for their potential to enhance the solubilization of phosphate rock and various K-silicates.

6.3   Pasture

Large parts of sub-Saharan Africa consist of natural grassland, and extensive cattle grazing on savanna land is common. There are only few areas where extensive grazing on improved grass-legume mixes is practiced, mostly in areas with more temperate climates. There are even fewer pasture schemes with intensive management in Africa. Fertilization of pastures is rarely done in sub-Saharan Africa, largely for economic reasons. Most research on phosphate rocks and liming materials in Africa is done to increase production of annual food crops. Research efforts on intensive pasture management in Africa and elsewhere concentrate on improvement of the grass-legume mixes and the introduction or maintenance of nitrogen fixing legumes.

In some parts of the world, the move to improve pastures includes the use of phosphate rocks. For example, in tropical Australia the need for P fertilization for intensive pasture management has been the focus of a major national research initiative: 'The role for reactive phosphate rock fertilisers for pasture in Australia' (Bolland *et al.* 1997; Sale *et al.* 1997; Simpson *et al.* 1997). The results of this research on direct application of cost-saving rock fertilizers for pasture are published in a book (Sale *et al.* 1997) and a special issue of the Australian Journal of Experimental Agriculture (Vol. 37, No. 8: 845-1098). Sale *et al.* (1997) conclude that under conditions of low pH, high rainfall and certain soil conditions, reactive phosphate rock is an effective P fertilizer in the short- or medium-term for permanent pasture.

Hedley and Bolan (1997) summarized the results of similar research on directly applied reactive phosphate rock in New Zealand. Here, the tests included partially acidulated phosphate rocks (PAPR). Experiments on volcanic soils illustrate the high agronomic effectiveness of PAPR on ryegrass-white clover permanent pasture (Rajan 1987b).

In Latin America, most of the directly applied PR fertilizers are used for improved pastures, especially in Brazil and Colombia (Appleton 1994). Best responses were obtained by applying both N and P sources. Steady yield increases over time have been found on Brazilian oxisols when applying the otherwise unreactive PR from Araxa (Leon *et al.* 1986). In East Africa, an example of base fertilization on pasture using phosphate rock comes from northwestern Kenya. Phosphate rock fines from the 'hard phosphates' of the Busumbu PR deposit in eastern Uganda were applied directly on pastures in the 1950s (Atkinson and Hale 1993; Mathers 1994).

Magnesium deficiencies have been identified in pastures on infertile acid soils of subtropical China. Here, correction with magnesium sources resulted in significant yield increases in subterranean clover (Michalk and Zhi-Kai 1992). Magnesium deficiencies of pasture soils can be addressed through the use of local Mg rock sources, specifically finely ground dolomitic limestone or calcined magnesite. In New Zealand some of the Mg inputs for pasture come from the addition of the Mg-rich silicate rocks dunite and serpentinite, and from superphosphate fertilizers (Chittenden *et al.* 1967). In some cases, fertilizers with micronutrient additions (for example Mo) are introduced in order to improve the composition of the grass-legume pasture.

The fertilization for intensive pasture production in sub-Saharan Africa is largely a function of costs. Small-scale farmers who cannot afford fertilizers for annual food crops are unlikely to use fertilizers or agrominerals for intensive pasture fertilization. Promising new directions include the use of low-cost locally available phosphate rocks to enhance fodder crop production near the cattle pens of zero-grazing farms and in phospho-composting systems (Odongo 2002).

7. Agrominerals and rocks in agroforestry systems

Agroforestry is an old and widely used land use practice in which trees are grown in association with agricultural crops or pastures. It combines elements of agricultural production with elements of forestry in a sustainable production system. Growing trees on farms alongside crops and livestock can improve the livelihoods of the rural poor and protect the natural resource base. Agroforesters follow interdisciplinary natural resource management strategies with the final aim of improving livelihoods of resource-poor farmers.

Trees can play many biophysical, economic and social roles in farming systems, including the function of enhancing soil fertility. Trees provide canopy, the litter may protect the soil from erosion and minimize soil temperature and moisture fluctuations, and roots can loosen topsoils and improve soil structure. Trees can capture and cycle nutrients from the air, from underlying rocks and from decomposing organic matter. In the case of nitrogen, trees can contribute to soil nitrogen pools in two ways: firstly through nutrient input, for example through biological nitrogen fixation, and secondly through nutrient cycling – transfer of nutrients from one compartment of the soil-plant system to another. The transfer of nitrogen from the air to soils in a cost-effective way can be effectively managed through the use of legumes and certain non-leguminous plants. Leguminous fallows of agroforestry tree species like *Sesbania sesban* can nodulate and fix nitrogen from the air and, in addition, capture nitrate from subsoil levels at depths beyond the reach of most crop roots. The transfer of the nitrogen to the topsoil is through leaf litter and biomass decomposition (Mekonnen *et al.* 1997; Sanchez *et al.* 1997). But soil fertility around trees will also be affected through other improvements of the soil, such as soil structure, organic matter contents, and related water and nutrient management.

So far, the attention of agroforestry research has focused largely on nitrogen cycling, and phosphorus cycling in agroforestry systems has only been addressed in recent years. As there is no phosphorus equivalent to biological nitrogen fixation, phosphorus must be either cycled, transferred from nearby organic sources or added from external sources. Agroforestry species may play a crucial role in cycling P from the soil into more plant available P forms. Trees have extended root zones and some species may be able to acquire P from a larger volume of soil through mycorrhizal acquisition. However, the potential cycling of P from subsoil capture is likely to be low as the available P concentrations in subsoils are normally very low.

Nutrient budgets indicate that most P added to the soils through tree prunings and litter is the result of nutrient cycling, not new nutrient inputs (Palm 1995). However, the amount of P provided though litter and tree prunings is insufficient to meet crop demands (Palm 1995). Some plants have relatively high P concentrations in their biomass, for example the roadside and hedge shrub *Tithonia diversifolia* (0.3 - 0.38% P) and for low P application rates the incorporation of this type of green manure can transfer some P into the soil. The advantage is that biomass transfer will contribute to P cycling, bringing less available inorganic forms of P into more available forms.

It has become evident that in order to overcome gross P deficiencies and to supply the soils with sufficient P for crop production, external phosphorus must be added. Since water-soluble P fertilizers are too expensive for most resource-poor farmers, alternative P sources must be introduced. Locally available PR sources have been tested as a component of agroforestry systems in Kenya and Uganda. Decomposing organic materials can produce organic acids, which, in turn, can enhance PR dissolution. Composting of PR and organic matter can increase the availability of P from PR under certain conditions. However, to be effective and practical, local solutions to the P-problem must be found. Most beneficial results of phosphate dissolution though phospho-composting results have been achieved when using a sedimentary or biogenic phosphate rock as inorganic P-source (Bangar *et al.* 1985; Lompo 1993; Mathur *et al.* 1986; Singh and Amberger 1991; Ikerra *et al.* 1994; Tian and Kolawole 1999). Applying composts with less reactive mainly igneous PR sources showed no positive responses in P-deficient soils of eastern Uganda and this practice remains a challenge (Oshier 2002). Phospho-composting with the same PR but with other organic matter and on other soils proved successful in Kenya (Odongo 2002).

The effect of P-sorption on soils could also be influenced by the release of organic anions from tree or shrub biomass (Iyamuremye and Dick 1996; Nziguheba et al. 1998). Researchers found that the addition of green manure in the form of prunings of the agroforestry species Tithonia diversifolia not only provided nutrients and increased soil microbial biomass of C, N and P, but the application of this green manure also decreased P adsorption on soils, thus contributing to greater available P sources in the soil solution (Nziguheba et al. 1998). However, little is known about P solubilization and the sorption-desorption process in soils when organic materials are applied together with inorganic fertilizers (Palm et al. 1997).

Under certain conditions it might be possible to cycle P from rocks to crops. Results from a survey in eastern Uganda of inherent soil fertility and P concentration in the biomass of the roadside shrub Tithonia diversifolia growing on soils over different parent materials showed that the mean P concentration of Tithonia diversifolia (measured as dry matter) was significantly higher on soils of the PR mine (mean = 0.553% P) than on soils overlying granite (0.326% P) (van Straaten et al. 2001). It has to be investigated whether the roots of Tithonia diversifolia have the ability to actively increase the dissolution of phosphate rock or whether the results are only a reflection of higher soil fertility. It may be possible that Tithonia diversifolia can contribute to P cycling by bringing less available inorganic forms of phosphorus (from the underlying rocks and soils) into more available organic forms in the plant tissue. Unpublished research data indicate that Tithonia diversifolia is ecto- and endo-mycorrhizal and may secrete citric acid to the rhizosphere, thus enhancing dissolution of nearby minerals (Sanchez, pers. comm. 2000).

An intriguing option is the application of a combination of inorganic and organic P sources on P-deficient soils. Research in Kenya has shown that the combination of biomass from agroforestry shrubs with high rates of PR (in this case the reactive Minjingu PR) increased maize yield up to five times (Sanchez et al. 1997). A practical method to replenish soil P in highly weathered and P deficient soils is through integrating locally available organic resources with commercial P fertilizers or, even more practically, with phosphate rock resources if available in close proximity.

Phosphorus isotope studies have illustrated the effects of green manures, especially the agroforestry multipurpose trees Gliricidia sepium, Acacia mangum, Leucena leucocephala, and Senna siamea, on the phosphate solubilization from PR. The results of a study by Zaharah and Bah (1997) show that the solubility of the less reactive PRs increased, while the solubility of the more reactive PRs was depressed. The reason for this is not entirely clear.

Evidence from various parts of Africa indicate that growing maize after legumes with added phosphate rock will increase yield and organic matter in soils (IITA 1999; Jama, pers. comm. 2001). The combination of Tithonia biomass with P fertilizers and phosphate rock have been shown to be effective (Nziguheba 2001). When Tithonia leaves decompose in the soil, soluble carbon and nutrients are released to the soil, which in turn may enhance P cycling and conversion of mineral forms of P into organic P forms (Nziguheba et al. 1998).

Large one-time applications of PR or P fertilizers along with subsequent maintenance P applications and sound agronomic practices have enabled farmers in the Cerrado region of Brazil, with their highly weathered and high P-sorbing soils, to increase their agricultural productivity (Goedert 1983). They became food exporters rather than food importers. This success story lends support to the concept of large, one-time P 'recapitilization' in parts of Africa, a concept that has been discussed widely in agronomic and economic circles. In contrast to the one-time heavy application of P (recapitilization) is smaller amount applications. Initial results from agroforestry research in western Kenya indicate that one time applications gave similar yield responses to annual P applications. Given the high initial investment for P recapitilization (application rate 125-250 kg ha^{-1}, which is about US $120-210 per hectare) the annual application rate seems more realistic under the current socio-economic conditions where most farmers make less than a dollar a day. Farmers, realizing the positive yield effect of Tithonia applications plus P fertilizers or PR, experimented with these resources and found that it was more profitable to apply these materials on high value crops, for example, vegetables, rather than on maize (Jama et al. 1997; Sanchez et al. 1997; Sanchez and Jama 2000).

The application of a combination of organic and inorganic sources, for example, organic sources from trees and shrubs, with inorganic PR sources, on high-value P-efficient crops like cabbage or kale could become key to successful N and P (and probably K) management in small holder farms.

Mycorrhizae play an important role in the acquisition and uptake of P by plants, including trees. The high efficiency of P uptake from various P sources by mycorrhizae-infected trees has been demonstrated in temperate climates (Finlay and Read 1986; Cumming and Weinstein 1990) but few data are available for sub-Saharan Africa. Direct application of PR with and without arbuscular mycorrhizae on multipurpose agroforestry trees has been carried out by Karanja et al. (2001). The results from greenhouse studies show that on nutrient-poor acid soils, the addition of 50 kg P ha^{-1} as Minjingu PR alone resulted in significant increases of height and root collar diameter compared to the control. Leucena leucocephala recorded the highest increase in height and root collar followed by Eucalyptus grandis, indicating a high efficiency in P utilization. Additionally, Karanja et al. (2001) showed that inoculating seedlings of legume trees with arbuscular mycorrhizae increased nodulation. Adequate P supply is essential for the host, and for the survival of rhizobia bacteria, nodulation and N$_2$ fixation (Azcon et al. 1979).

The glasshouse experiments of Karanja et al. (2001) illustrate the importance of mycorrhizal infection to P uptake of trees and the importance of P fertilization of agroforestry multipurpose trees, and specifically the use of phosphate rocks. It is important to carry out experiments under field conditions to verify the effectiveness of these methods and the fertilizing phosphate rock materials.

No information on the use of other nutrient-containing rocks and minerals, for example K- and Mg-containing micas (e.g. biotite, phlogopite) and leucite-bearing volcanics or liming materials (limestone, dolomite) have been reported in agroforestry systems. Some of these agrominerals certainly warrant testing as they are slow-release naturally occurring nutrient sources.

8. Small-scale mining and processing of agrominerals

In the foregoing chapters, accounts of various agrominerals and their agronomic importance have been discussed for various biomass production systems. Details of the occurrences of these agrominerals and pertinent agronomic experiments with these resources are provided in the country profiles that follow. The agrominerals discussed are mainly for small-scale and local agricultural use and for potential uses in forestry and horticulture. They are restricted to small-scale, site-specific and adapted use. Some of the agrominerals are available in sub-Saharan Africa but have not been tested for agricultural use, for example zeolites, pumice and the many 'waste' or byproducts from mineral related industries.

There are several large-scale agromineral deposits being mined in sub-Saharan Africa, for example, the phosphate ores in Togo, Senegal and South Africa. Emphasis in this book is on the many small-scale deposits and their potential use in agriculture, forestry, agroforestry and horticulture. One has to be reminded that for every very large deposit, there are many orders of magnitude more similar small- and medium-scale deposits. There are areas that are naturally endowed with minerals due to their geological setting, while others have clearly less potential. It is obvious, however, that there is enormous potential for the increased use of readily available agrominerals to maintain or enhance soil fertility.

To develop these small-scale resources one has to use similar but size-adapted methodologies and techniques. Fortunately there is already a large body of experience with appropriate mining and processing in many countries of sub-Saharan Africa. Most of the appropriate mining and processing techniques are used in other industries, for example the small-scale gold mining industry. But many of the techniques can be easily adapted and modified to suit the small-scale mining and processing of industrial minerals like phosphate rocks.

Appropriate processing techniques and equipment that could be used for agromineral processing include:

- locally available and locally built stamp mills used in the gold fields of Zimbabwe,
- the locally developed tractor driven ball mills in the small scale gold mining camps in northern Tanzania,
- the modified mobile concrete mixer for partial acidulated phosphates made in Zambia (Borsch 1993),
- the simple and robust phosphate blend pelletizer, developed in Zimbabwe and adapted in Uganda.

These are examples of simple and robust technologies 'made in Africa,' which could be used to crush, grind and even process geological resources near their sources. There are several small industries and support institutions in sub-Saharan Africa that provide assistance for appropriate processing technologies to small-scale operators. From another continent with similar constraints, the 'semi-mechanized' approach of small Indian mines seems particularly applicable to many other developing countries that have a large underemployed labor force and limited availability of foreign exchange to buy sophisticated mining equipment. Operating costs for small-scale open cast mining differs from place to place and commodity to commodity but are in the general range of US $1-10 per tonne. Depending on the size of the operation, on the appropriate equipment used, mineral hardness etc., crushing and grinding cost another US $4-10 per tonne. For many agrominerals such as scoria and some zeolites, 'mining' may simply involve excavation of the unconsolidated material with a shovel followed by screening and bagging and/or bulk transport.

Small-scale agromineral development is a labor-intensive activity (International Labour Organization 1999) that can significantly reduce not only mining and processing costs, but, by extracting and developing agromineral deposits closer to the farming sites, also reduce unit transportation costs. In addition to enhancing agricultural productivity and sustainability for resource poor farmers, small-scale mining and development of agrominerals will generate livelihood opportunities for many people directly or indirectly involved in these activities. Employment opportunities in rural areas and additional income-generating opportunities can substantially improve the livelihoods of many people and reduce poverty.

Small-scale mining is often seen as an unregulated illegal activity. Especially small-scale gold mining operations are often under-capitalized, under-mechanized, and the operators often lack technical and managerial skills (Noetstaler 1995). Small-scale miners often operate under poor living and working conditions, employ children and avoid taxes. In addition, small-scale mining can be hazardous to human health and detrimental to the environment. Positive sides of small-scale mining include: low investment costs and a short lead time from discovery to production. Small-scale miners often utilize otherwise unexploited small deposits, and they employ low-skill labour. Small-scale mining encourages indigenous entrepreneurship, creates employment and spin-off jobs, and, properly supported, can contribute to poverty alleviation and rural development.

To start small-scale development of the new agromineral sector it will be necessary

- to develop this sector in an orderly manner,
- to develop, together with the stakeholders, the adapted technologies needed for a successful venture,
- to invest with the stakeholders into basic and appropriate mining and processing equipment,
- to train the stakeholders in 'bottom-up centres,'
- to formalize and legalize their activities.

It is important to forge links and form partnerships between farmers, entrepreneurs, communities and government and non-governmental organizations.

In many development agencies the word 'mining' has the connotation of exploitation of natural resources with all the negative images of environmental degradation, social disruption and trans-national involvement and resource transfers. Mining seemingly contradicts the sustainable development paradigm. However, extraction of agrominerals should be viewed differently. These minerals and rocks are utilized for local agricultural needs, for development of infrastructure and for survival. With proper resource management practices, the development of these minerals can increase soil fertility and food production, and will contribute to food security and poverty reduction.

In contrast to small-scale mining of gold and diamonds, which is often illegal and unsupported by local authorities, the extraction of high bulk agrominerals like limestones and phosphate rock will be legal and supported by the community. Unlike precious metals and diamonds, agrominerals are bulky and not easily smuggled across borders.

Agromineral extraction and processing obviously depends on the size, grade, location etc. of the deposits. Large deposits are likely to be developed by larger enterprises, either local, national or international. Small scale agromineral operations can provide wide opportunities for local entrepreneurs (for example operating a crusher/grinder unit), and be run, after an initial setting up of the appropriate technologies, by local craftspersons and local labour. For these operations, the capital requirements are generally low. At some mini-scale agromineral operations, for example, small limestone operations, the mining and processing can be seasonal, run by farmers themselves in the off-season.

9. Environmental aspects and concerns

Most agrominerals are chemically benign and pose no additional risk to the health of miners or farmers. However, with phosphate rocks there are several environmental concerns that have to be addressed, not only for the large-scale and high-tech production of agrominerals but also for the small-scale sector. The inherent chemistry of several 'natural' sedimentary phosphates are characterized by elevated concentrations of Cd, U and As, which can pose potential health and environmental hazards. The cadmium problem especially has to be addressed, as its accumulation in soils and crops can have potentially harmful effects on humans. More phosphate rocks from sub-Saharan Africa, especially sedimentary PRs, should be analyzed for this potentially harmful element.

There are other environmental concerns with the extraction and use of naturally occurring agrominerals and the disposal of 'wastes' from these operations. Examples include the mining of bird guano from islands close to Madagascar or the Seychelles, which can have serious environmental impacts on marine wildlife. Unprotected extraction of bat guano from caves can have significant health effects through the inhalation of *Histoplasmosis* spores. The disposal of 'wastes' from agromineral operations has to be carefully planned and managed. The disposal of wastes from agromineral operations should be done using best management techniques. Dumping of 'wastes' into the ocean (e.g. from phosphate beneficiation processes in Togo) can have serious negative effects on the environment. Most of these potential damages can be prevented when following 'best environmental management practices' and educating both management and the persons mining and processing the ore.

General environmental concerns are also related to transport and energy uses. More efficient use of fuel wood for agricultural lime 'burning' for example can substantially reduce the environmental damage caused by this practice. It has been demonstrated that it is possible to reduce fuel wood consumption through better kiln designs and management practices. In many cases, the limestone or dolomite resources do not even need to be 'burnt' to be agronomically effective. Transport costs will generally be high if the deposits are not located close to the soils where they are most effective and alternative transportation methods may be required, particularly for small agromineral resources.

10. Outlook

The description of the geology, mineralogy and application of minerals and rocks for agriculture, forestry and related fields provides an insight into the potential of utilizing indigenous agrominerals in sub-Saharan Africa. The description of details of known agrominerals in 48 countries will follow in Part 2 of this book. The account focuses only on the 'supply side' of these resources in sub-Saharan Africa. It is obvious that this study has to be complemented with a solid assessment of the 'demand side,' specifically the distribution and extent of nutrient-deficient soils. Also, the effectiveness of the agrominerals has to be assessed along with an appraisal of risks, costs and benefits of agromineral development. Prior to developing these resources, several additional sources of information on the supply and demand side have to be collected. From the demand side, it is necessary to compile agronomic and soils data, and economic, social and environmental background information. In a wider context, development strategies must address whole systems and technologies, not only commodities.

Each agromineral deposit is unique and requires individual best mining, processing techniques and management practices. No blanket recommendations can be made for the most effective, efficient and environmentally sound practices, and recommendations tailored to the individual deposits and applications are required. In most cases, more detailed geological assessments, detailed mineralogical and chemical characterization of the agrominerals have to be undertaken, as well as the selection of adapted appropriate mining and processing techniques and equipments.

The utilization of indigenous agrominerals for raising soil productivity is still a relatively narrow, input-oriented approach. Agromineral extraction and use should be incorporated into a multi-faceted integrated agro-ecological land husbandry approach in which many stakeholders participate, including farmers with their indigenous knowledge and skills. The development of agromineral resources makes up only a small fraction of a whole package of measures necessary to address the problems of the resource-poor and food-insecure population of sub-Saharan Africa.

The concept of agromineral resource development using appropriate small-scale technologies for a more integrated self-sufficient and sustainable agriculture is based on the extraction and use of a nation's minerals and rocks, a 'capital stock.' Minerals are non-renewable stocks, at least in the time range of a few hundred thousand years. Although some of the agrominerals are plentiful and can last several decades or longer, they are finite. In general, minerals are fixed stocks that don't last forever. But agromineral stocks are sharply different from other minerals, in so far as their development redistributes their value from a mineral capital stock of a point source to a much larger land base in the region. For example, the local point-source phosphate rock deposit will be transformed to P-fertilizer or P-soil amendment that will improve large areas with P-deficient soils. The value of the land has increased through the use of the local mineral capital stock. In the long run, the geological fixed mineral stock will be transformed into a re-newable organic resource stock. Inorganic phosphate sources have turned into organic phosphate sources that can be recycled many times.

Agromineral development can have positive effects on the economic and social development of rural societies. It is expected that the locally available mineral capital stock will be transformed by appropriate mining and processing techniques into marketable effective products that will bring economic and social benefits to the local communities. The mineral capital stock will in part also be reinvested into human development and training. This kind of mineral extraction will provide local employment. It can enhance investment into the local infrastructure, including schools, hospitals, communication and access to water. Agrominerals are natural resources that can improve agricultural production, restore and maintain productivity of soils, and, in the long term, contribute to the self reliance of communities and nations. Their development will be a small but significant contribution to sustainable land management.

Obviously, this approach should be part of an overall integrated land management initiative. Farmers' participation and cross-linkages with other sectors and institutions is paramount in this approach. The projects that will emerge should be developed, from the planning stage onward, together with the stakeholders, including the farmers, the community and government, non-governmental organizations and the private sector. The planning and development of local agromineral resources should not only concentrate on technical matters, but also on community-led approaches to resource management, and to the promotion of locally-adapted forms of management.

Agromineral development projects should be part of integrated, more self-reliant and sustainable land management systems that will contribute to the long-term improvement of food security in sub-Saharan Africa. By achieving the objectives of improved soil productivity in a productive and healthily balanced agro-ecosystem, these projects will ultimately contribute to the reduction of poverty.

References:

Ae N, Arihara J, Okada K, Yoshihara T and C Johansen 1990. Phosphorus uptake by pigeon pea and its role in cropping systems of Indian subcontinent. Science 248:477-480.

Agbenin JO 1998. Phosphate-induced zinc retention in a tropical semi-arid soil. Europ. J. Soil Sci. 49:693-700.

Alva AK and ME Sumner 1989. Alleviation of aluminum toxicity to soybeans by phosphogypsum or calcium sulfate in dilute nutrient solutions. Soil Sci. 147:278-285.

Alva AK, Gasco GJ and Y Guang 1989. Gypsum material effects on peanut and soil calcium. Comm. Soil Sci Plant Anal. 20:1727-1744.

Anderson DL, Snyder GH and FG Martin 1991. Multi-year response of sugarcane to calcium silicate slag on Everglade histosols. Agron. J. 83:870-874.

Appleton JD 1990. Rock and mineral fertilizers. Appropriate Techn. 17:25-27.

Appleton JD 1994. Direct-application fertilizers and soil amendments - appropriate technology for developing countries? In: Mathers SJ and AJG Notholt (eds.) Industrial minerals in developing countries. AGID Report Series Geosciences in International Development No.18, pp. 223-256.

Asea PEA, Kucey RMN and JWB Steward 1988. Inorganic phosphate solubilization by two *Pennicillium* species in solution culture and soil. Soil Biol. Biochem. 20:459-464.

Atkinson H and M Hale 1993. Phosphate production in central and southern Africa, 1900-1992. Minerals Industry Intern. September 1993:22-30.

Ayres AS 1966. Calcium silicate slag as a growth stimulant for sugarcane on low-silicon soils. Soil Sci. 101:216-227.

Azcon R, Barea JM and DS Hayman 1976. Utilization of rock phosphate in alkaline soils by plants inoculated with mycorrhizal fungi and phosphate-solubilizing bacteria. Soil Biol. Biochem. 8:135-138.

Bakken AK, Gautneb H, and K Myhr 1997. The potential of crushed rocks and mine tailings as slow-releasing K fertilizers assessed by intensive cropping of Italian ryegrass in different soil types. Nutr. Cycl. Agroecosys. 47:41-48.

Bakken AK, Gautneb H, Sveistrup T and K Myhr 2000. Crushed rocks and mine tailings applied as K fertilizers on grassland. Nutr. Cycl. Agroecos. 56:53-57.

Banath CL 1969. Iron pyrites as a sulphur fertilizer. Aust. J. Agric. Res. 20:697-708.

Banath CL and JF Holland 1976. Iron pyrites as a sulphur fertilizer in an alkaline soil. Aust. J. Experim. Agric. and Animal Husbandry 16:376-381.

Banda DJ and BR Singh 1989. Establishment of critical levels of zinc for maize in soils of the high rainfall areas of Zambia. Norw. J. Agric. Sci. 3:221-227.

Bangar KC, Yadav KS and MM Mishra 1985. Transformation of rock phosphate during composting and the effect of humic acid. Plant Soil 85:259-266.

Banik S 1983. Variation in potentiality of phosphate-solubilizing soil microorganisms with phosphate and energy source. Zentralblatt fuer Mikrobiologie 138:209-216.

Barak P, Chen Y and A Singer 1983. Ground basalt and tuff as iron fertilizer for calcareous soils. Plant Soil 73:155-158.

Barrau EM and WA Berg 1977. Pyrite and pyritic mill tailings as a source of iron in a calcareous iron-deficient soil. Soil Sci. Soc. Am. J. 41:385-388.

Barbarick KA and HJ Pirela 1984. Agronomic and horticultural uses of zeolites: A review. In: Pond WG and FA Mumpton (eds.) Zeo-agriculture: Use of natural zeolites in agriculture and aquaculture. Westview Press Boulder, Colorado:93-103.

Barbarick KA, Lai TM and DD Eberl 1990. Exchange fertilizer (phosphate rock plus ammonium-zeolite) effects on sorghum-sudangrass. Soil Sci. Soc. Am. J. 54:911-916.

Bationo A, Chien SH, Henao J, Christianson CB and AU Mokunye 1990. Agronomic evaluation of two unacidulated and partially acidulated phosphate rocks indigenous to Niger. Soil Sci. Soc. Am. J. 54:1772-1777.

Belkacem S, Nys C and D Gelhaye 1992. Effects of fertilizer and lime on mature Norway spruce (*Picea abies*) biomass mineral content. Ann. Sci. Forestieres 49:235-252.

Bekele T, Cino BJ, Ehlert PAI, Van Der Maas AA and A Van Diest 1983. An evaluation of plant-borne factors promoting the solubilization of alkaline rock phosphates. Plant Soil 75: 361-378.

Bekele T and W Hofner 1993. Effects of different phosphate fertilizers on yield of barley and rape seed on reddish brown soils of the Ethiopian highlands. Fert. Res. 34:243-250.

Benetti M 1983. Rock fertilizer and other low-cost methods to increase crop yields. Benetti, Delaware Water Gap, Pennsylvania, USA: 113pp.

Berthelin J, Leyval C, Laheurte F and P de Giudici 1991. Involvement of roots and rhizosphere microflora in the chemical weathering of soil minerals. In: Atkinson D (editor) Plant root growth - An ecological perspective. British Ecolog. Soc. Blackwell Scientific Publ. 187-200.

Black R, Lameyre J and B Bonin 1985. The structural setting of alkaline complexes. J. Afr. Earth Sci.3:5-16.

Blum WEH, Herbinger B, Mentler A, Ottner F, Pollak M, Unger E and WW Wenzel 1989a. Zur Verwendung von Gesteinsmehlen in der Landwirschaft. I. Chemisch-mineralogische Zusammensetzung und Eignung von Gesteinsmehlen als Duengemittel. Z. Pflanzenernaehr. Bodenk. 152:421-425.

Blum WEH, Herbinger B, Mentler A, Ottner F, Pollak M, Unger E and WW Wenzel 1989b. Zur Verwendung von Gesteinsmehlen in der Landwirschaft. II. Wirkung von Gesteinsmehlen als Bodenverbesserungsmittel. Z. Pflanzenernaehr. Bodenk. 152:427-430.

Bojinova D, Velkova R, Grancharov I and S Zhelev 1997. The bioconversion of Tunisian phosphorite using *Aspergillus niger*. Nutr. Cycl. Agroecosyst. 47:227-232.

Bolland MDA, Lewis DC, Gilkes RJ and LJ Hamilton 1997. Review of Australian phosphate rock research. Aust. J. Exp. Agric. 37:845-859.

Borsch L 1988. The beneficiation of the Kaluwe and Nkombwa Hill brown soils - some preliminary laboratory test results on the extraction of phosphate. Internal MINEX report, 28pp.

Borsch L 1990. Potential of potash-rich rocks and minerals in agriculture: some preliminary tests. AGID 61/62, 2pp.

Borsch L 1993. Exploration and development studies of phosphate resources in Zambia - A case history. In: Pride C and P van Straaten (eds.) Agrogeology and small scale mining. Small Mining International, Bull. 5-6:15-16.

Bosse HR, Gwosdz W, Lorenz W, Markwich H, Roth W and F Wolff 1996. Limestone and dolomite resources of Africa. Geol. Jb., D 102, 532pp.

Butegwa CN, Mullins GL and SH Chien 1996. Agronomic evaluation of fertilizer products derived from Sukulu Hills phosphate rock. Fert. Res. 44:113-122.

Cabala-Rosand P and A Wild 1982a. Direct use of low grade phosphate rock from Brazil as fertilizer. I. Effect of reaction time in soil. Plant Soil 65:351-362.

Cabala-Rosand P and A Wild 1982b. Direct use of low grade phosphate rock from Brazil as fertilizer. II Effects of mycorrhizal inoculation and nitrogen source. Plant Soil 65:363-373.

Caires EF and CA Rosolem 1991. Root growth of peanut cultivars and soil acidity. In: Wright RJ, Baligar VC and RP Murrmann (eds.) Plant-Soil interactions at low pH. Kluwer Academic Publ. Dordrecht, Netherlands.

Caldas EF and MK Tejedor Salguero 1987. Mulch farming in the Canary Islands. In: Wachira JK and AJG Notholt (eds.) Agrogeology in Africa. Commonw. Sci. Council, Techn. Publ. Series 226:242-254.

Cekinski E and GA da Silva 1998. Technological characterization of Anitapolis (Brazil) phosphate rock as feedstock for fused magnesium phosphate production. Nutr. Cycl. Agroecosys. 52:31-35.

Cerezine P C, Nahas E and DA Banzatto 1988. Soluble phosphate accumulation by *Aspergillus niger* from fluorapatite. Appl. Microbiol. Biotechn. 29:501-505.

Chesworth W 1982. Late Cenozoic geology and the second oldest profession. Geoscience Canada 9:54-61.

Chesworth W 1987. Geology and agriculture. In: Wachira JK and AJG Notholt (eds.) Agrogeology in Africa. Commonw. Sci. Council, Techn. Publ. Ser. 226:5-11.

Chesworth W 1993. The first twenty-nine days: Prospects for agrogeology. In: Pride C and P van Straaten (eds.) Agrogeology and small scale mining. Small Mining International, Bulletin 5-6:2-3.

Chesworth W, Magias-Vasquez F, Acquaye D and E Thomson 1983. Agricultural alchemy: stones into bread. Episodes 1:3-7.

Chesworth W, van Straaten P, Semoka J and E Mchihiyo 1985. Agrogeology in Tanzania. Episodes 8:257-258.

Chesworth W, van Straaten P, Smith P and S Sadura 1987. Solubility of apatite in clay and zeolite bearing systems: Application to agriculture. Applied Clay Science 2:291-297.

Chesworth W, van Straaten P and JMR Semoka 1989. Agrogeology in East Africa: the Tanzania-Canada project. J. Afric. Earth Sci. 9:357-362.

Chien SH and LL Hammond 1978. A comparison of various laboratory methods for predicting the agronomic potential of phosphate rocks for direct application. Soil Sci. Soc. Am. J. 42:935-939.

Chien SH, Sompongse D, Henao J and DT Hellums 1987. Greenhouse evaluation of phosphorus availability from compacted phosphate rocks with urea and triple superphosphate. Fert. Res. 14:245-256.

Chien SH, Adams F, Khasawneh FE and J Henao 1987. Effects of combinations of triple superphosphate and a reactive phosphate rock on yield and phosphorus uptake by corn. Soil Sci. Soc. Am. J. 51:1656-1658.

Chien SH and LL Hammond 1989. Agronomic effectiveness of partially acidulated phosphate rock as influenced by soil phosphorus-fixing capacity. Plant Soil 120:159-164.

Chien SH and RG Menon 1995a. Agronomic evaluation of modified phosphate rock products. Fert. Res. 41:197-209.

Chien SH and RG Menon 1995b. Factors affecting the agronomic effectiveness of phosphate rock for direct application. Fert. Res. 41:227-234.

Chien SH, Menon RG and KS Billingham 1996. Phosphorus availability from phosphate rock as enhanced by water-soluble phosphorus. Soil Sci. Soc. Am. J. 60:1173-1177.

Chirenje T 1996. Phospho-composting to enhance solubilization of igneous apatites from Zimbabwe. M.Sc. thesis, University of Guelph, Guelph, Ontario, Canada, 140 pp.

Chittenden ET, Stanton DJ, Watson J and KJ Dodson 1967. Serpentinite and dunite as magnesium fertiliser. New Zeal. J. Agric. Res. 10:160-171.

Choudhary M, Peck TR and LD Bailey 1995. Dissolution of rock phosphate in silage leachate. Commun. Soil Sci. Plant Anal. 26:1095-1104.

Clifton RA 1987. Natural and synthetic zeolites. US Bureau of Mines Information Circular 9140.

Coroneos C, Hinsinger P and RJ Gilkes 1996. Granite powder as a source of potassium for plants: a glasshouse bioassay comparing two pasture species. Fert. Res. 45:143-152.

Conyers MK, Scott BJ, Fisher R and W Lill 1996. Predicting the field performance of twelve commercial liming materials from southern Australia. Fert. Res. 44:151-161.

Cumming JR and LH Weinstein 1990. Aluminium-mycorrhizal interaction in the physiology of pitch pine seedlings. Plant Soil 125:7-18.

Dahanayake K, Senaratne A, Subasinghe SMND and A Liyanaarachi 1991. Potential use of naturally occurring sulphuric acid to beneficiate poorly soluble phosphate from Eppawala, Sri Lanka. Fert. Res. 29:197-201.

De Geus JG 1973. Fertilizer guide for the tropics and subtropics. Centre d'Etude de l'Azote, Zurich, Switzerland, 774pp.

De Swart PH and A van Driest 1987. The rock-phosphate solubilizing capacity of *Pueraria javanica* as affected by soil pH, superphosphate priming effect and symbiotic N$_2$ fixation. Plant Soil 100:135-147.

D'Hotman de Villiers 1961. Soil rejuvenation with crushed basalt in Mauritius. Int. Sugar J. 63:363-364.

Dubey SK and RC Mondal 1993. Sodic soil reclamation with saline water in conjunction with organic and inorganic amendments. Arid Soil Res. Rehab. 7:219-231.

Eberl DD and Lai TM 1992. Slow-release nitrogen fertilizer and soil conditioner. U.S. Patent Appl. US 789,206, 15th Apr. 1992.

Feigenbaum S, Edelstein R and I Shainberg 1981. Release rate of potassium and structural cations from mica to ion exchangers in dilute solutions. Soil Sci. Soc. Am. J. 45:501-506.

Finlay RD and DJ Read 1986. The structure and function of the vegetative mycelium of ectomycorrhizal plants II. The uptake and distribution of phosphorus by mycelium interconnecting host plants. New Phytologist 103:143-156.

Flach EN, Quak W and A Van Diest 1987. A comparison of the rock phosphate-mobilizing capacity of various crop species. Tropical Agriculture 64:347-352.

Fleischel H 1972. Basic slag in German agriculture. Agri Digest 25:45-50.

Fried M 1953. The feeding power of plants for phosphates. Soil Sci. Am. Proc. 17:357-359.

Friesen DK, Juo ASR and MH Miller 1982. Residual value of lime and leaching of calcium in a kaolinitic ultisol in the high rainfall tropics. Soil Sci. Soc. Am. J. 46:1184-1189.

Friesen DK 1991. Fate and efficiency of sulfur fertilizer applied to food crops in West Africa. Fert. Res. 29:35-44.

Fyfe WS 1981. The environmental crisis: quantifying geosphere interaction. Science 213:105-110.

Fyfe WS 1987. Sustainable food production and agrogeology. In: Pride C and P van Straaten (eds.) Agrogeology and small scale mining. Small Mining Intern., Bulletin 5-6:4-5.

Fyfe WS 1989. Soil and global change. Episodes 12:249-254.

Fyfe WS 2000. The life support system - toward earth sense. In: WG Ernst (editor) Earth systems: processes and issues. Cambridge University Press, 506-515.

Fyfe WS, Kronberg BI, Leonardos OH and N Olorunfemi 1983. Global tectonics and agriculture: a geochemical perspective. Agr. Ecosyst. Env. 9:383-399.

Gillman GP 1980. The effect of crushed basalt scoria on the cation exchange properties of a highly weathered soil. Soil Sci. Soc. Am. J. 44:465-468.

Gillman GP, Burkett DC and RJ Coventry 2000. A laboratory study of application of basalt dust to highly weathered soils: effects ion soil cation chemistry. Aust. J. Soil Res.39:799-811.

Gock E and KH Jacob 1984. Conceptions for processing the pyrite-bearing phosphorite of Abu Tartur. Berliner Geowiss. Abh. 50:381-397.

Goedert WJ 1983. Management of the Cerrado soils of Brazil: a review. J. Soil Sci. 34:405-428.

Goenadi DH, Siswanto and Y Sugiarto 2000. Bioactivation of poorly soluble phosphate rocks with a phosphorus-solubilizing fungus. Soil Sci. Soc. Am. J. 64:927-932.

Goldschmidt VM 1954. Geochemistry. 730 pp.

Goma HC, Phiri S, Mapiki A and BR Singh 1991. Evaluation of fused magnesium phosphate in acid soils of the high rainfall zone of Zambia. In: Zambia Fertiliser Technology Development Committee (ZFTDC) Utilization of local phosphate deposits for the benefits of the Zambian farmer. Lusaka, Zambia, pp. 138-149.

Govere EM, Chien SH, and RH Fox 1995. Effects of compacting phosphate rock with nitrogen, phosphorus, and potassium fertilisers. E. Afr. Agric. For. J. 60:123-130.

Guardani R, Drahos J, Guiletti M and K Schuegerl 1989. Studies on calcination of aluminium phosphate rock in fluidized bed reactors. Fert. Res. 20:181-191.

Gupta AP, Manocha PK and NK Tomar 1988. Effect of decomposing cattle dung and pyrite on the utilization of mineral acid-soluble phosphate by mustard. Biol. Waste 25:161-169.

Habashi F 1989. In-situ and dump leaching technology: application to phosphate rock. Fert. Res. 18:275-279.

Habashi F 1994. Phosphate fertiliser industry: processing technology. Industrial Min. March 1994:65-69.

Habib MK, Hafez KHA and WM Shehata 2001. Saudi scoria and basalt - Occurrence, use and investment opportunity. Industrial Minerals November 2001:70-75.

Hammond LL, Chien SH and GW Easterwood 1986a. Agronomic effectiveness of Bayovar phosphate rock in soil induced phosphorus retention. Soil Sci. Soc. Am. J. 50:1601-1606.

Hammond LL, Chien SH and AU Mokwunye 1986b. Agronomic evaluation of unacidulated and partially acidulated phosphate rocks indigenous to the tropics. Adv. Agron. 40:89-140.

Hammond LL and LA Leon 1983. Agronomic effectiveness of natural and altered phosphate rocks from Latin America. IMPHOS 3rd International Congress on phosphorus compounds, Oct. 4-6, Brussels, Belgium, 503-58.

Hammond LL, Chien SH, Roy AH and AU Mokwunye 1989. Solubility and agronomic effectiveness of partially acidulated phosphate rocks as influenced by their iron and aluminum oxide content. Fert. Res. 19:93-98.

Harley AD and RJ Gilkes 2000. Factors influencing the release of plant nutrient elements from silicate rock powders: a geochemical overview. Nutr. Cycl. Agroecosyst. 56:11-36.

Hedley MJ and NS Bolan 1997. Developments in some aspects of reactive phosphate rock research and use in New Zealand. Aust. J. Exp. Agric. 37:861-884.

Hellums DT 1991. Factors affecting the efficiency of nonconventional phosphorus fertilizers in lowland and upland cropping systems. Ph.D. Thesis, Auburn University, Auburn, Alabama, USA.

Hensel J 1890. Das Leben. (in German) Verlag Boericke und Tafel, Leipzig, Germany.

Hensel J 1894. Bread from stones. AJ Tafel (ed.) Philadelphia, USA.

Hinsinger P 1998. How do plant roots acquire mineral nutrients? Chemical processes involved in the rhizosphere. Adv. Agr. 64:225-265.

Hinsinger P and RJ Gilkes 1996. Mobilization of phosphate from phosphate rock and alumina-sorbed phosphate by the roots of ryegrass and clover as related to rhizosphere pH. Europ. J. Soil Sc. 47:533-544.

Hinsinger P and B Jaillard 1993. Root-induced release of interlayer potassium and vermiculization of phlogopite as related to potassium depletion in the rhizosphere of ryegrass. J. Soil Sci. 44:525-534.

Hinsinger P, Elsass F, Jaillard B and M Robert 1993. Root-induced irreversible transformation of a trioctahedral mica in the rhizosphere of rape. J. Soil Sci. 44:535-545.

Hoffland E 1992. Quantitative evaluation of the role of organic acid exudation in the mobilization of rock phosphate by rape. Plant Soil 140:279-289.

Hoffland E, Findenegg GR and JA Nelemans 1989a. Solubilization of rock phosphate by rape. I. Evaluation of the role of the nutrient uptake pattern. Plant and Soil 113:155-160.

Hoffland E, Findenegg GR and JA Nelemans 1989b. Solubilization of rock phosphate by rape. II. Local root exudation of organic acids as a response to P-starvation. Plant and Soil 113: 161-165.

Huang Z, Zhang C, Luo J, Zheng S, Lu R and X Yan 2001. Utilization of rock phosphates as a source of phosphorus for sugarcane production on acid soils in south China. International meeting on direct application of phosphate rock and related technology: Latest developments and practical experiences, July 16-20 2001, Kuala Lumpur, Malaysia.

Huettl RF 1990. Nutrient supply and fertilizer experiments in view of N saturation. Pant Soil 128:45-58.

Huettl RF and HW Zoettl 1993. Liming as a mitigation tool in Germany's declining forests - reviewing results from former and recent trials. Water Air Soil Pollut. 61:325-338.

Ikerra TWD, Mnkeni PNS and BR Singh 1994. Effects of added compost and farmyard manure on P release from Minjingu phosphate rock and its uptake by maize. Norw. J. Agr. Sci. 8:13-23.

IFDC 1998. Potential use of calcined calcium iron aluminum phosphates for flooded rice production. IFDC Report December 1998, p 5.

IITA 1999. Plants that make fertilizers. Annual Report 1999. International Institute of Tropical Agriculture, Ibadan, Nigeria.

International Labour Organization 1999. Social and labour issues in small-scale mines. TMSSM/1999, 99 pp.

Iyamuremye F and RP Dick 1996. Organic amendments and phosphorus sorption by soils. Adv. Agron. 56:139-185.

Jama B, Swinkels RA and RJ Buresh 1997. Agronomic and economic evaluation of organic and inorganic sources of phosphorus in western Kenya. Agron. J. 89:597-604.

Johnston WB and RA Olson 1972. Dissolution of fluorapatite by plant roots. J. Soil Sci.114:29-36.

Kadeba O 1990. Fertilizer application in aid of plantation establishment in the savanna areas of Nigeria. Water, Air, Soil Poll. 54:641-649.

Kadeba O 1998. Above-ground nutrient dynamics of Caribbean Pine (*Pinus caribaea*) plantation ecosystems. In: Schulte A and D Ruhiyat (eds.) Soils of tropical forest ecosystems: Characteristics, ecology and management. Springer Verlag, pp. 125-132.

Kamasho JA and BR Singh 1982. Available copper and zinc status of some Tanzanian volcanic ash soils: A case study. Pedologie 32:209-224.

Kanabo IAK. and RJ Gilkes 1988. The effect of soil texture on the dissolution of North Carolina phosphate rock. J. Soil Sci. 39:191-198.

Kang BT and OA Osiname 1985. Micronutrient problems in tropical Africa. In: Vlek PLG (Ed.) Micronutrients in tropical food crop production. Martinus Nijhoff/Dr. W. Junk Publ. Dordrecht, Netherlands: pp. 131-150.

Kantor W, Schoenfeld G and E Gock 1990. Improvement of the solubility of rock phosphate by mechanical activation compared to chemical treatments. Paper presented at IFDC seminar on rock phosphates in Lome, Togo.

Karanja NK, Mwendwa KA, Okalebo JR and F Zapata 2001. Effect of phosphate rock fertilization and arbuscular mycorrhizae (AM) inoculation on the growth of agroforestry tree seedlings. International meeting on direct application of phosphate rock and related technology: Latest developments and practical experiences, July 16-20 2001, Kuala Lumpur, Malaysia.

Keller WD 1948. Native rocks and minerals as fertilizers. Sci. Monthly 66:122-130.

Keller WD, Balgord WD and AL Reesman 1963. Dissolved products of artificially pulverized silicate minerals and rocks. J. Sediment. Petrol. 33:191-204.

Khasawneh FE and EC Doll 1978. The use of phosphate rock for direct application to soils. Adv. Agron. 30:159-206.

King FH 1911. Farmers of forty centuries. Rodale Press, Emmaus, Pennsylvania, USA. 441 pp.

Kodama H, Schnitzer M and M Jaakkimainen 1983. Chlorite and biotite weathering by fulvic acid solutions in closed and open systems. Can. J. Soil Sci. 63:619-629.

Kpomblekou K and MA Tabatabai 1994. Effect of organic acids on release of phosphorus from phosphate rocks. J. Soil Sci. 158:442-453.

Kucey RMN 1983. Phosphate solubilizing bacteria and fungi in various cultivated and virgin Alberta soils. Can. J. Soil Sci. 63:671-678.

Kucey RMN 1987. Increased phosphorus uptake by wheat and field beans inoculated with a phosphorus-solubilizing *Pennicillium biliaji* strain and with vesicular-arbuscular mycorrhizal fungi. Appl. Environ. Microbiol. 53:2699-2703.

Lai TM and DD Eberl 1986. Controlled and renewable release of phosphorus in soils from mixture of phosphate rock and NH_4-exchanged clinoptilolite. Zeolites 6:129-132.

Leon LA, Fenster WE and LL Hammond 1986. Agronomic potential of eleven phosphate rocks from Brazil, Colombia, Peru and Venezuela. Soil Sci. Soc. Am. J. 50:798-802.

Leonardos OH, Fyfe WS and BI Kronberg 1987. The use of ground rocks in laterite systems: an improvement to the use of conventional soluble fertilizers? Chem. Geol. 60:361-370.

Leonardos OH, Theodoro SH and ML Assad 2000. Remineralization for sustainable agriculture: A tropical perspective from a Brazilian viewpoint. Nutr. Cycling Agroecosyst. 56:3-9.

Levinson AA 1974. Introduction to exploration geochemistry. Applied Publishing Ltd. Wilmette, USA, 612 pp.

Leyval C and J Berthelin 1989. Interactions between *Laccaria laccata*, *Agrobacterium radiobacter* and beech roots: Influence on P, K, Mg, and Fe mobilization from minerals and plant growth. Plant Soil 117:103-110.

Loganathan P, Hedley MJ and MR Bretherton 1994. The agronomic value of co-granulated Christmas Island Grade C phosphate rock and elemental sulphur. Fert. Res. 39:229-237.

Lombin G 1983. Evaluating the micronutrient fertility of Nigeria's semi-arid soil. 1. Zinc. Soil Sci. 136:142-147.

Lompo F 1993. Contribution a la valorisation des phosphates natureles du Burkina Faso: Etudes des effets de l'interaction phosphates natureles-materies organiques. These Docteur Ingenieur. Fac. Des Sciences et Techniques de L'Universite Nationale de Cote d'Ivoire, Abidjan.

Lowell K and RR Weil 1995. Pyrite enhancement of phosphorus availability from African phosphate rocks: A laboratory study. Soil Sci. Soc. Am. J. 59:1645-1654.

Lupin MS and ND Le 1983. Compaction - Alternate approach for granular fertilizer. Techn. Bull. T-25, Intern. Fert. Dev. Center, Muscle Shoals, Alabama, USA.

Lynch PB and EB Davies 1964. Top dressing of grassland with phosphate and lime. II. Residual effects. New Zeal. J. Agric. Res. 7:299-338.

MacKay AD, Syers JK and PEH Gregg 1984. Ability of chemical extraction procedures to assess the agronomic effectiveness of phosphate rock materials. NZ. J. Agric. Res. 27:219-230.

Mane JD, Modak HM, Ramaiah NA and SJ Jadhav 1988. Utilisation of sugarcane trash and other cellulosic wastes for production of oxalic acid. Biol. Wastes 25:171-176.

Markewicz FJ and W Lodding 1983. Glauconite. In: Industrial Minerals and Rocks. 5, Vol 2:745-756.

Martin G and P Fourier 1965. Les oligo-elements dans la culture de l'arachide du nord Senegal, Oleagineux 20:287-291

Mathers SJ 1994. Industrial mineral potential of Uganda. In: Mathers SJ and AJG Notholt (eds.) Industrial Minerals in Developing Countries. AGID Geosciences in International Development 18:144-166.

Mathur SP, Proulx JG, Levesque M. and RB Sanderson 1986. Composting of an igneous rock phosphate. In: Wachira JK and AJG Notholt (eds.) Agrogeology in Africa. Commonw. Sci. Council, Techn. Publ. Series 226:129-145.

Mattingley GEG 1968. Evaluation of phosphate fertilizers II. J. Agric. Sci. 70:139-156.

Mayer-Krapoll H 1969. Basic slag and its many-sided effects in forest fertilization. AgriDigest 18:3-10.

Mba CC 1997. Rock phosphate solubilizing *streptosporangium* isolates from casts of tropical earthworms. Soil Biol. Biochem. 29:381-385.

McClellan GH and JR Lehr 1969. Crystal chemical investigations of natural apatites. Amer. Mineralogist 54:1374-1391.

McClellan GH and AJG Notholt 1986. Phosphate deposits of tropical sub-Saharan Africa. In: Mokwunye AU and PLG Vlek (eds.) Management of nitrogen and phosphorus fertilizers in sub-Saharan Africa. Martinus Nijhoff Publishers, Dordrecht, Netherlands: 173-223.

McCray JM and ML Sumner 1990. Assessing and modifying Ca and Al levels in acid subsoils. Adv. Soil Sci. 14:45-75.

McDowell LR 1992. Minerals in animal and human nutrition. Academic Press Inc. New York, USA, 176-204.

McMichael B 1990. Pumice markets. Volcanic rise of stonewashing. Industrial Minerals May 1990:22-37.

McNeil DL 1987. Soil requirements for peanut growth. J Agric. Western Aust. 28:28-31.

Mekonnen K, Buresh RJ and B Jama 1997. Root and inorganic distributions of sesbania fallows, natural fallow and maize. Plant Soil 188:319-327.

Michalk DL and H Zhi-Kai 1992. Response of subterranean clover (*trifolium subterraneum*) to lime, magnesium, and boron on acid infertile soil in subtropical China. Fert. Res. 32:249-257.

Missoux 1853/54. Sur l'emploi de la poudre des roches granitiques comme excitant de la vegetation. Compt. Rend. Acad. Sci. (Paris) t 36: p.1136; t 37: p.245.

Mitchell AD, Loganathan P, Payn TW and RW Tillman 1999. Effect of calcined magnesite on soil and *Pinus radiata* foliage magnesium in pumice soils of New Zealand. Aust. J. Soil Res. 37:545-560.

Mnkeni PNS, Semoka JMR and EG Kaitaba 1994. Effects of Mapogoro phillipsite on availability of phosphorus in phosphate rocks. Trop. Agric. (Trinidad) 71:249-253.

Mnkeni PNS, Chien SH and G Carmona 2000. Effectiveness of Panda Hill phosphate rock compacted with superphosphate as source of phosphorus for rape, wheat, maize, and soybean. Comm. Soil Sci. Plant Anal. 31:3163-3175.

Mokwunye U, Chien SH and E Rhodes 1986. Phosphate reactions with tropical African soils. In: Mokwunye AU and PLG Vlek (eds.) Management of nitrogen and phosphorus fertilizers in sub-Saharan Africa. Martinus Nijhoff Publ., Dordrecht, Netherl., pp. 253-281.

Moormann FR and BT Kang 1978. Microavailability of soils in the tropics and its agronomic implications with special reference to West Africa. In: Diversity of soils in the tropics. Am. Soc. Agron., Spec. Publ. 34:29-43.

Mortveldt JJ 1985. Micronutrient fertilizers and fertilization practices. In: Vlek PLG (editor) Micronutrients in tropical food production. M. Nijhoff/Dr. W. Junk Publ. Dordrecht, Netherlands, pp. 221-235.

Mueller-Dombois D 1991. Forest decline and soil nutritional problems in Pacific areas. Water, Air, Soil Poll. 54:195-207.

Muleba N 1999. Effects of cowpea, crotolaria and sorghum crops and phosphorus fertilizers on maize productivity in semi-arid West Africa. J. Agric. Sci. 132:61-70.

Muleba N and M Coulibaly 1999. Effects of phosphorus fertilizer sources on cowpea and subsequent cereal crop productivity in semi-arid West Africa. J. Agric. Sci. 132:45-60.

Mumpton FA 1984. Natural zeolites. In: Pond WG and FA Mumpton (eds.) Zeo-agriculture: Use of natural zeolites in agriculture and aquaculture. Westview Press Boulder, Colorado, pp. 247-254.

Nahas E 1996. Factors determining rock phosphate solubilization by microorganisms isolated from soil. World J. Microbiol. Biotechn. 12:567-572.

Nahas E, Banzatto DA and LC Assis 1990. Fluorapatite solubilization by *Aspergillus niger* in vinasse medium. Soil Biol. Biochem. 22:1097-1101.

Narsian V and HH Patel 2000. *Aspergillus aculeatus* as rock phosphate solubilizer. Soil Biol. Biochem. 32:559-565.

Noetstaler R 1995. Keynote address to the International Roundtable on artisanal mining, World Bank, Washington D.C. May 17-19, 1995.

Noland DA, Spomer LA and DJ Williams 1992. Evaluation of pumice as a perlite substitute for container soil physical amendment. Commun. Soil Sci. Anal. 23:1533-1547.

Notholt AJG and DE Highley 1986. World phosphate resources, with particular reference to potential low-grade ores. Trans. Instn. Min. Metall. (Section B: Applied Earth Sci.) 95:A125-132.

Notholt AJG, Sheldon RP and DF Davidson (eds.) 1989. Phosphate deposits of the world. Vol 2. Phosphate rock resources, Cambridge University Press, Cambridge, UK, 566pp.

Nyamapfene KW 1986. The use of termite mounds in Zimbabwe peasant agriculture. Trop. Agric. (Trinidad) 63:191-192.

Nyandat NN and PN Ochieng 1976. Copper content and availability in soils. A survey of arable and range areas of Kenya. East Afric. Agric. Forestry J. 42:1-7.

Nykvist N 1998. Logging can cause a serious lack of calcium in tropical rainforest ecosystems. An example from Sabah, Malaysia. In: Schulte A and D Ruhiyat (eds.) Soils of tropical forest ecosystems: Characteristics, ecology and management. Springer Verl., 87-91.

Nziguheba G 2001. Improving phosphorus availability and maize production through organic and inorganic amendments in phosphorus efficient soils in western Kenya. Ph. D. Thesis. Dissertationes de agricultura, Kathol. Univ. Leuven, Belgium, 116pp.

Nziguheba G , Palm CA, Buresh RJ and P Smithson 1998. Soil phosphorus fractions and adsorption as affected by organic and inorganic sources. Plant Soil 198:159-168.

Nziguheba G, Merckx R, Palm CA and M Rao 2000. Organic residues affect phosphorus availability and maize yield in a nitisol of western Kenya. Biol. Fertil. Soils 32:328-339.

Obigbesan GO and H Kuhn 1974. Vergleichende Untersuchungen ueber die Wirksamkeit verschiedener Phosphatduengemittel auf humiden tropischen Boeden Westafrikas. Tropenlandwirt 75:49-57.

Odongo EN 2002. Livestock's contribution to phosphorus cycling in smallholder agriculture in Kenya. Ph. D. Thesis, University of Guelph, Canada, 176pp.

Ohno T and MS Erich 1990. Effect of wood ash application on soil pH and soil test nutrients. Agric. Ecosyst. Environm. 32:223-239.

Okalebo JR, Karanja NK, Maritim HK, Woomer PL, Obura PAS, Nekesa P and F Mwaura 2001. Nutrient replenishment in smallhold farms of Western kenya using the "Prep-Pac" product. International meeting on direct application of phosphate rock and related technology: Latest developments and practical experiences, July 16-20 2001, Kuala Lumpur, Malaysia.

Oshier R 2002. Use of local resources for soil phosphorus replenishment in eastern Uganda: composting of organic material and Busumbu phosphate rock. M. Sc. Thesis, University of Guelph, Ontario, Canada, 237pp.

Osiname OA, Kang BT, Schulte EE and RB Corey 1973. Zinc response of maize (*Zea mays* L.) grown on sandy inceptisols in western Nigeria. Agron. J. 65:875-877.

Palm CA 1995. Contribution of agroforestry trees to nutrient requirements of intercropped plants. Agroforestry Systems 30:105-124.

Palm CA, Myers RJK and SM Nandwa 1997. Combined use of organic and inorganic nutrient sources for soil fertility maintenance and replenishment. In: Buresh RJ, Sanchez PA and F Calhoun (eds.) Replenishing soil fertility in Africa. SSSA Special Publ. 51:193-217.

Parham W 1989. Natural zeolites: Some potential agricultural application for developing countries. Natural Resources Forum, May 1989:107-115.

Penot E, Syofyan S and T Fairhurst 1998. The use of phosphate rock in the establishment of rubber-based agroforestry systems in Indonesia. In: Johnston AE and JK Syers (eds.) Nutrient management for sustainable crop production in Asia. CAB International, pp. 348-349.

Pereira MLD 1995. The Eppawala phosphate deposit in Sri Lanka: Characterization and modification of apatite solubility. M. Sc. Thesis, University of Guelph, Ontario, Canada, 188 pp.

Powell, M 2001. Pers. Communication, University of Western Ontario, Canada.

Pijnenborg and Lie 1993. Effect of lime-pelleting on the nodulation of lucerne (*Medicago sativa* L.) in an acid soil: A comparative study carried out in the field, in pots and in rhizotrons Plant Soil 121:225-234.

Pride C and P van Straaten 1993. Small-scale mining and agromineral deposit development. Presentation, IFDC conference on indigenous resource development for the fertilizer sector, Florida, USA (unpubl.).

Quiñones MA, Borlaug NE and CR Dowswell 1997. A fertilizer-based green revolution for Africa. In: Buresh RJ, Sanchez PA and F. Calhoun (eds.) Replenishing soil fertility in Africa. SSSA Special Publ. 51:81-95.

Rajan SSS 1982. Influence of phosphate rock reactivity and granule size on the effectiveness of 'biosuper'. Fert. Res. 3:3-12.

Rajan SSS 1983. Effect of sulphur content of phosphate rock/sulphur granules on the availability of phosphate to plants. Fert. Res. 4:287-296.

Rajan SSS 1987a. Phosphate rock and phosphate rock/sulphur granules as phosphate fertilizers and their dissolution in soil. Fert. Res. 11:43-60.

Rajan SSS 1987b. Partially acidulated phosphate rock as fertiliser and dissolution in soil of the residual rock phosphate. New Zeal. J. Exp. Agric. 15:177-184.

Rajan SSS, Watkinson JH and AG Sinclair 1996. Phosphate rocks for direct application to soils. Adv. Agron. 57:77-159.

Raji BA and BW Jimba 1999. A preliminary chlorine survey of the savanna soils of Nigeria. Nutr. Cycl. Agroecosyst. 55:29-34.

Rausell-Colom JA, Sweatman TR, Wells CB and K Norish 1965. Studies in the artificial weathering of mica. In: Hallsworth EG and DV Crawford (eds.) Experimental Petrology, Butterworths, London UK, pp. 40-72.

Roschnik RK, Grant PM and WK Nduku 1967. The effect of incorporating crushed basalt rock into an infertile acid sand. Rhod. Zamb. Mal. J. Agric. Res. 5:133-138.

Rossi G 1978. Potassium recovery through leucite bioleaching: possibilities and limitations. In: Murr LE, Torma AE and JA Brierley (eds.) Metallurgical applications of bacterial leaching and related microbiological phenomena, Academic Press, New York USA, pp. 297-317.

Rowell AWG and PM Grant 1975. A comparison of fertilizer borate and colemanite incorporated in granular fertilizers. Rhod. J. Agr. Res. 13:63-66.

Sagoe CI, Ando T, Kouno K, and T Nagaoka 1998a. Effects of organic-acid treatment of phosphate rocks on the phosphorus availability to Italian ryegrass. Soil Sci. Plant Nutr. 43:1067-1072.

Sagoe CI, Ando T, Kouno K, and T Nagaoka 1998b. Relative importance of protons and solution calcium concentration in phosphate rock dissolution by organic acids. Soil Sci. Plant Nutr. 44:617-625.

Sahu SN and BB Jana 2000. Enhancement of the fertilizer value of rock phosphate engineered through phosphate-solubilizing bacteria. Ecol. Eng. 15:27-39.

Sale PWG, Simpson PG, Anderson CA and LL Muir 1997. The role for reactive phosphate rocks for pasture in Australia. CSIRO Publ. Melbourne, Australia.

Sale PWG and AU Mokwunye 1993. Use of phosphate rocks in the tropics. Fert. Res. 35:33-45.

Sanchez PA 1976. Properties and mangement of soils in the tropics. J. Wiley and Sons Inc. New York, 618pp.

Sanchez PA 2002. Soil fertility and hunger in Africa. Science 295:2019-2020.

Sanchez PA and G Uehara 1980. Management considerations for acid soils with high phosphorus fixation capacity. In: Khasawneh FE, Sample EC and EJ Kamprath (eds.) The role of phosphorus in agriculture. Am. Soc. Agron. Madison, Wisconsin, USA, 471-514.

Sanchez PA and JG Salinas 1981. Low-input technology for managing oxisols and ultisols in tropical America. Adv. Agron. 34:280-406.

Sanchez PA and C Palm 1996. Nitrogen and phosphorus in African soils - what role for agroforestry? Agroforestry Today, Oct-Dec 1996:14-16.

Sanchez PA and RRB Leaky 1997. Land-use transformation in Africa: three determinants for balancing food security with natural resource utilization. Eur. J. Agr. 7:1-9.

Sanchez PA, Shepherd KD, Soule MJ, Place FM, Buresh RJ and AN Izac 1997. Soil fertility replenishment in Africa: an investment in natural resource capital. In: Buresh RJ, Sanchez PA and F Calhoun (eds.) Replenishing soil fertility in Africa. SSSA Special Publ. 51:1-46.

Sanchez PA and BA Jama 2000. Soil fertility replenishment takes off in East and Southern Africa. Presentation. Intern. Symp. on balanced nutrient management systems for the moist savanna and humid forest zones of Africa. Cotonou, Benin, Oct. 9, 2000.

Sanz-Scovino JI and DL Rowell 1988. The use of feldspars as potassium fertilizers in the savannah of Colombia. Fert. Res. 17:71-83.

Sassi G, Ruggori B, Specchia V and A Gianetto 1991. Citric acid production by A. niger with banana extract. Biores. Techn. 37:259-269.

Schofield PE, Gregg PEH and JK Syers 1981. 'Biosuper' as a phosphate fertiliser: A glasshouse evaluation. New Zeal. J. Exp. Agric. 9:63-67.

Schnitzer M and H Kodama 1976. The dissolution of micas by fulvic acid. Geoderma 15:381-391.

Schumann AW and ME Sumner 2000. Chemical evaluation of nutrient supply from fly ash-biosolids mixtures. Soil Sci. Soc. Am. J. 64:419-426.

Schutte K 1954. A survey of plant minor element deficiencies in Africa. Afric. Soils 3:285-292.

Shainberg I, Sumner ME, Miller WP, Farina MPW, Pavan MA and MV Fey 1989. Use of gypsum on soils: a review. Adv. Soil Sci. 9:1-111.

Sheldon RP 1987. Industrial minerals- with emphasis on phosphate rock. In: McLaren DJ and BJ Skinner (eds.) Resources and World development. - Dahlem conferences 1987, Berlin, Germany, 347-361.

Sillanpaeae M 1982. Micronutrients and nutrient status of soils: a global study. FAO Soils Bull. 48, 444pp.

Simpson J 1998. Site specific fertiliser requirements of tropical Pine plantations. In: Schulte A and D Ruhiyat (eds.) Soils of tropical forest ecosystems: Characteristics, ecology and management. Springer Verlag, pp. 115-124.

Simpson PG, Sale PWG, Hepworth G, Gilbert MA, Blair GJ, Garden DL, Dann PR, Hamilton L, Stewart J, Hunter J, Cayley JWD, Ward GN, Johnson D, Lewis DC, Fleming NK, Bolland DA, Gilkes RJ and MJ McLaughlin 1997. National reactive phosphate rock project – aims, experimental approach and site characteristics. Aust. J. Exp. Agric. 37:885-904.

Singh CP, Ruhal DS and M Singh 1983. Solubilization of low grade rock phosphate by composting with a farm waste, pear-millet boobla. Agric. Wastes 8:17-25.

Singh CP and A Amberger 1990. Humic substances in straw compost with rock phosphate. Biol. Waste 31:165-174.

Singh CP and A Amberger 1991. Solubilization and availability of phosphorus during decomposition of rock phosphate enriched straw and urine. Biol. Agric. Hortic. 7:261-269.

Singh CP and A Amberger 1998. Organic acids and phosphorus solubilization in straw composted with rock phosphate. Biores. Techn. 63:13-16.

Sivasubramaniam S, Wickremasinghe KN and S Ayadurai 1981. The use of Eppawela apatite for tea in Sri Lanka. Tea Q. 50:4-10.

Smaling EMA 1995. The balance may look fine when there is nothing you can mine: nutrient stocks and flows in West African soils. In: Gerner H and AU Mokwunye (eds.) Use of phosphate rock for sustainable agriculture in West Africa. IFDC, Miscellaneous Fert. Studies, 11: 10-20.

Smaling EMA, Stoorvogel JJ and PN Windmeijer 1993. Calculating soil nutrient balances in Africa at different scales: II. District scale. Fert. Res. 35: 237-250.

Smaling EMA, Nandwa SM and BH Jansen 1997. Soil fertility in Africa is at stake. In: Buresh RJ, Sanchez PA and F Calhoun (eds.) Replenishing soil fertility in Africa. SSSA Spec. Publ. 51, Soil Sci. Soc. Am. Madison Wisconsin USA:47-61.

Smith JP and Lehr JR 1966. An x-ray investigation of carbonate apatites. J. Agric. Food Chem. 14:242-249.

Smithson PC 1999. Interactions of organic materials with phosphate rocks and triple superphosphates. Agrofor. Forum 9:37-40.

Smithson P, Jama B, Delve R, van Straaten P and R Buresh 2001. East African phosphate resources and their agronomic performance. Intern. meeting on direct application of phosphate rock and related technology: Latest developments and practical experiences, July 16-20 2001, Kuala Lumpur, Malaysia.

Smyth TJ and PA Sanchez 1982. Phosphate rock dissolution and availability in Cerrado soils as affected by sorption capacity. Soil Sci. Soc. Am. J. 46:339-345.

Song SK and PM Huang 1988. Dynamics of potassium release from potassium-bearing minerals as influenced by oxalic and citric acids. Soil Sci. Soc. Am. J. 52:383-390.

Sperber JI 1958. Solution of apatite by soil microorganisms producing organic acids. Aust. J. Agric. Res. 9:782-788.

Spiropoulos J 1991. Small-scale mineral industries - Their role in rural development. In: DA Stow and DJC Laming (eds). Geoscience in Development, AGID Rep.14, Balkema, Rotterdam 197-208.

Stewhouwer RC, Dick WA and P Sutton 1999. Acidic soil amendment with a magnesium-containing fluidized bed combustion by-product. Agron. J. 91:24-32.

Stoorvogel JJ, Smaling EMA, and BH Jansen 1993. Calculating soil nutrient balances in Africa at different scales: I. Supra-national scale. Fert. Res. 35:227-235.

Sumner ME 1995. Amelioration of subsoil acidity with minimum disturbance. Adv. Soil Sci. 19:147-185.

Suzuki Y and N Kohyama 1988. Carcinogenic and fibrogenic effect of erionite, mordenite and synthetic zeolite $A. In: Kallo D and HS Sherry (eds.) Occurrence, properties and utilization of natural zeolites. Academiai Kiado, Budapest, Hungary, pp. 829-840.

Swaby RJ 1975. Biosuper-biological superphosphate. In: McLachlan KD (editor) Sulphur in Australasian agriculture. Sydney University Press, pp. 213-220.

Syers JK and AD MacKay 1986. Reactions of Sechura phosphate rock and single superphosphate in soil. Soil Sci. Soc. Am. J. 50:480-485.

Tan KH 1980. The release of silicon, aluminum and potassium during decomposition of soil minerals by humic acid. Soil Sci. 129:5-11.

Tennakone K, Weerasuriya SVR, Jayatissa DL, Damyanthi MLWD and LHK Silva 1988. Non hygroscopic superphosphate fertilizer from apatite and hydrochloric acid. Fert. Res. 16:87-96.

Tian G and GO Kolawole 1999. Phosphorus availability of phosphate rock incubated with plant residues with various chemical compositions. Agroforestry Forum 9:40-42.

Tiwari KN, Dewivedi BS and AN Parthak 1985. Iron pyrites as sulphur fertiliser for legumes. Plant Soil 86:295-298.

Truong B and D Montange 1998. The African experience with phosphate rock, including Djebel Onk, and case studies in Brazil and Vietnam. In: Johnston AE and JK Syers (eds.) Nutrient management for sustainable crop production in Asia. CAB International 133-148.

Ure AM and ML Berrow 1982. The elemental constituents of soils. In: HJM Bowen (editor) Environmental Chemistry Vol. 2. Royal Soc. Chem. London, pp. 94-204.

Van den Berghe CH 1996. The effect of Matongo rock phosphate and urea as compared to di-ammonium phosphate in the composting process and the yield of potatoes in the Mugamba region of Burundi. Fert. Res. 45:51-59.

Van der Pol F 1993. Soil mining. An unseen contributor to farm income in southern Mali. Royal Trop. Institute Amsterdam, Bull. 325, 48 pp.

Van Diest A 1991. Various forms of root action influencing the availability of soil and fertilizer phosphorus. In: McMichael BL and H Persson (eds.) Plant roots and their environment. Elsevier Sci. Publ., Amsterdam, pp. 164-170.

Vandre R, Kaupenjohann M and W Zech 1991. Long term effects of liming measures in emission damaged woodlands vegetation and soil chemical status of soil structural elements. Mitteilungen der Deutschen Bodenkundlichen Gesellschaft 66:745-748.

Van Kauwenbergh SJ 1995. Mineralogy and characterization of phosphate rock. In: Dahanayake K, Van Kauwenbergh SJ and DT Hellums (eds.) Proceeding of Intern. Workshop: Direct Application of phosphate rock and appropriate technology fertilizers in Asia: What hinders acceptance and growth? Institute of Fundamental Studies, Kandy, Sri Lanka, pp. 29-47.

Van Kauwenbergh SJ and GH McClellan 1990. Comparative geology and mineralogy of the Southeastern United States and Togo phosphorites. In: Notholt AJG and I Jarvis (eds.) Phosphorite research and development. Geol. Soc. Spec. Publ. 52:139-155.

Van Kauwenbergh SJ and DT Hellums 1995. Direct Application Phosphate Rock: A contemporary snapshot. Phosphorus and Potassium 200:27-37.

Van Ray B and A van Diest 1979. Utilization of phosphate from different sources by six plant species. Plant Soil 51:577-589.

Van Straaten P 1987. Agrogeological resources in eastern and southern Africa. In: Wachira JK and AJG Notholt (eds.) Agrogeology in Africa. Commonw. Sci. Council, Techn. Publ. Ser. 226:12-36.

Van Straaten P and W Chesworth 1985. Low cost fertilisers: Local geological resources for subsistence farmers in Eastern Africa. In: United Nations Economic Commission for Africa. Second Regional Conference on the Development and Utilisation of Mineral Resources in Africa. Lusaka, Zambia, 4-9.

Van Straaten P and C Pride 1993. Agrogeological resources for small scale mining. In: Pride C. and P van Straaten (eds.) Agrogeology and small scale mining. Small Mining Intern. Bull. 5-6:5-9.

Van Straaten P and TRC Fernandes 1995: Agrogeology in Eastern and Southern Africa: a survey with particular reference to developments in phosphate utilization in Zimbabwe. In: Blenkinsop, T.G. and P.L. Tromp (eds.) Sub-Saharan Economic Geology. Geol. Soc. Zimbabwe Spec. Publ. 3, Balkema Publishers, Netherlands, pp. 103-118.

Van Straaten P, Maroko J, Voroney P and D Fallow 2001. Inherent soil fertility reflected in phosphorus content of *Tithonia diversifolia* leaf tissue. Poster presented at the Canadian Soil Science Soc. Meeting 2001, Guelph, Ontario, August 2-4 2001.

Vassilev N, Baca MT, Vassileva M, Franco I and R Azcon 1995. Rock phosphate solubilization by *Aspergillus niger* grown on sugar-beet waste medium. Appl. Microbiol. Biotech. 44:546-549.

Vlek PLG and WL Lindsay 1978. Potential use of disintegrated iron pyrite in sodic and iron-deficient soils. J. Environ. Qual. 7:111-114.

Von Fragstein P, Pertl W and H Vogtmann 1988. Verwitterungsverhalten silikatischer Gesteinsmehle unter Laborbedingungen (in German). Z. Pflanzenern. Bodenk. 151:141-146.

Waggaman WH 1952. Basic slag, degreased bone and dicalcium phosphate. In: WH Waggaman (editor) Phosphoric acid, phosphate and phosphatic fertilizers. Reinhold Publ. Corp. New York, USA, pp. 356-375.

Walker ME 1975. Calcium requirements for peanuts. Comm. Soil Sci. Plant Anal. 6:299-313.

Watson JP 1977. The use of mounds of the termite *Macrotermes falciger* (Gerstaecker) as a soil amendment. J. Soil Sci. 28:664-672.

Weerasuriya TJ, Pushpakumara and PI Cooray 1993. Acidulated pegmatitic mica: A promising new multi-nutrient mineral fertilizer. Fert. Res. 34:67-77.

Weil RR 2000. Soil and plant influences on crop responses to two African phosphate rocks. Agr. J. 92:1167-1175.

Weil RR and SK Mughogo 2000. Sulfur nutrition of maize in four regions of Malawi. Agron. J. 92:649-656.

Werner W 1969. Die Bedeutung kalk- und silikathaltiger Phosphatduenger fuer die Duengung von Latosolen. Tropenlandwirt 70:57-61.

Wilmot TR, Ellsworth DS and MT Tyree 1996. Base cation fertilization and liming effects on nutrition and growth of Vermont sugar maple stands. For. Ecol. Managem. 84:123-134.

Wilson GCS 1985. New perlite system for tomatoes and cucumbers. Acta Horticult. 172:151-156.

Wilson MA and BG Ellis 1984. Influence of calcium solution activity and surface area on the solubility of selected rock phosphates. Soil Sci. 138:354-359.

Woomer PL, Bekunda MA, Karanja NK, Moorhouse T and JR Okalebo 1998. Agricultural resource management by smallhold farmers in East Africa. Nature and Resources 34:22-33.

Woldeab A, Assefa A, Yematawork A, Abera S, van Straaten P, Groenevelt P and W Chesworth 1994. Report on the results of the Ethiopia-Canada Agrogeology Project - Rock Mulch. Report, LRS-University of Guelph, Canada, 76pp.

Yamoah CF, Burleigh JR and VJ Eylands 1992. Correction of acid infertility in Rwandan Oxisols with lime from indigenous source for sustainable cropping. Exp. Agric. 28:417-424.

Yusdar H and MM Hanafi 2001. Use of phosphate rock for perennial and annual crops cultivation in Malaysia: a review. International meeting on direct application of phosphate rock and related technology: Latest developments and practical experiences, July 16-20 2001, Kuala Lumpur, Malaysia.

Zaharah AR and AR Bah 1997. Effect of green manures on P solubilization and uptake from phosphate rocks. Nutr. Cycl. Agroecosyst. 48:247-255.

Zin ZZ, Khalid H, Tarmizi M and AB Hamdan 2001. Use of phosphate rock fertilizers for oil palm in Malaysia. International meeting on direct application of phosphate rock and related technology: Latest developments and practical experiences, July 16-20 2001, Kuala Lumpur, Malaysia.

Zoysa AKN, Loganathan P and MJ Hedley 1999. Phosphate rock dissolution and transformation in the rhizosphere of tea (*Camellia sinensis* L.) compared with other plant species. Europ. J. Soil Sci. 49:477-486.

Part 2 – Agrominerals of sub-Saharan Africa

Terms and Definitions

ERA		PERIOD	EPOCH		MA
Phanerozoic	Cenozoic	Quaternary	Holocene		0
			Pleistocene		0.1
					1.8
		Neogene (Tertiary)	Pliocene		5
			Miocene		24
		Paleogene (Tertiary)	Oligocene		34
			Eocene	Lutetian	41
					49
				Ypresian	55
				Thanetian	61
			Paleocene	Danian	65
	Mesozoic	Cretaceous	Maastrichtian		72
			Campanian		83
			Santonian		86
			Coniacian		89
			Turonian		93
			Cenomanian		98
			Albian		112
			Aptian		120
					144
		Jurassic			205
		Triassic			248
	Paleozoic	Permian			295
		Carboniferous			354
		Devonian			416
		Silurian			442
		Ordovician			495
		Cambrian			544
Proterozoic	Neoproterozoic				1000
	Mesoproterozoic				1600
	Paleoproterozoic				2500
Archean					4600

The term **palygorskite** ($Mg_2Al_2Si_8O_{20}(OH)_2(OH)_4 \cdot 4H_2O$) is used throughout this text in place of **attapulgite**. This magnesium-rich clay is often associated with sedimentary phosphate deposits. Palygorskite-rich sediments often precede phosphate deposition, for instance, in Niger, Nigeria, Senegal and Togo.

Phosphorite is a sedimentary rock with a high enough content of minerals to be of economic interest (Glossary of Geology).

Reserves versus Resources

A mineral *resource* is a concentration or occurrence of material of economic interest in or on the Earth's crust in such form, quantity and quality that there are reasonable prospects for eventual economic extraction. The location, quantity, grade and continuity are known, estimated or interpreted from specific geological evidence and knowledge. Mineral resources are subdivided in order of decreasing geological confidence into *inferred*, *indicated* and *measured* categories.

Mineral *reserves* constitute a realistic inventory of mineralization, which under assumed and justifiable technical and economic conditions, might become economically extractable.

Angola

Total population (July 2000 estimate): 10,145,000
Area: *1,246,700 km^2
Annual population growth rate (2000): 2.15%
Life expectancy at birth (1998): 47.0 years
People not expected to survive to age 40 (1998): 37.7% of total population
GDP per capita (1998): US $1,821

* includes the Cabinda enclave, located between the Republic of Congo and the Democratic Republic of Congo.

Angola, the second largest country in sub-Saharan Africa, consists of various landscapes, from a coastal lowland, 20-30 km wide in the south and 100 km wide in the north, to a dissected tableland at altitudes around 1,500-2,000 m that slopes gently eastward towards the Congo and Zambezi Basins.

Angola's agriculture is mainly based on subsistence farming with about 75% of the Angolan population dependent on agricultural production. At present, only 3% of the total land area is under cultivation. In 1999, the agricultural sector accounted for 12% of the GDP. Major food crops are cassava, maize, bananas, sweet potatoes, millet, rice, sugar cane and beans. The main export crop is coffee.

Angola is a country well endowed with mineral and energy resources. This industry is currently dominated by the production of oil and diamonds. The enclave of Cabinda to the north of the country is the source of approximately 70% of Angola's total oil production. Angola is the second-largest oil producer in sub-Saharan Africa (after Nigeria) and has significant reserves of natural gas (1.6 trillion cubic feet). Some 85% of this natural gas is currently burned off (flared) due to lack of infrastructure.

Much of Angola's large mineral resource potential remains undeveloped due to a long-lasting civil war that has displaced about one million Angolans.

Geological outline

The geology of Angola is dominated by Proterozoic rocks. Neoproterozoic rocks of the Bembe Group occur in the western part of the country. The 'Schisto-Calcaire,' which is part of the Neoproterozoic West Congolian Supergroup that outcrops mainly in the northwest of the country. The lower part of the 'Schisto-Calcaire' is made up of stromatolitic and oolitic limestones and rests on tillites. In the coastal basin, a 4,000 m thick sequence of Cretaceous to Tertiary and Quaternary sediments rests unconformably on the Precambrian. Kalahari sands cover the eastern part of the country.

AGROMINERALS

Phosphates

There are several distinct phosphate regions in Angola, most of them in the coastal region (Figure 2.1). The phosphates are grouped into at least four clusters:

1.   the Cabinda phosphates (9 known deposits),
2.   the Lucunga River phosphates (3 major deposits),
3.   the Luanda phosphate (1 occurrence),
4.   phosphates associated with carbonatite complexes (reported in 6 of 11 known carbonatite complexes).

1.   The Cabinda phosphates.

Extensive sedimentary phosphate deposits are located in the central part of the Cabinda District in areas of relatively low-lying terrain. The phosphate beds, Upper Cretaceous (Maastrichtian) to Lower Eocene in age, are concentrated in two zones. The lower phosphate zone has three beds, 3 m, 12 m and 9 m thick, and the upper phosphate zone has bed thickness ranging from 13-23 m. The phosphatic beds are made up of pellets, oolites and organic fragments (fish teeth, scales and bones). The P_2O_5 content of the lower beds is 10-20% and the grade of the upper beds is 15-20% P_2O_5. Weathering and leaching extend to depths of 100 m or more and in some places have increased the grade of the phosphate beds to 32-38% P_2O_5 (Hodge and Partners 1978).

The phosphate-bearing beds are faulted and mildly folded into northwest striking broad anticlines and synclines, which continue across the border into the neighbouring Democratic Republic of Congo (Figure 2.2).

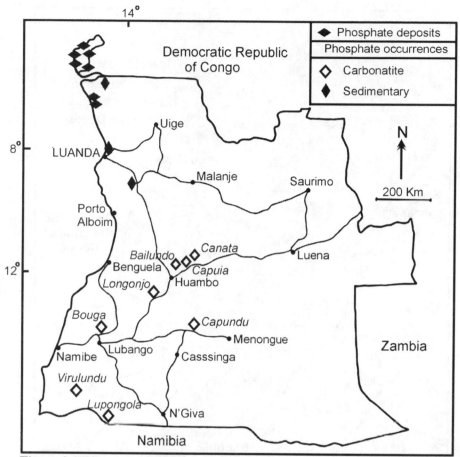

Figure 2.1: Location of phosphate resources of Angola (after Hodge and Partners 1978).

Prospecting in the Cabinda enclave was initially carried out during the late 1960s and early 1970s by Companhia de Fosfatos de Angola (COFAN). It included rotary drilling (201 boreholes, total length = 19,232 m), core drilling (29 holes, length = 626 m), sinking of 9 shafts (total depth = 131 m), as well as gamma-ray and resistivity logging, microscopic studies and chemical analyses. The data obtained were re-evaluated by, among others, Hodge and Partners (1978) and Terraconsult (1983).

Terraconsult (1983) described several phosphate outcrops of the Cabinda District (Figure 2.2) in detail:

- At Mongo Tando (10 km northeast of Landana, along the Itombe Creek): the 3-4 m thick phosphorite layer contains 17-30% P_2O_5.
- At Chibuete, along Lake Massabi, layers contain 15-26% P_2O_5 over a strike length of 6 km.
- At Cacata (some 30 km east of Landana, along the Nhenha Creek): a lenticular phosphorite sequence, up to 14 m thick, contains up to 35% P_2O_5.
- Near Cambota (10 km east of Dinge, at the left bank of the Sanzo River): phosphorite beds contain 12-26% P_2O_5.
- At Chivovo (10 km north of Dinge, at the Tuma Creek): lenticular phosphatic sandstones contain 29% P_2O_5.

Reserve estimates of the phosphates in the Cabinda District differ considerably. Notholt *et al.* (1989) estimated that five groups of deposits in Cabinda contain 16 million tonnes of phosphates, of which 3.3

million tonnes are in the proven category. This is in contrast to the results of the Phase I results of COFAN, which indicated 110 million tonnes of high grade recoverable phosphate concentrates at 34-38% P_2O_5 and a further 50 million tonnes of concentrates containing 32-34% P_2O_5.

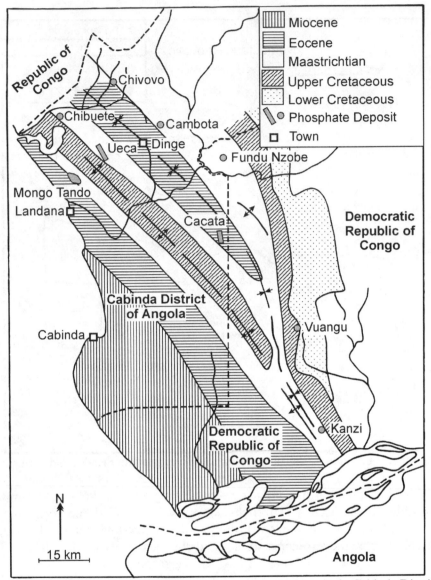

Figure 2.2: Location of phosphate occurrences and deposits in Cabinda District, Angola, and the Bas Congo area, Democratic Republic of Congo.

Hodge and Partners (1978) re-visited the COFAN Phase I and Phase II investigations (412 rotary boreholes, 40 cored boreholes). These findings confirmed probable reserves of 21 million tonnes ranging from 2.1-16.5% P_2O_5 (weighted average 10.1% P_2O_5) within a one square kilometer central section of the Mongo Matonde area of Cabinda District. The thickness of the phosphate beds range from 6.6-18.2 m with a waste-to-ore ratio ranging from 0.0:1-4.5:1. Chemical results from outcropping rock sequences confirm the high phosphate grades. For instance, Hodge and Partners (1978) provide chemical analyses of the original ore (not beneficiated) from the uppermost bed (3 m thick) of the upper phosphate zone in an old quarry at Mango Tando. The composition of the phosphates is: 37.50% P_2O_5, 51.57% CaO, 0.94% Fe_2O_3, 1.62% SiO_2 and 3.84% F. Analyses of the reactivity of a 37% P_2O_5 concentrate from Cabinda showed a neutral ammonium citrate (NAC) solubility of 4.5%, indicating high solubility (McClellan and Notholt 1986).

The evaluation of the exploration work indicated that the previous work had some shortcomings, especially with regard to core recovery. Hodge and Partners (1978) indicated that the resource estimates may be too high.

The high-grade near-surface phosphate beds with a high reactivity could be easily extracted and processed by small-scale methods for local consumption. Based on the relatively high solubility of the phosphate rocks, the agronomic effectiveness is expected to be high in phosphorus-deficient acid soils. So far, no data are available on their agronomic effectiveness in Angolan soils.

2.   The Lucunga River phosphates

The second largest potential for Tertiary phosphate development exists in the Lucunga River area east of Quinzau, approximately 40 km north of the port city of Ambrizete. The phosphate beds are of the unconsolidated nodular type. The deposits of Coluge and Lendiacolo are middle-upper Eocene in age and the reworked phosphate deposit of Quindonacaxa is of Pleistocene age (Hodge and Partners 1978; El-Kadi 1980). Antonio Martins (1963) started to investigate the Quindonacaxa deposit in detail in the early 1960s. A Bulgarian team (Bulgargeomine) and Geomina studied the deposit in 1979 using both geological and geophysical methods. The phosphate reserves at Quindonacaxa alone, based on data of Antonio Martins (1963), are 20,255,903 tonnes at 18.54% P_2O_5. Agronomic work by Melo (1984) indicated good agronomic effectiveness of Quindonacaxa PR applied directly on acid soils (pH< 5.5). The study concluded that 2.5 times more P in the form of PR are required to obtain the same yield results as with superphosphate.

A small phosphate resource in a selected area, 0.5 km^2 in size, within the Qindonacaxa zone was proposed for phosphate extraction. The reserves in this small area were calculated to be 199,652 tonnes of concentrate at 30.96% P_2O_5 (El-Kadi 1980), sufficient to run a pilot plant for about 6 years at an annual production rate of 30,000 tonnes, or about 12 years at 15,000 tonnes. This part of the deposit has been mined and operated intermittently between 1981 and 1984 by the state owned company Fosfatos de Angola (FOSFANG) under a joint venture with Bulgaria (Premoli 1994).

Total resources in the three main deposits of the Lucunga valley have been estimated at some 28 million tonnes of phosphate rock with 18-26% P_2O_5. The phosphate beds are commonly 0.2-2.0 m thick with localized areas having a thickness of over 5 m. Overburden varies from 0.1 m in the Lendiacola area to 2.4 m in the Quindonacaxa area.

3.   Other sedimentary phosphate occurrences

Sedimentary phosphates of various grades and volumes are reported from Pedra do Feitico close to the Zaire River at the border to the Democratic Republic of Congo, and small occurrences south of the Lucunga phosphate zone.

Calcareous phosphorites of unknown quality and quantity are found near Sassalemba, 40 km northeast of Luanda, and at Lunga Riamica, 15 km south of Dondo (Terraconsult 1983). McClellan and Notholt (1986) describe a very low grade (5% P_2O_5) phosphate occurrence at Subinda, south of Namibe (previously called Mocamedes).

4.   Phosphates associated with carbonatites.

Igneous phosphates are known from several Cretaceous carbonatite complexes in Angola. Details on these carbonatite complexes that occur along a northeast-southwest striking structural line (passing west of Huambo) have been published by De Sousa Machado (1958, quoted in Heinrich 1980), Gittins (1966), Issa Filho *et al.* (1991), and Alberti *et al.* (1999). Following this line from northeast to southwest, the main phosphate-bearing carbonatites are: Canata, Capuia, Bailundo, Longonjo, and Bonga (Figure 2.1). South of this line, but following the same structural trend, are the phosphate-containing Capunda, Lupongola and Virulundo carbonatites.

The apatite-bearing Canata carbonatite, 10 km southwest of Andulo, contains in its centre titaniferous magnetite and strongly radioactive minerals. This is a mineral association often found together with apatite enrichments in carbonatites. The Bailundo carbonatite contains phoscorites (apatite-forsterite-magnetite) with apatite cumulates reaching up to 39% P_2O_5 (Alberti *et al.* 1999). The Longonjo carbonatite complex, 4 km southwest of Longonjo (Figure 2.1) contains abundant apatite, barite and magnetite (Premoli 1994). In grab samples collected from the Bonga carbonatite, which contains approximately 800 million tonnes of Niobium ore at 0.5% Nb_2O_5, the phosphate content reached up to 10% P_2O_5 (Terraconsult 1983). Other carbonatite complexes with known phosphate occurrences are Virulundo, Lupongola, and Capunda (Terraconsult 1983; Alberti *et al.* 1999). According to Issa Filho *et al.* (1991), the Bailundo and Bonga carbonatites contain the highest concentration of phosphates in the unweathered rocks.

Most of the surveys were carried out in the primary (unweathered) carbonatite environment. No data are available on enrichments in the weathered residual soil environment of the carbonatites, which in other countries provide the largest and most easily extractable phosphate resources.

Limestone/dolomite

Coastal sediments form the best resources for extracting limestones, but also carbonatites and Neoproterozoic 'Schisto-Calcaire' metasediment with stromatolitic and oolitic limestones and dolomitic limestones have good potential.

Sedimentary limestones for the production of cement is abundant in the coastal zone. The carbonatites in various parts of the country may provide good resources for liming material, but no thorough assessment has been made.

A different source of carbonate that could be used for agricultural purposes is the waste from marble quarrying. These wastes can amount to 30% of total production and in 1994, Angola produced 244,000 m³ marble in the southwest of the country (Kronsten 1994).

Gypsum/anhydrite/sulphur

Gypsum/anhydrite is known from the Cretaceous coastal basins of Angola, with small occurrences of anhydrite reported from the lower Cretaceous Cuanza Basin. Gypsum occurrences are reported from near Cabo Ledo (80 km north of Luanda), and Dombe Grande, 50 km south of Benguela. In the Dombe Grande area, the gypsum deposit ('Dombe Grande Gypsum') of lower Cretaceous (Aptian) age is up to 50 m thick (Duarte Morais and Sgrosso 2000). In both the Cabo Ledo and Dombe Grande gypsum deposits, there are also fine layers and 'small pockets' of elemental sulphur (Terraconsult 1983).

Angola produced approximately 20,000 tonnes of gypsum per year in the 1980s.

Glauconite

A 'considerable glauconite deposit' is known from Giraul, close to the port city of Namibe (previously called Mocamedes) (Terraconsult 1983). However, no detailed information on the deposit, including thickness and overburden, is provided.

Agromineral potential

The agromineral potential of Angola is good. The development of Angola's agromineral resources depends on soil needs, on market demands, and on infrastructural and political stability factors. From the resource side it is evident that widespread sedimentary phosphorites with high grades occur close to the surface in the Cabinda District and in the Lucunga River area. Other phosphates along the coastal zone have been discovered but not studied in detail, for example, the phosphates of Sassalemba. The few reliable data on chemistry and mineralogy of the sedimentary phosphates of Angola indicate that the phosphorites described as bone fragments, pellets and oolites are largely francolites with a high agronomic potential, especially in acid P-deficient soils. Initial pot trials with Quindonacaxa PR indicate potentially good agronomic effectiveness on acid soils.

Additional attention should be given to possible phosphate mineralizations in the Neoproterozoic of the West Congolian Supergroup. Chakravarty (1982) indicated positive tests on phosphates from a stromatolitic specimen from southern Angola.

Apart from the sedimentary phosphates, there are phosphate-enriched carbonatites in Angola, especially Bonga and Bailundo. The core of the Bailundo carbonatite reportedly contains apatite cumulates. A good potential exists to delineate phosphate enrichments in residual soils over these and other carbonatites.

The potential of developing limestone/dolomite deposits from coastal sediments, dolomitic metasediments and from carbonatites is considered good.

The gypsum deposits of the Dombe Grande area should be investigated for their potential to reduce Al-toxicities in acid soils, and for the amelioration of sodium-affected soils.

The potential of using glauconite for local perennial crop or tree crop production in coastal areas needs to be tested.

References:

Alberti A, Castorina F, Censi P, Comin-Chiaramonti and CB Gomes 1999. Geochemical characteristics of Cretaceous carbonatites from Angola. J. Afr. Earth Sci. 29:735-759.

Antonio Martins J 1963. Rochas fosfatados de Angola (Bacio do Lucunga). Luanda: Junta de Desdenvolvimento Industrial, 120pp.

Chakravarty SC 1982. Sedimentary phosphate resources of Angola. Report, UN-TCD-NRED, United Nations, New York, 56pp.

Cunha Guveiha JA 1960. Notas sobre os fosfatos sedimentares de Cabinda. Bolm. Servs. Geol. Minas, Angola 1:49-65.

De Sousa Machado FJ 1958. The volcanic belt of Angola and its carbonatites. Comm. Tech. Co-op. Africa South of the Sahara, Reg. Comm. Geol. Publ. 44:309-317.

Duarte Morais ML and Sgrosso I 2000. The Meso-Cenozoic succession of the Kwanza Basin exposed in the surroundings of Benguela between Lobito and Dombe Grande; Field excursion guide book. GEOLUANDA International Conference 2000, 24pp.

El-Kadi MB 1980. Quindonacaxa phosphate deposit, Congo basin, Angola. Report UNDP Project ANG 78/017, United Nations, New York, 7pp.

Gittins J 1966. Summaries and bibliographies of carbonatite complexes. In: Tuttle OF and J Gittins (eds.) Carbonatites. Interscience Publ. New York, 417-570.

Heinrich EW 1980. The geology of carbonatites. Krieger Publishing Co, Huntington, New York, 585pp.

Hodge BL and Partners 1978. Report on the copper and phosphate potential of Angola. Unpubl. Report for Minmet Financing Company, 23pp.

Issa Filho A, Dos Santos ABRMD, Riffel BF, Lapido-Loureiro FEV and I McReath 1991. Aspects of the geology, petrology and chemistry of some Angolan carbonatites. J. Geochem. Expl. 40:205-226.

Kronsten G 1994. Angola. Mining Annual Review 1994, Mining Journal Ltd. London, p. 134.

Melo JASC 1984. Utilização directa das fosforites de Angola. Estimativa de eficácia: I. Ensaios em Vaso. Inst. Investigatção Agronómica, Communcacao 2:1-9.

McClellan GH and AJG Notholt 1986. Phosphate deposits of sub-Saharan Africa. In: Mokwunye AU and PLG Vlek (eds.) Management of nitrogen and phosphorus fertilizers in sub-Saharan Africa. Martinus Nijhoff, Dordrecht, Netherlands:173-224.

Notholt AJG 1994. Phosphate rock in developing countries. In: Mathers SJ and AJG Notholt (eds.) Industrial minerals in developing countries. AGID Report Series Geosciences in International Development 18:193-222.

Notholt AJG, Sheldon RP and DF Davidson 1989. Phosphate deposits of the world. Vol. 2. Phosphate rock resources, Cambridge University Press, Cambridge, UK; Chapter 26: Africa-Introduction, 164-170.

Pacheco A 1976. Interesse das fosfatos na economia de Angola. Div. Servs. Geol. Minas Angola, Mem.1,18pp.

Premoli C 1994. Industrial minerals in Angola and Mozambique: a multi-country approach. In: Mathers SJ and AJG Notholt (eds.) Industrial minerals in developing countries. AGID report series Geosciences in International Development 18:135-144.

Terraconsult AG 1983. A review of the mineral resources of the People's Republic of Angola. Zurich, 100pp.

Benin

Total population (July 2000 estimate): 6,396,000
Area: 112,620 km^2
Annual population growth rate (2000): 3.03%
Life expectancy at birth (1998): 53.5 years
People not expected to survive to age 40 (1998): 28.9% of total population
GDP per capita (1998): US $867

Benin is a tropical, long and narrow, north-south striking country between Togo and Nigeria. The landscape of Benin consists of a narrow sandy coastal strip enclosing a chain of lagoons, and an extensive plateau area. Several isolated mountain ranges occur with altitudes between 300 m and 1,500 m.

Agriculture is the dominant sector of Benin's economy. Subsistence farming produces mainly food crops like cassava, maize, yams, sorghum and millet. Other agricultural products are cotton, palm products, cocoa, cashew nuts and sugar cane. In 1999, the agricultural sector contributed 38% to the GDP and employed an estimated 65% of the labour force.

There is little mining activity in the country, except for extraction and quarrying of industrial minerals for construction.

Geological outline

Most of Benin is underlain by migmatites, gneisses and granites of the Neoproterozoic Dahomeyan Belt. Strongly folded quartzites and mica schists (Badagba quartzites) within the Dahomeyan Belt occur in a north-south striking belt across the country (Wright *et al.* 1985). Neoproterozoic to early Cambrian rocks of the Voltaian, a clastic sedimentary sequence that is mainly exposed in neighbouring Togo and Ghana, occur in the far northwest of the country. In southern Benin, a thick sequence of east-west striking sediments of Cretaceous to Tertiary age unconformably overlie the Dahomeyan. This sequence itself is overlain by continental sediments of the Tertiary 'Continental Terminal.'

AGROMINERALS

Phosphates

Two types of sedimentary phosphates are known from Benin:

- the southern phosphates of Eocene age, similar to the phosphates of neighbouring Togo,
- the northern phosphates of Neoproterozoic age, similar to the phosphates in neighbouring Niger.

Both phosphate rock deposits have been investigated in great detail by the Direcion des Mines de la Géologie et des Hydrocarbons (DMGH) of Benin, by the United Nations Development Programme (UNDP), and by the United Nations Revolving Fund for Natural Resources Exploration (UNRFNRE). The southern phosphates have also been studied by the oil company Shell.

The southern phosphate rock deposits are part of the coastal basin sediments that strike along the coast from Nigeria, across Benin into Togo and Ghana. In Benin, Eocene (Lutetian) phosphatic sediments occur in the striking continuation of phosphate rock deposits of neighbouring Togo where the Hahotoe phosphatic sandstone beds are currently being mined. To test whether mineable phosphate rocks such as those found in Togo continue into Benin, a series of geological and geochemical exploration programs were carried out. Altogether 367 pits were dug by various exploration teams. In addition, a total of 44 boreholes (Shell: 37, UNDP: 7) were sunk in prospective areas. The results of the pitting and drilling program were disappointing, as were the geochemical surveys. Only thin (up to 0.7 m) and irregular phosphate beds were discovered in the Kpome, Pobe, Toffo, and Lokossa areas. The main phosphate beds are intercalated with greenish glauconitic clays containing phosphate nodules

An evaluation of the phosphate exploration work was made for UNRFNRE by a consultant. He concluded that the small and marginal phosphate deposits in Benin would be unable to compete with the nearby extensive Hahotoe phosphate deposit in neighbouring Togo (Exploratech 1979b).

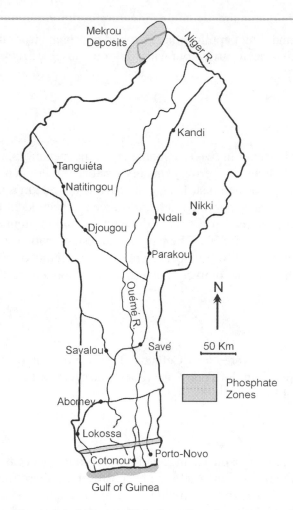

Figure 2.3: Location of the two phosphate zones in Benin.

The phosphates in northern Benin have been studied in detail by UNDP exploration teams (Barry 1981). The phosphate mineralization is located more than 800 km from the coast in a remote northern area at the Mekrou River close to the border with Burkina Faso and Niger (12°09' N, 2°25' E) (Figure 2.3). The phosphate beds are part of the middle-Voltaian Mekrou Formation of Neoproterozoic age, comparable to the ones in neighbouring Niger and Burkina Faso (Trompette *et al.* 1980; Trompette 1989). The phosphates occur as very hard, dark gray, massive phosphate rocks within a folded sedimentary sequence consisting of dark organic shales and cherts. The average thickness of the phosphate bed is 2.2 m.

UNDP geologists calculated near surface 'proven' reserves of 3,265,500 tonnes at 25.1% P_2O_5 covering an area of 0.225 km^2 with a waste to ore ratio of 2.6:1. Additionally, 'indicated reserves' are 2,204,900 tonnes with a grade of 25.77% P_2O_5 (Barry 1981).

Investigations of the phosphate rock concentrate by the Bureau de Recherches Géologiques et Minières (BRGM) indicated a 2% citric acid solubility of 19.1% and a neutral ammonium citrate (NAC) solubility of 5.6% (quoted in Barry 1981). In contrast to the data obtained by the International Fertilizer Development Center (IFDC) reports a NAC solubility only 1.9% (McClellan and Notholt 1986).

The evaluation reports of Exploratech (1979a,b) and Barry (1981) indicate that mining and production of superphosphates and/or phosphoric acid would be not economic using large-scale mining and processing techniques. However, on economic grounds, Exploratech (1979a,b) recommended the investigation of small-scale extraction and direct application of ground phosphate from the Mekrou river area. Whether any agronomic testing has been carried out with Mekrou phosphate rocks is not known.

Other agrominerals

Limestone/Dolomite

Carbonate rocks occur in Benin in two environments, in the metamorphosed Neoproterozoic to early Paleozoic Dahomeyan Belt and in Tertiary (mainly Paleocene) sediments. Several occurrences of marble in the Dahomeyan Belt are located near Dadjo, approximately 50 km north-northwest of Save in the central part of Benin. A 6-million tonne marble resource has been identified and is exploited by a Benin-Libyan company. Paleocene limestones, approximately 90 million tonnes, occur near Onigbolo north of Pobe, close to the border with Nigeria. The biogenic limestone with a strike length of 3 km and a width of more than 500 m is used as feed for the local cement plant at a rate of 500,000 tonnes per year (Lorenz 1996; Thiriot 1996). The French company Lafarge leases and manages the cement company 'Ciments d'Onigbolo.'

Peat

Peat deposits have been discovered near Cotonou. The 12.5 million tonnes of peat resources are in addition to the peat deposits in the Tono Lake (Lac Tono) area east of Lokossa and at Kpakpatan in Mono Region (Mining Annual Review 1998).

Agromineral potential

The potential of developing phosphates in Benin is very limited since the southern phosphate occurrences are too small to be economic and the Mekrou phosphates in northern Benin are uneconomical from a large-scale perspective. However, they might be useful for small-scale application on acid soils in northern Benin. Agronomic testing of these phosphates in crushed and ground form should be considered on P-deficient acid soils. Modification techniques using locally available organic waste products should also be tested. The phosphates from neighbouring Togo should be agronomically tested on soils of the southern parts of Benin. The development of liming materials should be tried, particularly on acid, aluminum toxic soils.

References:

Barry GS 1981. Study of the Mekrou phosphates mineral survey phase III, People's Republic of Benin. Report to United Nations Development Programme UN/TCD BEN/76-004, United Nations New York, 87pp.

Exploratech Ltd 1979a. Evaluatory study of the Mekrou phosphates, People's Republic of Benin. Report to United Nations Revolving Fund for Natural Resources Exploration, United Nations New York, 31pp.

Exploratech Ltd 1979b. Preliminary study of the coastal phosphates, People's Republic of Benin. Report to United Nations Revolving Fund for Natural Resources Exploration, United Nations New York, 10pp.

Lorenz W 1996. Benin. In: Bosse H-R, Gwosdz W, Lorenz W, Markwich, Roth W and F Wolff (eds.) Limestone and dolomite resources of Africa. Geol. Jb., D, 102:74-78.

McClellan GH and AJG Notholt 1986. Phosphate deposits of sub-Saharan Africa. In: Mokwunye AU and PLG Vlek (eds.) Management of nitrogen and phosphorus fertilizers in sub-Saharan Africa. Martinus Nijhoff, Dordrecht, Netherlands:173-224.

Mining Annual Review 1998. Benin. Mining Journal, London, p. 204.

Thiriot F 1996. Benin. Mining Annual Review 1996. Mining Journal, London, p.160.

Trompette R, Affaton P, Joulia F and J Marchand 1980. Stratigraphic and structural controls of Late Precambrian phosphate deposits of the northern Volta Basin in Upper Volta, Niger, and Benin, West Africa. Econ. Geol. 75:62-70.

Trompette R. 1989. Phosphorites of the northern Volta Basin (Burkina Faso, Niger and Benin). In: Notholt AJG, Sheldon RP and DF Davidson (eds.) Phosphate deposits of the world. Vol. 2. Phosphate rock resources, Cambridge University Press, Cambridge, UK: 214-218.

Wright JB, Hastings DA, Jones WB and HR Williams 1985. Geology and mineral resources of West Africa. Allen and Unwin, London, UK, 187pp.

Botswana

Total population (July 2000 estimate): 1,576,000
Area: 600,370 km^2
Annual population growth rate (2000): 0.76%
Life expectancy at birth (1998): 46.2 years
People not expected to survive to age 40 (1998): 37.1% of total population
GDP per capita (1998): US $6,103

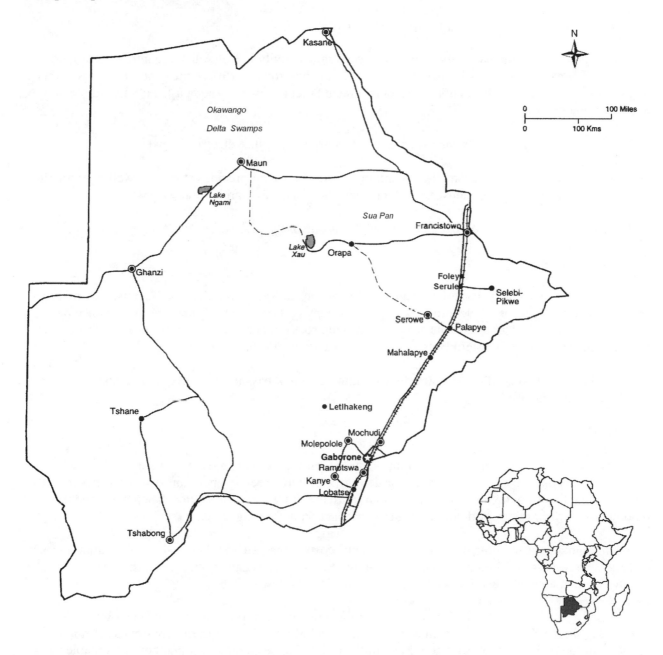

Botswana is a landlocked country in the centre of southern Africa. The eastern third of the country is comprised of undulating plains with isolated hills made up of Precambrian rocks. This part of Botswana is called the hardveld. The remaining two-thirds of the country is covered by Kalahari Sands, with deep sandy soils of very low agricultural productivity.

Near-desert conditions prevail in large parts of the country. Average annual rainfall in the southwest of the country is less than 250 mm and even this falls erratically. Droughts are common and can last for several years. About 22% of the population is engaged in agriculture, specifically pastoralism and agricultural crop production. Arable agriculture depends on extensive rain-fed cultivation of sorghum, millet, pulses, and watermelon. The most limiting factor for crop production is precipitation.

Animal products and meat are major export products.

Mining of diamonds remains the most important economic activity in Botswana. It contributes around one-third of Botswana's Gross Domestic Product (GDP) and provides 75% of the export earnings. Other major mining activities include copper-nickel mining at Selebi-Pikwe and soda ash and salt mining at the Sua Pan brine deposit.

The main energy source in Botswana is coal, which is used to produce electrical power.

Other mining activities include small-scale mining of gold and semi-precious stones, as well as extraction of construction materials. No industrial minerals have been used for agricultural purposes.

At US $6,103 Botswana's GDP per capita in 1998 was one of the highest in sub-Saharan Africa.

Geological outline

The geology of Botswana is largely obscured by Cretaceous to Recent Kalahari Beds, consisting mainly of aeolian sands. Archean and Paleoproterozoic rocks occupy parts of eastern Botswana. A sequence of Mesoproterozoic and Neoproterozoic, northeast-striking rocks, that are continuations of Proterozoic rocks from Namibia, cross into western Botswana (Kampunzu *et al.* 2000).

Karoo sediments, mainly of continental-fluvial origin, and thick basaltic lavas overlie Precambrian rocks in the east of the country.

AGROMINERALS

No phosphate occurrences are reported from Botswana. However, there are extensive limestone, dolomite and calcrete deposits in the country. Small-scale lime kilns have been in operation at several sites, mainly for the production of quicklime for use as mortar, plaster and for soil stabilization. There has been no reported use of limestones or dolomites for crop production in farming areas.

Limestones, marbles and dolomites have been identified at several sites (Figure 2.4). In Precambrian rocks considerable reserves of dolomitic marble and dolomitic limestones have been located in eastern Botswana in an area between Francistown and Mahalapye (Gwosdz 1996).

Superficially developed calcrete deposits with varying chemical composition are known around Letlhakeng, in the Kanye area, as well as near Ghanzi and Maun. Many of these limestones are not suitable for the production of cement because of their high magnesium content but they are suitable for quicklime burning. The Geological Survey Department of Botswana published an inventory of carbonate deposits and their potential for quicklime production in Botswana (Gwosdz and Modisi 1983, 1984).

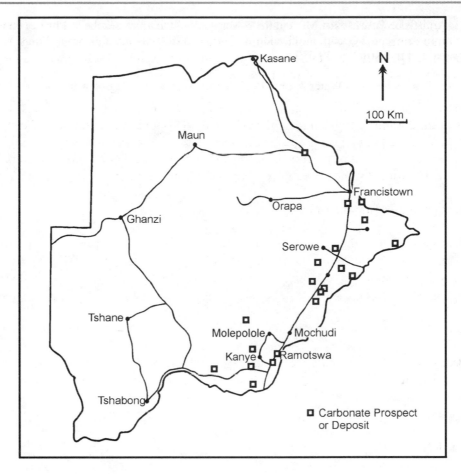

Figure 2.4: Limestone occurrences in Botswana (after Ministry of Minerals and Water Affairs, 1985).

Gypsum

Gypsum resources are located west of Foley and near Bojanamane, southwest of Serule. Whether they are extracted and used for improving soil structure, among other things, is not known.

Agromineral potential

The use of agrominerals in Botswana is very limited due to the small area of crop production and the unsuitable harsh climatic and physical conditions.

References:

Gwosdz W 1996. Botswana. In: Bosse H-R, Gwosdz W, Lorenz W, Markwich, Roth W and F Wolff (eds.) Limestone and dolomite resources of Africa. Geol. Jb., D, 102:78-90.

Gwosdz W and MP Modisi 1983. The carbonate resources of Botswana. Geol. Surv. Botswana Min. Res. Rep. 6,167pp.

Gwosdz W and MP Modisi 1984. The potential for quicklime production in Botswana. Geol. Surv. Botswana Min. Res. Rep. 7,50pp.

Kampunzu AB, Armstrong RA, Modisi MP and RBM Mapeo 2000. Ion microprobe U-Pb ages on detrital zircon grains from the Ghanzi Group: implications for the identification of a Kibaran-age crust in northwest Botswana. J. Afr. Earth Sci. 30:579-587.

Ministry of Mineral Resources and Water Affairs 1985. Small scale mining in Botswana, 30pp.

Burkina Faso

Total population (July 2000 estimate): 11,946,000
Area: 274,200 km^2
Annual population growth rate (2000): 2.71%
Life expectancy at birth (1998): 44.7 years
People not expected to survive to age 40 (1998): 39.9% of total population
GDP per capita (1998): US $870

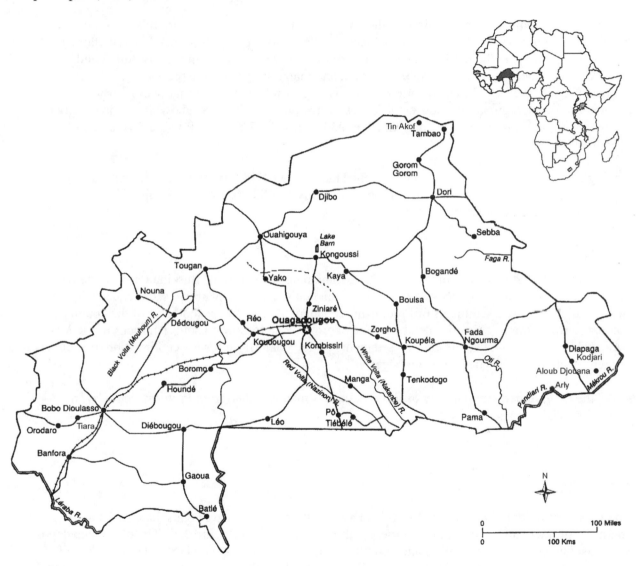

Burkina Faso is a landlocked country south of the Sahara Desert. Much of northern Burkina Faso lies in the Sahel zone at the fringe of the Sahara. The climatic and agroecological zones change from near desert in the north via a central plateau zone into areas of wooded savanna in the south. Annual rainfall increases from less than 200 mm in the north to 1,100 mm in the south of the country.

Burkina Faso's economy is largely founded on agricultural and livestock based production. In 1999, the agricultural sector accounted for 31% of the GDP and provided a livelihood to more than 90% of the population. Crop production is mainly at the subsistence level, but some larger farms cultivate cotton for export. The agro-pastoral land use system is based largely on the production of pearl millet, sorghum, cowpeas and groundnuts.

The main soil productivity constraints on the predominantly sandy acid soils are related to climatic conditions and nitrogen and phosphorus deficiencies (Bationo et al. 1998, 1992). Unpredictable rainfall distribution patterns in the north of the country limit the growth of the main cereals, millet and sorghum. In the central plateau zone where millet, sorghum and maize are grown, the pressure on soils is the greatest (Teboh et al. 1997). Degradation of soils is largely related to water and wind erosion as well as nutrient removal. Regional soil nutrient balances for the period 1979-1988 show that annual nutrient removal without replacement are approximately 23 kg/ha of N, 5 kg/ha of P_2O_5, and 16 kg/ha of K_2O (Teboh et al. 1997).

Mining only accounts for a small amount of Burkina Faso's GDP. The main mineral commodity produced is gold, much of which is extracted by the approximately 60,000-70,000 small-scale gold miners (International Labour Organisation 1999).

Geological outline

Metamorphosed Paleoproterozoic rocks of the Birimian underlie most of Burkina Faso. In the far west of the country Paleoproterozoic rocks dip below continental and marine platform sediments of the Taoudenni Basin, which comprise sediments of Proterozoic to Paleozoic age. In the southeast of the country the Paleoproterozoic rocks are concealed beneath Neoproterozoic to Lower Cambrian rocks of the Volta Basin. These largely unmetamorphosed sediments of the Volta Basin form a continuation of sedimentary sequences in Ghana, Togo, Benin and Niger.

Gold, the main mineral commodity of Burkina Faso is mainly mined from Proterozoic rocks and alluvial/eluvial deposits.

AGROMINERALS

Phosphates

The most important agrominerals of Burkina Faso are the Neoproterozoic phosphate rocks in the extreme southeast of the country close to the borders with Benin and Niger (Figure 2.5). The phosphate deposits were discovered in the early 1970s and described in detail by Lucas et al. (1980), Trompette et al. (1980), Maurin et al. (1989), and Trompette (1989). The sedimentary phosphate rock deposits belong to the Neoproterozoic Pendjari Group of the Volta Basin (Figure 2.5). They are located at Aloub Djouana (12° 8' N; 1°45' E), Kodjari (12° 1' N; 1°55' E) and Arly (11° 35' N; 1°25' E). The age of the deposit is 660 ± 8 million years indicating a Neoproterozoic age (Trompette 1989).

The phosphates were deposited at the southeastern flanks of the West African craton in the passive margin Volta Basin, characterized by epicontinental unmetamorphosed sediments. The succession is increasingly folded and deformed towards the east, at the contact with the Neoproterozoic Pan-African Dahomeyan front. The Kodjari and Arly deposits are part of the flat lying Voltaian sediments, the Aloub Djouana phosphate deposit occurs at the eastern side of the Volta Basin, in a strongly deformed thrust zone.

The approximately 100 m thick Kodjari Formation of the Pendjari Group consists of, from bottom to top: breccia (0.1 m), tillite (0-15 m), dolomitic limestone 0.5 - 3 m (often associated with barite), bedded cherts (25-30 m) and argillaceous siltstones or phosphorites (> 10 m). The association of tillite, limestone (with barite) and 'silexite' (a term used by French writers to denote massive chemically precipitated cherts) are commonly referred to as a 'triad' (Wright *et al.* 1985). The tillite is one of the stratigraphic markers in the Neoproterozoic to Cambrian in West Africa. Neoproterozoic 'triads' are also known from other parts of west Africa, especially in the Taoudenni Basin (Slansky 1986).

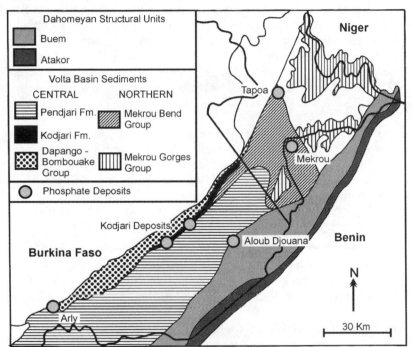

Figure 2.5: Location of Neoproterozoic phosphate deposits in Burkina Faso, Benin and Niger (after Trompette *et al.* 1980).

Detailed mineralogical and chemical characterization of the apatites in the Kodjari and Arly phosphates are described by Lucas *et al.* (1980) and McClellan and Notholt (1986). The apatites of the Kodjari phosphates occur as subrounded grains in a siliceous matrix. The unit cell a-value of the francolite is a = 9.355 Å, (McClellan and Saavedra 1986) and the citrate solubility is 2.3% P_2O_5 (McClellan and Notholt 1986). All chemical and mineralogical data are indicative of a low carbonate-substituted francolite and consequently low reactivity phosphate rock (Kpomblekou and Tabatabai 1994). The trace element analyses of Kodjari phosphate rocks (Kodjari PR) reveal low Cd and As concentrations, <4 mg/kg and <20 mg/kg respectively (McClellan and Notholt 1986).

The lower parts of the 10 m thick, fine grained, well-bedded Kodjari phosphate deposit with micronodules and illite and kaolinite clays were most likely deposited in a low-energy, reduced environment (Lucas *et al.* 1980). The upper parts of the sequence are characterized by more silt and sand size fractions, indicative of increasing energy environments and reworking. Lateritic alteration has resulted in higher Al and Fe concentrations in the upper parts of the deposit (Lucas *et al.* 1980).

The Arly phosphate rock (Arly PR) deposit, located approximately 100 km southwest of Kodjari occurs in a similar stratigraphic position to the phosphates of Kodjari. This phosphate bed, up to 1.5 m thick, is mainly composed of poorly bedded coarse-grained detrital phosphorites with a much higher silicate content than the Kodjari phosphates. Lucas *et al.* (1980) interpreted the coarse-grained Arly phosphorites as reworked phosphates deposited in a high-energy environment.

At the structurally complex Aloub Djouana deposit, east of Kodjari, the phosphatic sandstones are coarse-grained with abundant allochthonous fragments (mainly quartz and feldspars). These phosphatic sandstones are interpreted as sediments formed in turbulent depositional environments with widespread reworking (Trompette *et al.* 1980; Maurin *et al.* 1989).

Agronomic Testing of Kodjari Phosphates

The Kodjari phosphates have been agronomically tested as direct application phosphate fertilizers by nationally and internationally supported agricultural research projects. However, the reactivity of Kodjari PR is low and consequently the yield responses were generally low as well. While maize responded only slightly to Kodjari PR application, cowpea, a legume dependent on vesicular-arbuscular mycorrhizae (VAM) colonization for uptake of sparce soil P, responded more strongly to the application of Kodjari PR (Muleba and Coulibaly 1999). Also, the application of Kodjari PR had significant residual effects in two soils in Burkina Faso for up to two years (Muleba and Coulibaly 1999).

Experiments using modified Kodjari PR were more successful. In combination with organic 'wastes' the PR was more effective than PR alone (Lompo 1993). Also, growth chamber experiments using energy intensive 'mechanically activated' Kodjari PR increased the solubility considerably, resulting in significantly higher yields (Kantor *et al.* 1990, quoted in Hoffmann *et al.* 1991, see chapter Malawi). Research by Kpomblekou and Tabatabai (1994) showed that organic acids could release greater amounts of P from the low reactivity Kodjari PR than from Florida phosphate rock of medium reactivity. It seems that complexation plays a major role in the increased release of P from Kodjari PR.

The reserves of the various phosphate rock (PR) deposits, cited by McClellan and Notholt (1986), are: Aloub Djouana: 224 million tonnes at 15% P_2O_5, Kodjari: 80 million tonnes, and Arly: 4 million tonnes.

Reserve estimates by Trompette *et al.* (1980) are slightly different: Kodjari = 60 million tonnes at 27.5% P_2O_5, Arly = 2.8 million tonnes at 29% P_2O_5. Detailed investigations at Kodjari included drilling at two hills (Hill A and B). Reserves estimates by Maurin *et al.* (1989), and Teboh *et al.* (1997) are: 44 ± 8 and 19 ± 4 million tonnes for Hill A and Hill B respectively at a cut-off grade of 18% P_2O_5. The maximum overburden is 20 m.

So far, only the Kodjari PR deposit has been mined. At Hill A of Kodjari the phosphorites have been extracted from an open pit since 1978. Approximately 20 million tonnes of the Kodjari PR can be extracted after simple removal of the vegetation and the 0.5 m thick soil cover. The reserves at this hill alone are estimated at 44 million tonnes with 25-27% P_2O_5 to a depth of 20 m (Teboh *et al.* 1997). In the late 1990s the Kodjari PR was mined at a rate of 3,000 tonnes per year, using hand-held jackhammers and a loader, The ore was transported to Diapage for crushing and grinding. Some of the phosphates were mixed in compost pits before application.

The ex-factory costs for Kodjari PR were US $65 per tonne. Extraction (mining) with jackhammers and a front-end loader cost US $0.64 per tonne. Transportation from the mine to the grinding mill at Diapaga (42 km away) cost US $5.48 per tonne, and grinding at the plant in Diapaga cost US $42.00 per tonne. The remaining costs were administrative (Teboh *et al.* 1997). A grinding mill with a capacity of 2.5 tonne per hour was used in 1988. It has been operating at less than one-third of its intended capacity due to the relatively small size of the market. A new 5 tonne per hour grinding mill at equipment costs of US$ 1.6 million (!) has been considered (Teboh *et al.* 1997).

Limestone/dolomite/marble

Slightly folded limestones and dolomites occur in northern Burkina Faso close to the border with Mali near Tin Akof with resources of more than 30 million m^3 (Wolff 1996). Precambrian dolomites occur in the west of the country close to Bobo-Dioulasso and Orodara. In some places the dolomites are high in silica and iron and have total reserves in the range of 20 million m^3. Dolomitic marbles with thickness of more than 15 m are reported from Tiara, 32 km west of Bobo-Dioulasa. The decorative marble of Tiara is used for the production of ornamental stone (Wolff 1996). Operations of this kind usually produce considerable 'wastes' some of them fine sized materials. Whether any of these liming materials is used for agricultural purposes is not known.

Agromineral potential

The main potential of agromineral development in Burkina Faso lies in the development of the near surface phosphate resources of Kodjari. There are strong agricultural needs for phosphates in the region. Because the Kodjari phosphates are characterized by low reactivity, the agronomic effectiveness as a direct application P fertilizer is low. However, in combination with organic acids and organic wastes (phospho-composting) the Kodjari phosphates show considerable promise (Lompo 1993; Kpomblekou and Tabatabai 1994). Also, early indications show good agronomic response of PR from Burkina Faso on upland rice (Bado and Hien 1998). Modification techniques such as blending and compaction or pelletizing should be tested to improve the reactivity of these locally available phosphate rocks.

At present, the ex-factory price of this phosphate rock is high (US $152.6 per tonne). Reasons for the high price are low rate of production and high costs of energy and imported machinery. In the current situation the import of TSP is more profitable. However, TSP procurement and timely supply is not always secured and small-scale farmers often cannot afford the purchase of imported fertilizers (Teboh *et al.* 1997).

Considering the main constraints of energy and imported machinery, it is strongly recommended to explore possibilities using more labour intensive and alternative technologies with lower energy requirements and capital costs (for instance low-cost adapted crushing and grinding technologies) that are more appropriate and adapted. With the current PR production of less than 1,000 tonnes per year the possibilities of using low-cost small-scale processing techniques should be considered.

Developing low cost phosphate products by combining processed Kodjari PRs with organic matter seems to have good potential (Lompo 1993; Sanchez *et al.* 1997). Transfer and upscaling of successful strategies to increase phosphorus availability from low reactivity phosphate rocks using organic wastes or blending techniques should be encouraged. Plants like rapeseed and local *brassicaceae* that are able to extract P from relatively unreactive phosphate rocks (Weil 2000) should be tested.

References:

Bado VB and V Hien 1998. Efficacité agronomique des phosphates naturels du Burkina Faso sur le riz pluvial en sol ferralitique. Cahiers Agriculture 7:236-238.

Bationo A, Christianson BC, Baethgen WE and AU Mokwunye 1992. A farm-level evaluation of nitrogen and phosphorus fertiliser use and planting density of pearl millet production in Niger. Fert. Res. 31:175-184.

Bationo A, Lompo F and S Koala 1998. Research on nutrient flows and balances in West Africa: state-of-the-art. Agric. Ecosyst. Envir. 71:19-35.

International Labour Organization 1999. Social and labour issues in small-scale mines. TMSSM/1999, 99pp.

Kantor W, Schoenfeld G and E Gock 1990. Improvement of the solubility of rock phosphate by mechanical activation compared to chemical treatments.- Paper presented at IFDC seminar on rock phosphates in Lome, Togo. Quoted in Hoffmann R 1991. Present and potential utilization of agrominerals in Malawi. Techn. Cooperation Proj. 89.2028.2, Malawi-Fed. Rep. Germany, Zomba, 49pp.

Kpomblekou A and MA Tabatabai 1994. Effect of organic acids on release of phosphorus from phosphate rocks. J. Soil Sci. 158:442-453.

Lompo F 1993. Contribution à la valorisation des phosphates naturales du Burkina Faso: Etudes des effets de l'interaction phosphates natureles-materiels organiques. These Doctor Ingenieur. Fac. des Sci. et Techn. de l'Universite National de Côte d'Ivoire, Abidjan.

Lucas J, Prevot L and R Trompette 1980. Petrology, mineralogy and geochemistry of the late Precambrian phosphate deposit of Upper Volta (W Africa). J. Geol. Soc. London, 137:787-792.

Maurin G, Giot D, Sustrac G and E Zoungrana 1989. The Kodjari and Aloub Djouana phosphate deposits, Burkina Faso. In: Notholt AJG, Sheldon RP and DF Davidson (eds.) Phosphate deposits of the world. Vol 2. Phosphate rock resources, Cambridge University Press, Cambridge, UK:219-225.

McClellan GH and FN Saavedra 1986. Proterozoic and Cambrian phosphorites - specialist studies: chemical and mineral characteristics of some Precambrian phosphorites. In: Cook PJ and JH Shergold (eds.) Phosphate deposits of the world, Vol. 1. Proterozoic and Cambrian phosphorites. Cambridge University Press, Cambridge, UK:244-267.

McClellan GH and AJG Notholt 1986. Phosphate deposits of sub-Saharan Africa. In: Mokwunye AU and PLG Vlek (eds.) Management of nitrogen and phosphorus fertilizers in sub-Saharan Africa. Martinus Nijhoff, Dordrecht, Netherlands:173-224.

Muleba N and M Coulibaly 1999. Effects of phosphorus fertilizer sources on cowpea and subsequent cereal productivity in semi-arid West Africa. J. Agric. Sci. 132:45-60.

Sanchez PA, Shepherd KD, Soule MJ, Place FM, Buresh RJ, Izac A-MN, Mokwunye AU, Kwesiga FR, Ndiritu CG and PL Woomer 1997. Soil fertility replenishment in Africa: An investment in natural resource capital. In: Buresh RJ, Sanchez PA and F. Calhoun (eds.). Replenishing soil fertility in Africa. Soil Sci. Soc. Am. Special Publ. 51:1-46.

Slansky M 1986. Proterozoic and Cambrian phosphorites - regional overview: West Africa. In: Cook PJ and JH Shergold (eds.) Phosphate deposits of the world. Vol. 1. Proterozoic and Cambrian phosphorites. Cambridge University Press, Cambridge, UK:108-115.

Teboh JF, Cisse AC, Lompo F and LM Zigani 1997. Phosphate rock initiative: A case study of Burkina Faso. Report to the World Bank, 18pp.

Trompette R, Affaton P, Joulia F and J Marchand 1980. Stratigraphic and structural controls of Late Precambrian phosphate deposits of the northern Volta Basin in Upper Volta, Niger, and Benin, West Africa. Econ. Geol. 75:62-70.

Trompette R 1989. Phosphorites of northern Volta Basin (Burkina Faso, Niger and Benin). In: Notholt AJG, Sheldon RP and DF Davidson (eds.): Phosphate deposits of the world. Vol. 2. Phosphate rock resources, Cambridge University Press, Cambridge, UK:214-218.

Weil RR 2000. Soil and plant influence on crop response to two African phosphate rocks. Agron. J. 92:1167-1175.

Wolff F 1996. Burkina Faso. In: Bosse H-R, Gwosdz W, Lorenz W, Markwich, Roth W and F Wolff (eds.) Limestone and dolomite resources of Africa. Geol. Jb., D, 91-96.

Wright JB, Hastings DA, Jones WB and HR Williams 1985. Geology and mineral resources of West Africa. Allen and Unwin, London, UK, 187pp.

Burundi

Total population (July 2000 estimate): 6,055,000
Area: 27,830 km^2
Annual population growth rate (2000): 3.15%
Life expectancy at birth (1998): 42.7 years
People not expected to survive to age 40: Not available
GDP per capita (1998): US $570

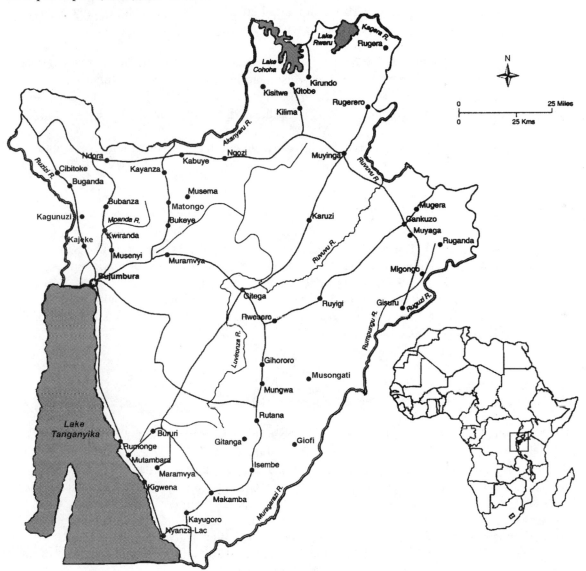

Burundi is a landlocked densely populated mountainous country in central Africa, north of Lake Tanganyika. The mountain ranges of Burundi reach altitudes of 2,600 m. Between the mountains and Lake Tanganyika lies a 3 km wide alluvial plain, which widens towards the north into the 20 km wide Ruzizi Plain.

The economy of Burundi is largely based on agricultural production, with 90% of the population dependent on subsistence farming. In 1999, the agricultural sector accounted for 52% of the GDP. The main food crops are maize, beans, rice, potatoes, bananas, and cassava. The main cash crop is coffee, contributing approximately 80% of the country's foreign exchange earnings. Most soils in Burundi are highly degraded, with soil acidity, aluminum toxicity and low available nutrient contents, especially phosphorus, being the main limiting factors. Fertilizer imports into this landlocked country are expensive and alternative means to maintain and increase soil productivity are required.

The mining sector is small, with only low-volume gold, cassiterite and colombo-tantalite and wolframite deposits being mined. A large lateritic nickel deposit at Musongati in southeast Burundi (approximately 6% of the world's nickeliferous laterite) has not yet been developed. Artisanal mining of alluvial gold in the northwestern province of Cibitoke continued even during the civil war and the blockade.

In the last few years, political instability and civil war have affected both the development of Burundi.

Geological outline

Geologically, folded and slightly metamorphosed clastic sediments of the Mesoproterozoic Kibaran belt underlie most of Burundi. Rocks of this belt extend from the Democratic Republic of Congo through Burundi and Rwanda into northwest Tanzania and Uganda in an east-northeast direction. The Kibaran rocks are intruded by granites, and along a 350 km long 'alignment,' a narrow zone of mafic and ultramafic intrusions (Deblond and Tack 1999). The Kibaran is flanked in the eastern part of the country by Neoproterozoic shallow water sediments of the Malaragazi Supergroup (Tack 1995) with basal conglomerates, schists, dolomitic limestones and lavas. Tertiary and Quaternary sediments fill parts of the Western Rift at the northern tip of Lake Tanganyika.

AGROMINERALS

Phosphates

Only igneous and residual phosphate accumulations have been found in Burundi so far. The residual igneous phosphate deposit at Matongo, 70 km north of Bujumbura (3° 4' S; 29° 37' E) was discovered in 1975 during an airborne geophysical survey (Songore 1991). The residual phosphates overlie a strongly weathered carbonatite, which is part of the much larger Neoproterozoic Upper Ruvubu alkaline complex (Tack et al. 1984). The residual phosphatic zone is up to 55 m thick. The composition of the ore varies strongly. A typical sample from the weathered phosphate ore contains approximately 30% fluor-apatite and 17% caxonite (an iron-phosphate mineral), the rest is composed of clay, feldspar and limonite (Kurtanjek and Tandy 1989). The solubility of the Matongo apatite is low: the citric acid soluble P of the phosphate concentrate is 1.6% (IFDC, quoted in van den Berghe 1996).

Over the last few decades, the deposit was appraised by the United Nations, by the British Sulphur Corporation and various other agencies and institutions. The detailed feasibility study showed reserves of 17.3 million tonnes of ore at 11.0% P_2O_5 (cutoff 5% P_2O_5) or 40 million tonnes at 5.6% P_2O_5 (Kurtanjek and Tandy 1989). The engineering company MacKay and Schnellmann completed test work for the feasibility study of phosphate fertilizer production and concluded that there was insufficient high-grade material to support a super-phosphate plant (Songore 1996).

Composting with Matongo Phosphate Rock and Urea

Agronomic experiments using Matongo phosphate concentrate as direct-application fertilizer have been generally unsuccessful. This is likely a result of the nature of the unreactive phosphate ore. However, experiments where the unreactive Matongo phosphates were mixed with urea in a composting system showed improved performance and higher agronomic effectiveness (van den Berghe 1996).

Limestone/dolomite/travertine

Widespread Neoproterozoic dolomitic limestones of the Musindozi Group (dolomitic limestones, calcareous shales and lavas) and of the Mosso Group (silicified dolomitic limestones and lavas) exist in southeastern Burundi, mainly northeast and southeast of Rutana, close to the border with Tanzania (Tack and Thorez 1990). The resources are large. Dolomitic limestones of more than 130 million tonnes are reported from east of Rutana. The high magnesium contents render these deposits unsuitable as raw material for cement production but suitable for the production of lime or ground dolomitic limestone for agricultural purposes (Sinzumusi 1989; Ntahindurwa 1990). Lime is produced in Giofi, Bukemba, Muramba and Shaka, south and east of Rutana. In addition, small dolomitic limestones are reported from Kajeke and Kagunuzi, both north of Bujumbura (Lorenz 1996).

Travertine deposits, much smaller in volume and variable in composition, are located in the northwest of Burundi, in Cibitoke, Busiga, Gihungwe, and Ruhanga (Verhaeghe 1964; Lorenz 1996). The individual travertine deposits are commonly less than 1 million tonnes in size, the largest being in Cibitoke with estimated reserves of approximately 1 million tonnes (Lorenz 1996). These resources could be used for local agricultural lime production or as agricultural limestone.

Another potential source of liming material, the carbonatite of Matongo is extensive (1,800 m long, and up to 250 m wide) but is deeply weathered. 'Fresh' carbonates are encountered only at depths below 45 m. Underground mining has been considered to extract the carbonates as a possible source for cement manufacture, but proved technically difficult and uneconomic.

Limestones and dolomites are calcined at several locations in the east of the country. At present the calcined material is used mainly for building purposes and whitewash. The Agronomy Department of the University of Burundi encourages the use of ground dolomitic limestone for agricultural purposes on the acid soils of Burundi (Wouters, pers. comm. 1984; Niyondezo 1987; Sinzumusi 1989; Ntahindurwa 1990).

Peat

Peat resources in excess of 300 million tonnes are located in Buyongwe near Ngozi (Niyondezo 1987). There are, however, environmental concerns with the extraction of peat from wetlands in Burundi.

Composting experiments using peat and organic residues in combination with the relatively insoluble Matongo phosphate rock have been proposed by Mathur (pers. comm. 1987). This composting technique with peat and unreactive PR has been successfully applied in Canada (Mathur *et al.* 1987).

Agromineral potential

The potential of utilizing the igneous, relatively insoluble phosphate resources of Matongo are limited because the low-grade iron-rich phosphate deposit requires considerable upgrading and processing. However, should the phosphates be mined on a larger scale the concentrate should be tested in composting systems in a similar fashion as described by van den Berghe (1996).

There are very extensive sources of dolomites in Burundi and efforts should be made to utilize these resources to ameliorate the predominantly acid soils in the country.

References:

Deblond A and L Tack 1999. Main characteristics and review of mineral resources of the Kabanga-Musongati mafic-ultramafic alignment in Burundi. J. Afr. Earth Sci. 29:313-328.

Kurtanjek MP and BC Tandy 1989. The igneous phosphate deposits of Matongo-Bandaga, Burundi. In: Notholt AJG, Sheldon RP and DF Davidson (eds.) Phosphate deposits of the world. Vol. 2. Phosphate rock resources. Cambridge University Press, Cambridge, UK: 262-266.

Lorenz W 1996. Burundi. In: Bosse H-R, Gwosdz W, Lorenz W, Markwich, Roth W and F Wolff (eds.) Limestone and dolomite resources of Africa. Geol. Jb., D, 102:97-101.

Mathur SP, Proulx JG, Leveque M and RB Sanderson 1987. Composting of an igneous rock phosphate. In: Wachira JK and AJG Notholt (eds.) Agrogeology in Africa. Commonwealth Sci. Council, Technical Publ. Series 226:129-145.

Niyondezo S 1987: Agrogeologic resources of Burundi. In: Wachira JK and AJG Notholt (eds.) Agrogeology in Africa. Commonwealth Sci. Council, Technical Publ. Series 226:63-66.

Ntahindurwa N 1990. Contribution a l'étude du comportement agrochimique des dolomies de Kabizi-Mugeni (Kayogoro-Mosso). Thesis, Dept. Sci. de la Terre, Univ. Burundi, 108pp.

Sinzumusi A 1989. Contribution a l'étude des roches carbonatées du Mosso et de Busiga (Burundi) comme gisements d'amendments calcaro-magnésiens. Thesis, Dept. Sci. de la Terre, Univ. Burundi, 65pp.

Songore T 1991. The Matongo phosphate deposit of Burundi. Fert. Res. 30:151-153.

Songore T 1996. Burundi. Mining Annual Review 1996. Mining Journal Ltd. London, p. 149.

Tack L 1995. The Neoproterozoic Malaragazi Supergroup of SE Burundi and its equivalent Bukoban System in NW Tanzania: A current review. Musée royal de l'Afrique centrale, Tervuren (Belg.), Annales Sciences Géologiques 101:121-129.

Tack L, De Paepe P, Deutsch S and J-P Liegois 1984. The alkaline plutonic complex of the upper Ruvubu (Burundi): Geology, age, isotopic geochemistry and implications for the regional geology of the Western Rift. In : Klerkx J and J Michot (eds.) Géologie Africaine - African Geology, Musée Royale de l'Afrique centrale - Tervuren: 91-114.

Tack L and J Thorez 1990. Sedimentology of the Munsindozi Group, Malagarasian (Upper Proterozoic), Burundi. IGCP 255 Newsletter/Bull. 3:89-92.

Van den Berghe CH 1996. The effect of Matongo rock phosphate and urea as compared to di-ammonium phosphate in the composting process and the yield of potatoes in the Mugamba region of Burundi. Fert. Res. 45:51-59.

Verhaeghe M 1964. Inventaire des gisement calcaires, dolomies et travertins du Kivu, du Rwanda et du Burundi. Département Géologie et Mines du Burundi, 95pp.

Cameroon

Total population (July 2000 estimate): 15,422,000
Area: 475,440 km^2
Annual population growth rate (2000): 2.47%
Life expectancy at birth (1998): 54.5 years
People not expected to survive to age 40 (1998): 27.4% of total population
GDP per capita (1998): US $1474

Cameroon stretches from the bend of West Africa at the Atlantic Ocean to the Lake Chad area in the north. It is a country with varying climates and ecological zones, reaching from semi-arid savannah landscapes in the north to dense tropical rainforests in the south and southwest. The central part of the country is largely composed of upland savanna. A chain of volcanic centres straddles the coast along the border with Nigeria in a northeasterly direction.

Cameroon is a country well endowed with natural resources. The economy is largely dependent on income from crude oil production and agricultural production.

Food and export crops as well as livestock, fishing and forestry form the backbone of the agricultural economy of Cameroon. The agricultural sector provides 44% of the GDP and employs approximately 60% of the labour force. The main agricultural products for local consumption are cassava, bananas/plantains, maize and sorghum. The main export crop is cocoa, followed by coffee, cotton and rubber. In 1999, sugar production in Cameroon reached 1.35 million tonnes.

Cameroon is sub-Saharan Africa's fifth largest oil producer (in 2000: 84,800 barrels per day). Revenues from crude oil production account for approximately one third of government revenues. The planned Chad-Cameroon oil pipeline will cross Cameroon from the northeast to the southwest and deliver oil from Chad to the export facilities at Kribi at the Gulf of Guinea.

Cameroon hosts a number of small gold deposits, which are worked by small-scale miners. At present, Cameroon imports alumina from Guinea and processes it at the smelter at Edea, but is planning to develop some of its own bauxite resources.

Geological outline

Cameroon can be geologically subdivided into Precambrian rocks, Cretaceous sediments and Tertiary-Quaternary sedimentary sequences. Large parts of the Precambrian are undifferentiated gneisses and migmatites. Mesoproterozoic and the Neoproterozoic rocks are exposed in the southeastern part of the country. Some of these sequences are interpreted as platform or continental margin sediments at the edge of the Archean Congo craton, represented in Cameroon by the Ntem complex in the south (Toteu *et al.* 1994).

Cretaceous sediments overlie the Precambrian. In northern Cameroon the sedimentary facies of the Cretaceous is largely continental, while the Cretaceous in the coastal zone is mainly marine.

A zone of volcanic massifs and anorogenic complexes crosses Cameroon in a east-northeasterly direction. This 'Cameroon line' probably follows a major structural zone (Deruelle *et al.* 1991; Kampunzu and Lubala 1991).

AGROMINERALS

Phosphates

Little information exists on the phosphate rocks of Cameroon. Visse (1953) reported siliceous phosphatic nodules in the Bongue River valley (near Kompina), 50 km north-northwest of Douala on the coast. Here, slightly radioactive phosphatic nodules (1-3 cm in diameter) occur in black, 1-2 m thick lower Eocene marls (Dizangue Formation, Série de Bongue). The nodules contain 15-18% P_2O_5. At the top of the slightly phosphatic sequence (5-8% P_2O_5), are calcareous beds with phosphate pebbles containing 12-18% P_2O_5 (Visse 1953). The extent of these beds is not known.

Other agrominerals

Alkaline meta-igneous rocks from the Yaounde area contain some 'biotitites' with K_2O contents up to 11% and slightly elevated P concentrations (up to 2.9% P_2O_5) (Nzenti 1998).

There are several Precambrian marble deposits in the north of the country near Figuil, and in the south near Mintom. Some of the marbles are used as ornamental stone. Whether any of the Precambrian marbles are used for lime production is not known.

Cretaceous limestones occur in northern Cameroon, near Figuil. In the Cretaceous coastal basin, limestones are exposed near Kampina, Bongue River, Lagbadjeck/Dizangue and at the Mabanga River (Gwosdz 1996). Travertine deposits of Ngol village at the Nyock River are small but may lend themselves to small-scale limestone extraction.

Agromineral potential

Little information on agromineral resources is available from Cameroon. Extensive parts of Cameroon are covered by tropical nutrient-poor soils and it would be worthwhile to study the occurrences of phosphates and liming materials in this part of the country. In particular, the Eocene Bongue phosphates should be investigated for quantity and quality as well as for their potential extraction and subsequent use on P-deficient acid soils.

In addition, the 'biotitites' and magnetite-rich pyroxenites in southern Cameroon should be investigated for possible phosphate and potassium enrichment zones.

Cameroon's limestone/dolomite resources should be assessed on their potential as soil amendments on acid soils.

References:

Deruelle B, Moreau C, Nkoumbou C, Kambou R, Lissom J, Njongfang E, Ghogomu RT and A Nono 1991. The Cameroon Line: a review. In: Kampunzu AB and RT Lubala (eds.) Magmatism in extensional structural settings. Springer Verlag, Berlin, Germany. 274-327.

Gwosdz W 1996. Cameroon. In: Bosse H-R, Gwosdz W, Lorenz W, Markwich, Roth W and F Wolff (eds.) Limestone and dolomite resources of Africa. Geol. Jb., D, 102:102-105.

Kampunzu AB and RT Lubala (eds.) 1991. Magmatism in extensional structural settings. Springer Verlag Berlin, Germany.

Nzenti JP 1998. Neoproterozoic alkaline meta-igneous rocks from the Pan-African North Equatorial Fold Belt (Yaounde, Cameroon): biotitites and magnetite rich pyroxenites. J. Afr. Earth Sci. 26:37-47.

Toteu SF, Van Schmus WR, Penaye J and JB Nyobe 1994. U-Pb and Sm-Nd evidence for Eburnian and Pan-African high-grade metamorphism in cratonic rocks of southern Cameroon. Precambrian Res. 67:321-347.

Thiriot F 1997. Cameroon. Mining Annual Review 1997. Mining Journal Ltd. London, p.151.

Visse LD 1953. Sur la présence d'accumulation phosphatées au Cameroun, au Dahomey et au Togo. C. R. Hbd. Seanc. Acad. Sci, Paris, 237(19):1171-1173.

Cape Verde

Total Population (July 2000 estimate): 401,000
Area: 4,033 km^2
Annual population growth rate (2000): 0.98%
Life expectancy at birth (1998): 69.2 years
People not expected to survive to age 40 (1998): 10.1% of total population
GDP per capita (1998): US $3,233

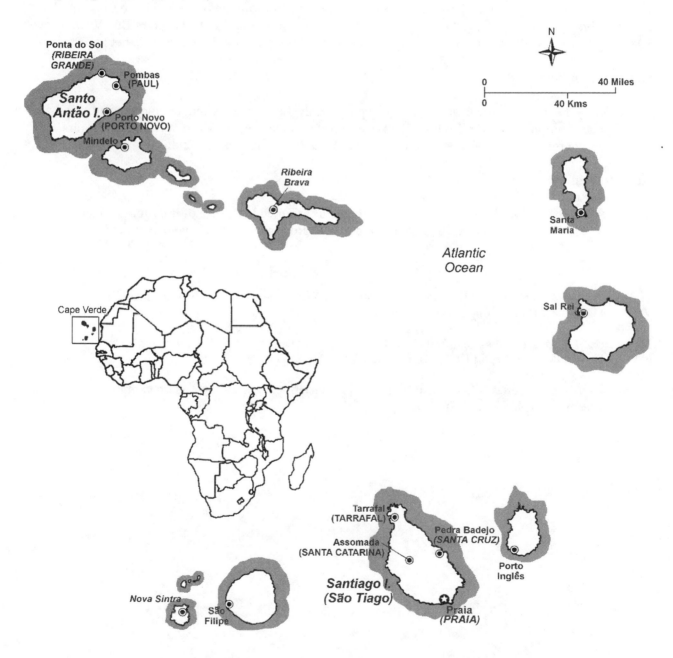

The islands of Cape Verde, located some 500 km west of the Senegalese coast in the Atlantic Ocean, consist of 12 islands, 9 of which are inhabited. The climate is arid. Only about 15% of the land base of these mountainous islands is suitable for farming. Cape Verde is an important trade and transportation centre.

The agricultural sector contributes about 13% to the GDP and employs approximately 25% of the population. Primary food crops are maize, bananas and coconuts. Bananas are the main agricultural export product.

The 'mining industry' in this island state is minimal. Apart from quarrying of pozzolana (some of which was exported to Portugal in the past) and dimension stone and the winning of solar salt, no substantial mineral development activities take place. A small lime operation exists on the island of Boa Vista (Meyer 1981). Whether any of the lime or unprocessed limestone is being used for agriculture is not known.

Geological outline

Geologically, the Cape Verde islands are made up of mainly Tertiary and younger volcanics, primarily of basaltic composition. However, Le Bas (1984) has reported some oceanic Mg-rich carbonatites. Jurassic limestones are found on the islands of Maio and Boa Vista (Stillman *et al*. 1982).

Agromineral potential

The potential of small-scale agrogeological development is limited to the use of limestones. Data relating to soil and crop needs are required to assess whether any agromineral-based development is useful.

References:

Le Bas MJ 1980. Oceanic carbonatites. In: J Kornprobst (ed.) Kimberlites. I: Kimberlites and related rocks. Elsevier Science Publishers, Amsterdam, Netherlands: 169-178.

Meyer H 1981. Cap Vert - Mission d'évaluation des ressources minérales. Rapport de mission 3-7 Dec 1980. Unpubl. Mission Report UNDP-DTCD, New York, 12pp.

Stillman CJ, Furnes H, LeBas MJ, Robertson AHF and J Zielonka 1982. The geological history of Maio, Cape Verde Islands. J. Geol. Soc. 139:347-361.

Central African Republic

Total population (July 2000 estimate): 3,513,000
Area: 622,984 km^2
Annual population growth rate (2000): 1.77%
Life expectancy at birth (1998): 44.8 years
People not expected to survive to age 40 (1998): 40.4% of the total population
GDP per capita (1998): US $1,118

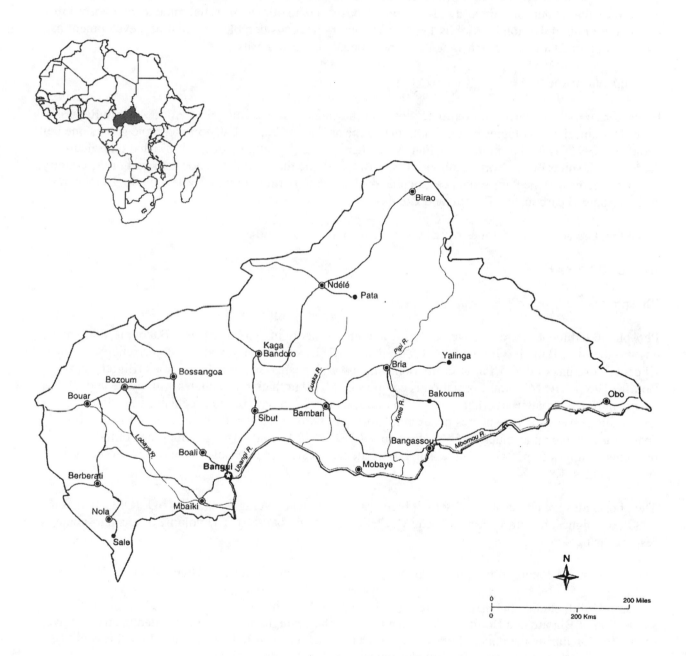

The landlocked country of the Central African Republic lies close to the equator, north of the Congo Basin. The countryside consists of a rolling plateau with average altitudes around 600-700 m. Most rivers drain into the Congo Basin. There are three distinct agro-ecological zones: tropical in the south, Sudan-Guinea type vegetation and climate in the centre of the country, and Sahelian in the north.

The economy of the Central African Republic is based on agricultural exports of coffee, cotton and tobacco, and of minerals, especially diamonds. Most of the farmers grow food crops like cassava, yams, bananas, rice and groundnuts on a subsistence basis. In 1999, the agricultural sector contributed about 55% of the GDP. Approximately 80% of the labour force is employed in the agricultural sector.

The mining sector of the Central African Republic contributes 4% of the country's GDP. The main economic mineral deposits are alluvial diamond deposits. Up to 40,000 artisanal miners are involved in riverbed mining of diamonds (Mobbs 1995). The country has considerable potential for development in the gold mineralizations in greenstone belts and alluvial/eluvial deposits.

Geological outline

Precambrian rocks underlie approximately 60% of the country. In the southern Central African Republic occur Precambrian lithologies belonging to the Archean Congo Craton. Palaeoproterozoic greenstone belts (Poidevin 1994) as well as high grade Pan-African granulites (Pin and Poidevin 1987) and other Pan-African rock suites of the North Equatorial Fold Belt underlie the central and northern part of the country. Neoproterozoic sedimentary sequences include the Bakouma Formation with tillites, fluvioglacial deposits and widespread carbonates (Bigotte and Bonifas 1968).

Flat-lying Cretaceous sandstones overlie parts of western and central areas.

AGROMINERALS

Phosphates

Phosphatic sediments were discovered during a uranium survey in 1959-1961 near Bakouma, 480 km east-northeast of Bangui (OECD/NEA 1980). Phosphatic lenses are intercalated with organic-rich silts and siliceous horizons of the M'Patou Formation, which was deposited in karst depressions (Bigotte and Bonifas 1968). The M'Patou Formation is composed of 0-20 m thick black shales with pyrite and abundant organic matter, overlain by a 20-25 m thick succession with brown, reddish and yellow phosphatic lenses. The phosphates occur in the form of microcrystalline, carbonate-substituted fluor-apatites that make up as much as 50% of the rock (OECD/NEA 1980). The general grade of the phosphates ranges from 9-35% P_2O_5. The phosphate lenses are highly weathered and contain secondary Al-phosphates.

The phosphates are characterized by their high uranium content, averaging 0.26% U_3O_8 (OECD/NEA 1980), the highest in sub-Saharan Africa (McClellan and Notholt 1986). The volume of this phosphate resource is not known.

The age of the M'Patou Formation is proposed as late Cretaceous to Eocene (Bigotte and Bonifas 1968).

Miauton (1980) studied the origin of these localized phosphates in karst depressions. He contests the suggestion of Bigotte and Bonifas (1968) that the phosphates might have been deposited in an extensive sea ingression during the upper Cretaceous to Eocene. Miauton (1980) disproves this hypothesis by demonstrating that these newly formed phosphates are of continental origin.

Other agrominerals

Limestones and dolomites of the Neoproterozoic are the main carbonates in the Central African Republic. Fine-grained but very pure limestones at Fatima, 8 km southwest of the capital Bangui are used for the local cement industry. The United Nations Development Programme (UNDP) undertook detailed exploration on the 'Calcaires de Fatima' with a total of 4,168 m drilled to outline blocks of extractable limestone for the cement industry (PNUD/UNDP 1974). Proven reserves are 8 million tonnes (Gwosdz 1996).

Apart from a few Proterozoic limestones and dolomites there are considerable resources of Cretaceous ferruginous limestones near Bakouma (Gwosdz 1996).

Agromineral potential

A thorough assessment of agricultural and soil needs are required before the potential use of the known agromineral resources can be assessed.

The Bakouma phosphates need geological evaluation on grade and volume. The potential of these resources hinges on the local soil and crop requirements for phosphorus. The uranium content of the Bakouma phosphates is very high. Uranium is reported to be partially replacing calcium in the crystal structure of the apatite in the Bakouma phosphates (OECD/NEA 1980), and considering the high concentration of uranium in the apatites, it will be necessary to remove/recover the uranium from the phosphate rock prior to its agricultural application.

Local limestone and dolomite resources should be assessed for their potential as liming materials on acid soils under high rainfall conditions, especially in the south of the country.

References:

Bigotte G and G Bonifas 1968. Faits nouveaux sur la géologie de la région Bakouma. Chron. Mines Rech. Min. 36:370, 43-46.

Gwosdz W 1996. Central African Republic. In: Bosse H-R, Gwosdz W, Lorenz W, Markwich, Roth W and F Wolff (eds.) Limestone and dolomite resources of Africa. Geol. Jb., D, 106-110.

McClellan GH and AJG Notholt 1986. Phosphate deposits of sub-Saharan Africa. In: Mokwunye AU and PLG Vlek (eds.) Management of nitrogen and phosphorus fertilizers in sub-Saharan Africa. Martinus Nijhoff, Dordrecht, Netherlands:173-224.

Miauton JD 1980. Bakouma, genèse et gîtologie d'un gisement néoforme continental phosphato-uranifère. Thèse 3° cycle, University of Nancy, France, 160pp.

Mobbs PM 1995. The mineral industry of the Central African Republic. Minerals Yearbook, vol. III, United States of the Interior, Geological Survey, 17-18.

OECD/NEA 1980. World uranium - Geology and resource potential. Intern. Uranium Resource Evaluation Project, Miller Freeman Publ. Inc. San Francisco, 524pp.

Pin C and JL Poidevin 1987. U-Pb zircon evidence for Pan-African granulite facies metamorphism in Central African Republic. A new interpretation of the high-grade series of the northern border of the Congo craton. Precambr. Res. 36:303-312.

PNUD/UNDP 1974. Etude des dépôts calcaires de Fatima. Rapport sur les résultats, conclusions et recommandations du projet, United Nations, New York, 33pp.

Poidevin JL 1994. Boninite-like rocks from the Paleoproterozoic greenstone belt of Bogoin, Central African Republic: geochemistry and petrogenesis. Precambr. Res. 68:97-113.

Chad

Total population (July 2000 estimate): 8,425,000
Area: 1,284,000 km^2
Annual population growth rate (2000): 3.31%
Life expectancy at birth (1998): 47.5 years
People not expected to survive to age 40 (1998): 36.9% of total population
GDP per capita (1998): US $856

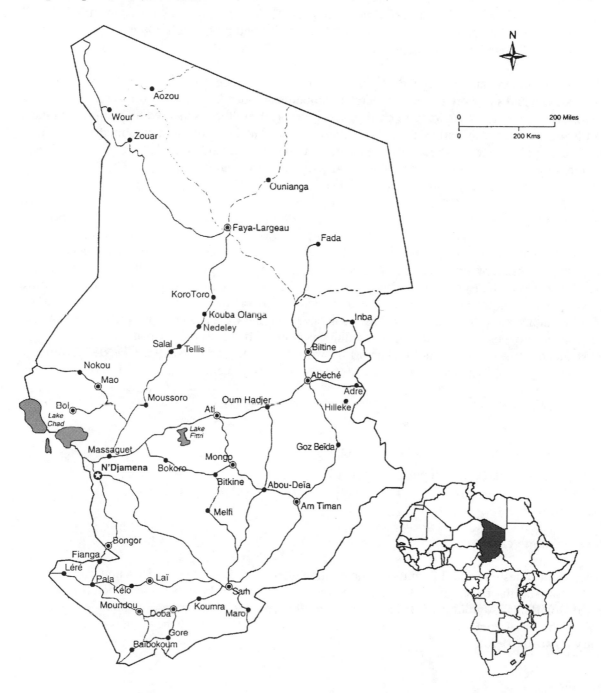

Chad is a landlocked country in the centre of the African continent with three distinct climatic and vegetation zones:

- the northern parts consist of Sahara desert environments (average annual precipitation 25 mm),
- the central part is bush-covered steppe (average annual precipitation 250-500 mm),
- the southern part is wooded savannah with average annual rainfall in excess of 500 mm.

Chad consists of a large peneplain deeply cut by rivers that drain into Lake Chad.

The national economy of Chad is largely based on subsistence agriculture. More than 90% of the population is involved in pastoralist or agricultural activities. The agricultural sector accounts for 36% of the GDP. The main food crops are mainly sorghum, millet, maize and groundnuts. Other major crops are rice and sugar cane. The major export crop is cotton.

Until recently, the mineral and energy industry of Chad did not play a significant part in the national economy. Soda ash and salt were the only mineral commodities produced, primarily for domestic consumption. However, this situation will change with revenues from the discovered oil resources in the Doba - Sarh area of southern Chad (Kusnir and Moutaye 1997). The Doba oil field is estimated to contain 1 billion barrels of oil. Three hundred wells are expected to produce 225,000 barrels a day. The building of a 1070 km long pipeline to an export terminal near Kribi in Cameroon is in progress. Crude oil is expected to start flowing through this pipeline in 2003.

Geological outline

The geology of Chad is characterized by Precambrian and younger sediments surrounding the central Chad Basin. Precambrian rocks occur in the Tibesti Mountains in the north and consist of undifferentiated granites and gneisses in the eastern part of the country. Lower Paleozoic sandstone sequences in the Kufra Basin in the northeast (at the border with Libya and Sudan) are overlain by Nubian sandstones. The Lower Cretaceous is characterized by continental clastic sequences and the Upper Cretaceous includes up to 400 m thick marine sediments. Tertiary continental sediments cover parts of southern Chad. Lacustrine sediment sequences (the Chad Formation) comprise large parts of the Chad basin (OECD/NEA 1980). Kusnir and Moutaye (1997) provide a summary of the geology and mineral resources of Chad.

AGROMINERALS

Phosphates

To date, no phosphates have been reported from Chad.

Other agrominerals

Limestone/dolomite/calcrete

Large reserves of limestone and dolomite are known in the Lere area along the border with Cameroon and from M'Boursou, north of Lere. In eastern Chad, dolomites and marbles have been described from near Hilleke and Goz Beida (Abdoul *et al*. 1973; Kusnir and Moutaye 1997). Calcretes are common in the area south and southwest of Pala (Abdoul *et al*. 1973), and along the road from Abeche to Fada in the east of the country (Gwosdz 1996).

Gypsum

Several impure gypsum occurrences are noted along the Barh el Gazal between Nedeley and Tellis (Abdoul *et al.* 1973). Most are occurrences of impure gypsum mixed with clays and diatomite in lacustrine sequences.

Agromineral potential

The potential of agromineral development in Chad is limited due to the small resource base and the harsh climatic conditions.

References:

Abdoul O, Becker J and ML Ferrante 1973. Six substances minérales à développement industriel possible. Unpubl. report. Service Géologique du Tchad. Projet Minier PNUD/CHD/72/00, 280pp.

Gwosdz W 1996. Chad. In: Bosse H-R, Gwosdz W, Lorenz W, Markwich, Roth W and F Wolff (eds.) Limestone and dolomite resources of Africa. Geol. Jb., D, 110-113.

Kusnir I and HA Moutaye 1997. Ressources minérales du Tchad: une revue. J. Afr. Earth Sci. 24:549-562.

OECD/NEA 1980. World uranium - Geology and resource potential. Intern. Uranium Resource Evaluation Project, Miller Freeman Publ. Inc. San Francisco, USA,524pp.

Comoros

Total population (July 2000 estimate): 578,000
Area: 2,170 km^2
Annual population growth rate (2000): 3.05%
Life expectancy at birth (1998): 59.2 years
People not expected to survive to age 40 (1998): 20.1% of total population
GDP per capita (1998): US $1,398

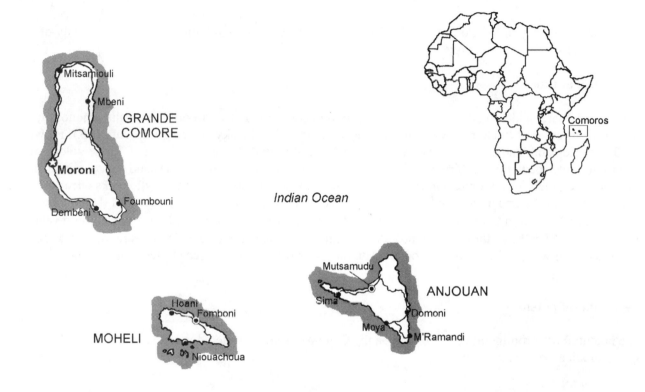

The Comoro Archipelago consists of a number of islands located at the northern end of the Mozambique Channel in the Indian Ocean. The islands of Grand Comore, Moheli and Anjouan make up the State of The Comoros. The island of Mayotte is under French administration. The Comoros are densely populated, and more than 80% of the population of about 580,000 obtain their livelihood from agriculture. The agricultural sector accounts for approximately 40% of the GDP with the main food crops being bananas, cassava, sweet potatoes, rice and maize. Almost all of Comoros' export earnings are derived from the sale of agricultural products such as vanilla, essence of ylang-ylang (an aromatic oil derived from a flowering tree), copra and cloves.

Intensive farming practices, combined with heavy population pressure and uncontrolled deforestation have caused serious soil erosion on the Comoro islands.

The mineral industry of the Comoros is limited to the production of local building materials, mainly of volcanic rocks.

Geological outline

The Comoros are made up of volcanic rocks, primarily undersaturated alkali olivine basalts. Phonolitic and small volumes of trachytic lavas have also been reported (Pavlovsky and de Saint-Ours 1953; Flower 1973; Emerick and Duncan 1982). The volcanic rocks have been differentiated into the 'Phase volcanique supérieure, intermédiaire et inférieure.' In all phases, basaltic lavas prevail. Scorias and puzzolanic tuffs have been reported from Grand Comore, Moheli and Anjouan. Phonolitic and trachytic rocks occur on Mayotte (Pavlovsky and de Saint-Ours 1953). The age of the volcanics increases eastward (Hajash and Armstrong 1972), from Grand Comoros (0.01 ± 0.01 million years) to Anjouan (1.52 ± 0.1 million years) to Mayotte (3.65 ± 0.1 million years) indicating that the volcanic chain of the Comoros represents a 'hot spot trace' that was produced as the Somali plate moved over a mantle source (Emerick and Duncan 1982).

Agromineral potential

The potential of agromineral development on the Comoros is very limited due to the lack of suitable agrogeological resources.

References:

Emerick CM and RA Duncan 1982. Age progressive volcanism in the Comoro Archipelago, western Indian Ocean and implications for Somali plate tectonics. Earth Planet. Sci. Lett. 60: 415-428.

Flower MFJ 1973. Evolution of basaltic and differentiated lavas from Anjouan, Comores Archipelago. Contrib. Mineral. Petrol. 38: 237-260.

Hajash A and RL Armstrong 1972. Paleomagnetic and radiometric evidence for the ages of the Comores Island, west central Indian Ocean, Earth Planet. Sci. Lett. 16:231.

Pavlovsky R and J de Saint-Ours 1953. Etude Géologique de l'Archipelago des Comores. Service Géologique, Tananarive, Madagascar, 55pp.

Congo (Democratic Republic of Congo)

Total population (July 2000 estimate): 51,965,000
Area: 2,345,410 km^2
Annual population growth rate (2000): 3.19%
Life expectancy at birth (1998): 51.2 years
People not expected to survive to age 40 (1998): 31.7% of the total population
GDP per capita (1998): US $822

The Democratic Republic of Congo (DRC), previously called Zaire, is a vast, resource-endowed country with mining and agricultural sectors as the cornerstones of the economy. But despite its rich natural resource base, the DRC is among the least developed countries in sub-Saharan Africa.

Historically, the DRC has been a major mining country, a producer of copper/cobalt, diamonds and gold. The mining sector accounted for 25% of the GDP and three quarters of the total export revenue. Both large mining companies and artisanal miners extracted the mineral resources of the DRC. Artisanal miners have historically accounted for the extraction of the largest portion of diamonds (Coakley 1995). Despite civil war and insecurity, artisanal miners continued to mine diamonds and, in addition, produced approximately 9,000 kg of gold in 1994.

Continued civil war and the general breakdown of the formal economy and existing infrastructure have disrupted much of the mineral production in the country. Presently, copper production is only at 5% of capacity.

The International Labour Organisation (1999) reports the activities of 150,000 small scale gold and diamond miners.

The agricultural sector is largely subsistence based. In 1999 agriculture contributed approximately 58% to the GDP. The main food crops are maize, bananas/plantains, sweet potatoes, cassava and rice. Coffee is the main export crop.

Geological outline

The Congo Basin, made up largely of Mesozoic and Quaternary sediments, occupies large areas in the west and centre of the country. Precambrian metamorphosed sediments and Proterozoic platform sediments occur in the eastern part of the country. Dolomites and Neoproterozoic sediments of the Katanga Supergroup (Cahen and Lepersonne 1967) occur in the Shaba Province in the southeast of the country.

Along the Western Rift, in the eastern part of the country are numerous Tertiary to Recent volcanoes, and some carbonatites.

AGROMINERALS

Phosphates

Sedimentary phosphates have been reported in the Bas Congo region, close to the Atlantic Ocean, at the border with Angola and the Cabinda enclave. The area northwest of Boma was intermittently surveyed before 1960. Between 1969 and 1971 the United Nations Development Programme (UNDP/PNUD) carried out exploration work on the 100 km long and 10-20 km wide zone with Upper Cretaceous (Maastrichtian) beds which occur in the Cabinda enclave of Angola and continue into the Democratic Republic of Congo. Several layers of sedimentary phosphates have been found in Angola and the DRC at shallow depth (see Figure 2.2 on page 72 in the chapter on Angola).

During a subsequent project between 1978 and 1980 UNDP/PNUD carried out advanced exploration, including the drilling of 30 boreholes and sinking of 54 pits in areas of phosphate-bearing sediments (Barry 1981). Specifically, the exploration focused on three areas along the northwesterly striking sediments, Fundu Nzobe, Vuangu, and Kanzi (Figure 2.2, page 74).

Work at Fundu Nzobe in the north, close to the border with Angola's Cabinda enclave, showed five phosphate bearing layers of upper Cretaceous (Maastrichtian) to lower Eocene age. The thickness and grade of these sedimentary phosphate beds are: Bed I: 11.5 m, 11.5-18.5% P_2O_5; Bed II: 5.5 m, 18-19.4% P_2O_5; Bed III: 20 m, 18-19.7% P_2O_5; Bed IV: 5.1 m, 20.6% P_2O_5; Bed V: 10.7 m, 31% P_2O_5. The geological conditions for mining are complicated as a result of structural deformation (open folding and faulting) and overburden. Superficial sand overburden reaches 20 m and more in some places. The resources in the Fundu Nzobe area are substantial but have not been assessed with certainty due their complex structural setting (Barry 1981).

In contrast to the area of Fundu Nzobe, the area of Kanzi in the south, close to the mouth of the Congo River, is tectonically less complicated. The phosphate mineralization consists of one layer of phosphorite only and is relatively uniform. The 8-10 m thick layer at 14% P_2O_5 is covered by a thick sandy overburden. The 'waste-to-ore' ratio ranges from 2:1-10:1. Twelve boreholes were drilled with a total length of 1,460 m (Barry 1981).

Geotechnical studies on samples from Kanzi showed that the ore could be upgraded to 34% P_2O_5 by removal of clay slimes and conventional double flotation methods (Zellars-Williams 1980).

On the basis of the existing borehole and pit data, the total phosphate resources at Kanzi alone were estimated at 20-28 million tonnes of phosphate ore, or 5-7 million tonnes of concentrate (Barry 1981).

The project was undertaken with the aim of developing a phosphate fertilizer plant with the capacity to process 150,000 to 500,000 tonnes of phosphate concentrate per year. The ore was to be mined with large draglines like in Florida and the concentrate was to be processed into phosphoric acid-based P fertilizers. The plan was to combine it with large-scale (100,000 tonnes per year) production of N fertilizers (ammonia). The project was not followed up for various reasons including concerns of economic and technical feasibility (Barry 1981). At the time, no consideration was given to small-scale extraction at sites where overburden is minimal.

Other phosphate resources available in the DRC include igneous phosphate resources, mainly associated with carbonatites.

Two carbonatites, located in the eastern part of the DRC, have been studied in greater detail: the Lueshe and the Bingo carbonatites. The Lueshe carbonatite (1°0'S; 29°8'E) is mainly made up of a syenite and carbonatite, with little apatite as an accessory mineral (Maravic and Morteani 1980). Biotite and vermiculite occur along the contacts of the dolomitic carbonatite, which is 822 ± 22 million years old (Kampunzu *et al.* 1998). The carbonatite is Nb-rich (de Kun 1961; Verhaeghe 1964), with a grade of 1.34% Nb_2O_5 in the residual soils. The principal niobium mineral is pyrochlore. An average chemical analysis of the lateritic residual soils is 5-9% P_2O_5 (Maravic *et al.* 1983).

Following the discovery of 3 million tonnes of pyrochlore-bearing ore at the Lueshe carbonatite, a pilot plant for the extraction of pyrochlore was started in 1986 by the German led company SOMIKIVU (Mining Annual Review 1985). The pilot operation with a production of 2 tonnes per hour came to an end in the fall of 1993 when the security situation worsened.

The Bingo carbonatite (0°5'N; 29°31'E) is mentioned by Verhaeghe (1964) and Lubala *et al.* (1985) as a carbonatite with large phosphate reserves, 'la réserve des phosphates semble énorme' (Verhaeghe 1964, p.23). Recent investigations at Bingo concentrated on the mineralogy of the Nb-bearing mineral, pyrochlore (Woolley *et al.* 1995; Williams *et al.* 1998). No detailed work on phosphate seems to have been carried out in recent years.

Limestone/dolomite/travertine

The limestone/dolomite resources of the DRC are substantial. Proterozoic marbles and dolomites are reported from near Lubudi where marble is used for the local cement industry (Buffard and Vicat 1975). Carbonates for the production of cement are also found around Lubumbashi in the 'copper-belt,' near Kalemie on the shores of Lake Tanganyika, north and northwest of Lake Kivu, near Kisangani, and in the Central Kasai Province (near Gandajika). Verhaeghe (1964) describes 16 metamorphic limestone occurrences in the North Kivu area and 12 from the South Kivu area alone. Precambrian calcareous metasediments are also found in the extreme west of the country (between Kinshasa and the coast) as part of the 'Schisto-Calcaire' sequence of the West Congo Series. Cretaceous limestones are exploited for use in cement production at Lukula in the west of the country.

The carbonatite of Lueshe contains considerable amounts of carbonates along with phosphates and pyrochlore. The Bingo carbonatite contains only small carbonate resources.

There are numerous travertine occurrences in the east of the country, along Lake Kivu and Lake Edward (Verhaeghe 1964; Gwosdz 1996). From the 19 travertine occurrences in the Kivu area, as described in detail by Verhaeghe (1964), some have resources in excess of 2 million tonnes. Many of these resources are of local importance.

Limestone is used for cement industries at five sites (near Likasi, Kalemie, Kimpese, Lubudi and Lukula). At the end of the 1970s, lime was produced on an industrial scale and by numerous small local industries with a total production of 120,000 tonnes (Gwosdz 1996).

Agromineral potential

The Democratic Republic of Congo is endowed with considerable agromineral resources. So far only a few systematic surveys have been carried out and it is likely that considerable amounts of additional agrominerals are yet to be discovered in the DRC. Resources of sedimentary and igneous phosphates have already been found.

The potential for developing the upper Cretaceous to Eocene sedimentary phosphates on a small scale for local consumption is high, especially in the Bas Congo area. These phosphates, located in the striking continuation of the Angolan phosphatic sediments, occur close to the surface and can be easily extracted.

Igneous residual phosphates may be extracted from the known mineralized carbonatites of Bingo and, as a by-product from Nb mining, from the Lueshe carbonatite complex.

The unmetamorphosed Neoproterozoic sequences of the West Congolian Supergroup overlying tillite horizons should be explored for their phosphate potential. The structural and stratigraphic position of the phosphate occurrence in the neighbouring Republic of Congo provides a good initiative to explore for phosphates in the Neoproterozoic Schisto-Calcaire.

Limestone and dolomite occurrences are widespread and may be developed on a small-scale in areas close to acid soils.

References:

Barry GS 1981. Evaluation des gisements de phosphate Bas Zaire, République du Zaire. Projet ZAI/75-009. Report to DTCD, United Nations, New York, 41pp.

Buffard R and JP Vicat 1975. Le calcaires stromatoliques de Lububi, Haut Shaba. Ann. Soc. Geol. Belgique, 98: 483-492.

Cahen L and J Lepersonne 1967. The Precambrian of the Congo, Rwanda and Burundi. In: Rankama K (editor) The Precambrian, Vol. 3. Interscience Publishers, New York:143-290.

Coakley GJ 1995: The mineral industry of Zaire. Minerals Yearbook Vol. III, US Department of the Interior, Geological Survey:123-126.

de Kun N 1961. Die Niobkarbonatite von Afrika. Neues Jb. Mineral. Mh. 1961(6):124-135 (in German).

Gwosdz W 1996. Zaire. In: Bosse H-R, Gwosdz W, Lorenz W, Markwich, Roth W and F Wolff (eds.) Limestone and dolomite resources of Africa. Geol. Jb., D, 102:482-494.

International Labour Organization 1999. Social and labour issues in small-scale mines. TMSSM/1999, 99pp.

Kampunzu AB, Kramers JD and MN Makutu 1998. Rb-Sr whole rock ages of the Lueshe, Kirumba and Numbi igneous complexes (Kivu, Democratic Republic of Congo) and the break-up of the Rodinia supercontinent. J. Afr. Earth Sci. 26:29-36.

Lubala RT, Kampunzu AB and MN Makutu 1985. Inventaire des complexes alcalins a l'Est du Zaire. J. Afr. Earth Sci. 3:169-174.

Maravic H v and G Morteani 1980. Petrology and geochemistry of the carbonatite and syenite complex of Lueshe (N.E. Zaire). Lithos 13:159-170.

Maravic H v, Morteani G and GA Roethe 1983. Die niobiumreichen Verwitterungserze des Karbonatits von Lueshe/Zaire. Erzmetall 36:29-35 (in German).

Mining Annual Review 1985. Zaire. Mining Journal Ltd. London, 443-445.

Verhaeghe M 1964. Inventaire des gisement calcaires, dolomies et travertins du Kivu, du Rwanda et du Burundi. Département Géologie et Mines du Burundi, 95pp.

Williams CT, Wall F, Woolley AR and S Phillipo 1998. Compositional variation in pyrochlore from the Bingo carbonatite, Zaire. J. Afr. Earth Sci. 25:137-145.

Woolley AR, Williams CT, Wall F, Garcia D and J Moute 1995. The Bingo carbonatite-ijolite-nepheline syenite complex, Zaire: geology petrography, mineralogy and petrochemistry. J. Afr. Earth Sci. 21:329-348.

Zellars-Williams 1980. Report of laboratory tests conducted on Kanzi phosphate samples. Report to United Nations, ZAI/75/009, United Nations, New York, 14pp.

Congo (Republic of Congo)

Total population (July 2000 estimate): 2,831,000
Area: 342,000 km^2
Annual population growth rate (2000): 2.23%
Life expectancy at birth (1998): 48.9 years
People not expected to survive to age 40 (1998): 34.4% of total population
GDP per capita (1998): US $995

The Republic of Congo (also called Congo-Brazzaville) lies on the equator at the west coast of Africa. The main geographical zones of the Republic of Congo (RC) are, from west to east: the low, treeless coastal plain, the Mayombe Range and Chailu Massif covered by rainforest, the vast depression of the Niari valley, and the Bateke plateau and northern parts of the country covered with equatorial rainforests.

The economy of the Republic of Congo with its capital Brazzaville is largely based on the export of crude oil and natural gas. The RC is sub-Saharan Africa's fourth-largest oil producer, pumping 265,000 barrels per day from its offshore deposits. Oil contributes more than 50% to the GDP. The natural gas reserves of the RC are 3.2 trillion cubic feet (TCF), the third-largest known gas resources in sub-Saharan Africa (after Nigeria and Cameroon). All of Congo's gas output is currently flared due to a lack of infrastructure.

Congo's agriculture is predominantly subsistence in nature. Food crops are cassava, plantains, maize, groundnuts and rice. Other crops are sugar cane, palm oil, citrus, pineapple and coffee. Agriculture contributes only 10% to the GDP but provides a livelihood for about 60% of the population.

Geological outline

Geologically, the Republic of Congo is characterized by Precambrian rocks in the central part of the country, which are overlain by continental Cretaceous and Tertiary sediments. Quaternary alluvial sediments cover the eastern part of the country. The coastal basin is made up of Cretaceous to Quaternary marine sediments, including phosphatic sequences and evaporites. The coastal basin borders the Precambrian Mayombe Range to the east. The Neoproterozoic West Congolian Supergroup occurs in the Nyanga syncline with feldspathic sediments overlain by dolomites, cherts and dolomitic limestones with stromatolites. Alvarez and Maurin (1991) and Alvarez (1995) provide a detailed sedimentological analysis of the Neoproterozoic rocks of the Comba trough.

AGROMINERALS

Phosphates

The Republic of Congo has considerable resources of sedimentary phosphates. These phosphate deposits, Upper Cretaceous - Lower Eocene (Ypresian) in age, form a string of outcrops extending over 50 km along the coast (Giresse 1980).

Sedimentary phosphates are exposed 50-80 km east to northeast of Pointe Noire within a 750 m wide belt of the Upper Cretaceous (Maastrichtian) Holle Series and younger sediments (Giresse 1980). These phosphate beds continue into the Cabinda enclave of Angola, and into Gabon. The phosphate deposits were discovered during exploration for oil. In total, the phosphate rock sequence of this area contains 15 million tonnes of phosphate ore at 21-25% P_2O_5. The phosphate deposit of Kola, in the northwestern extension of the Holle Series, contains 0.3 million tonnes at 21% P_2O_5 (McClellan and Notholt 1986). The most researched phosphate deposit is located in the Holle area at Bas Tchivoula, approximately 40 km east of Pointe Noire, with 5 million tonnes at 23% P_2O_5. The phosphates are exposed at the surface in two facies, siliceous fossiliferous, and coprolitic-quartzose, representing open sea and deltaic facies respectively (Giresse 1980). Crystallographic investigations of the apatite (unit-cell a-value = 9.30 to 9.35 Å) show that the apatites are francolites (Giresse 1980). However, some aluminum phosphates reported at the top of the formation, weathering products of the underlying phosphates.

Other phosphate deposits in the Republic of Congo are located offshore. In the early 1970s researchers from the Bureau de Recherches Géologiques et Minières (BRGM) reported unconsolidated phosphatic sediments of Miocene and Holocene age in offshore deposits near Pointe Noire (Barusseau et al. 1988). These deposits are probably reworked unconsolidated sediments and occur in shallow water at a depth of about 40 m, less than 20 km from the coast. In 1982, the United Nations Revolving Fund for Natural Resources Exploration (UNRFNRE), through contractors, carried out detailed offshore investigations in an area between Point Noire and the border to the Cabinda enclave. The investigations included seismic profiling and dredge sampling, and outlined an area of about 81 km^2 with near-surface unconsolidated enrichments of phosphorite pellets and calcareous shells. The probable reserves are reported as 7 million tonnes of phosphorites and 25.5 million tonnes of calcareous shells (UNRFNRE 1984).

Samples from the mixed phosphorite/shell deposit (10.5% P_2O_5) were tested agronomically at the Research Station of Loudima in Congo, but no results are available. Large samples of phosphate pellets and calcareous shells were also evaluated by the Agronomy Department of the Mississippi State University (Pettry 1985) to assess their mineralogy and agronomic effectiveness.

Mineralogical and chemical studies of the screened samples show that the phosphate minerals are francolite. The unit-cell a-value of a phosphate sample provided by the International Fertilizer Development Center (IFDC) was 9.3247 Å, and has confirmed francolitic composition. Baresseau *et al.* (1988) report a-values from these offshore phosphorites from 9.155 to 9.347 Å. The total P_2O_5 content of the 'pure' phosphorites was 30.06-31.07% (Pettry 1985). Finely ground phosphorites were evaluated in a greenhouse study using an ultisol with a pH of 5 and high P-fixing capacities from Mississippi State as test soil and wheat as the test crop. The greenhouse study showed that plant uptake P-levels for the 0.25, 1, and 3 tons per acre applications of finely ground phosphorite (less than 60 mesh) exhibited increased yields of 20, 113, and 165% respectively above the control (Pettry 1985).

McClellan and Notholt (1986) mentioned phosphate nodules (28-35% P_2O_5) in the Neoproterozoic Schisto-Calcaire in the middle Niari Valley, near Comba, 110 km west of Brazzaville. Alvarez (1995) noted authigenic apatites in lagoonal sediments of the Neoproterozoic West Congolian Supergroup. So far, however, the grade, extent and volume of these occurrences are not known. This phosphate occurrence, though of unknown extent and quality, is extremely important as it represents the only known phosphate occurrence in the Schisto-Calcaire of the Neoproterozoic West Congolian Supergroup in West Africa.

Potash

The Republic of Congo is one of the few countries in sub-Saharan Africa with extensive potash resources. The Lower Cretaceous potash deposit of Holle in the coastal region of Congo was mined in the 1970s (de Ruiter 1979). The potash deposit at Holle occurs at depths of 400-700 m below sea level. The potassium-salts in the Holle potash deposit are rich in carnallite and sylvite. Production of sylvite (KCl) reached 450,000 tonnes per year in the 1970s but was halted when the mine flooded in 1977 (de Ruiter 1979; Kronsten 1996). De Ruiter (1979) describes layers of 1.9 m and 3 m thickness with K_2O contents of 18 and 38% respectively and mineable reserves of 17 million and 26 million tonnes K_2O respectively.

Limestone/dolomite

Abundant limestones and dolomites are found in the Neoproterozoic Schisto-Calcaire of the West Congolian Supergroup in the west of the country. The oolitic limestone at the base of the Schisto-Calcaire is up to 30 m thick with very large reserves. A limestone quarry near the town of Loutete provides limestone material for the local cement industry. At another site, at Mandingu, west of Loutete the quarried limestone is used for quicklime production. The lime kiln has an annual capacity of 30,000 tonnes (Gwosdz 1996). Other carbonate horizons of the Schisto-Calcaire are dolomitic in composition. There are also widespread Cretaceous - Tertiary marine sediments in the coastal area of Congo, some of which are limestones. Shell samples from dredging operations offshore, discussed in the section on phosphates, contained limestone shells with $CaCO_3$-equivalent contents of 81-89%, which is comparable to commercial agricultural liming material (Pettry 1985).

Agromineral potential

The Republic of Congo is endowed with a variety of agrominerals, including Cretaceous, Miocene and Holocene phosphates, as well as extensive potash and limestone/dolomite resources. The phosphorites of the Upper Cretaceous Holle Series near Bas Tchivoula should be assessed for their potential as direct application phosphate fertilizer using small-scale mining and appropriate processing technologies.

There is a strong need to investigate the stratigraphic and structural controls of Neoproterozoic phosphates of the Schisto-Calcaire and compare them to the Neoproterozoic phosphates of West Africa (Burkina Faso, Benin, Niger) and the Brazilian deposits of the Bambui Group (Dardenne *et al.* 1986). This could potentially lead to new discoveries of phosphates in the Republic of Congo and in other parts of the Neoproterozoic in neighbouring countries with similar rock sequences. The upper Cretaceous to Tertiary phosphorites of the Holle area should be studied on their potential as direct application phosphate fertilizer on local acid and phosphorus deficient soils. The potential of the limestone resources depends largely on the proximity of these resources to acid soils, on agronomic response, and on economic considerations.

References:

Alvarez P 1995. Les facteurs de controle de la sédimentation du Supergroup Ouest-Congolien (Sud-Congo). Rampe carbonatée et activité biologique au Proterozoic Supérieur. Documents du BRGM 239, 231pp.

Alvarez P and Maurin JC 1991. Evolution sédimentaire et tectonique du bassin proterozoique supérieur de Comba (Congo): stratigraphie sequentielle du Supergroupe Ouest-Congolien et modèle d'amorttissement sur decrochements dans le contexte de la tectogenèse panafricaine. Precambr. Res. 50:137-171.

Barusseau JP, Giresse P and L Manongo 1988. Genesis of a Holocene phosphate placer deposit on the continental shelf of Congo. J. Coastal Res. 4:369-379.

Dardenne MA, Trompette R, Magalhaes LF and LA Soares 1986. Proterozoic and Cambrian phosphorites - regional review: Brazil. In: Cook PJ and JH Shergold (eds.) Phosphate deposits of the world, Vol. 1: Proterozoic and Cambrian phosphorites, Cambridge University Press, Cambridge,UK: 116-131.

De Ruiter PAC 1979. The Gabon and Congo Basins Salt Deposits. Econ. Geol. 74:419-431.

Giresse P 1980. The Maastrichtian phosphate sequence of the Congo. Soc. Econ. Paleont. Mineral, Spec. Publ. 29:193-205.

Giresse P and R Baloka 1996. Les phosphates meso-cénozoiques du bassin du Congo et leurs paléoenvironments. Bull. Soc. Geol. Fr. 5:585-600.

Gwosdz W 1996. Congo. In: Bosse H-R, Gwosdz W, Lorenz W, Markwich, Roth W and F Wolff (eds.) Limestone and dolomite resources of Africa. Geol. Jb., D, 114-117.

Kronsten G 1996. Congo. Mining Annual Review 1996. Mining Journal Ltd. London, p.149.

McClellan GH and AJG Notholt 1986. Phosphate deposits of sub-Saharan Africa. In: Mokwunye AU and PLG Vlek (eds.) Management of nitrogen and phosphorus fertilizers in sub-Saharan Africa. Martinus Nijhoff, Dordrecht, Netherlands:173-224.

Pettry DE 1985. Evaluation of shell/phosphorite deposits as soil liming and fertilizer materials. Rep. to UNRFNRE. Agron. Dept. Mississippi Agric. For. Exper. Station, Mississippi State Univ./ UN, New York, 25pp.

UNRFNRE (United Nations Revolving Fund for Natural Resources Exploration) 1984. Exploration pour phosphates au large des côtes du Congo (Secteur de Pointe Noire). Internal report, UN, New York, 20pp.

Côte d'Ivoire

Total population (July 2000 estimate): 15,981,000
Area: 322,460 km^2
Annual population growth rate (2000): 2.58%
Life expectancy at birth (1998): 46.9 years
People not expected to survive to age 40 (1998): 37% of total population
GDP per capita (1998): US $1,598

Geographically and climatically, the Côte d'Ivoire (Ivory Coast) consists of at least three major zones. Low-lying land and lagoons with an equatorial tropical climate are found in the southern zone adjacent to the Atlantic Ocean. Tropical forest zone lies north of the lagoonal zone, and a wooded savanna zone with sparse vegetation and dry climate exists in the north of the country.

The economy of Côte d'Ivoire is largely export-driven. The main exports are agrarian and forestry products, specifically cocoa, coffee, rubber-based latex, and timber. Agriculture accounts for approximately 26% of Côte d'Ivoire's GDP and an estimated 70% of the country's export earnings. Roughly 70% of the labour force is involved in the agricultural sector. The main food crops are yams, cassava, plantains, rice and maize. Other crops include sugar cane, and export commodities such as cocoa beans, cocoa paste, coffee, cotton and pineapple.

So far, the mining industry plays only a minor role in the development of the Côte d'Ivoire. Mineral exploration has focused on gold and lateritic nickel and relatively small amounts of oil were produced from offshore sources between 1978 and 1988. Recent exploration has confirmed the existence of additional oil and natural gas resources offshore.

Geological outline

The oldest rocks of Côte d'Ivoire are part of the Archean West Africa craton and occur in the west of the country. Undifferentiated granites and gneisses as well as Paleoproterozoic north-northeast striking rock sequences of the Birimian with predominantly metasediments (conglomerates, sandstones and shales) and subordinate metavolcanics (Wright *et al.* 1985) underlie most of the country. No Neoproterozoic rocks or Paleozoic rocks occur in Côte d'Ivoire. Sandy-clayey sediments of the Cretaceous and Quaternary were deposited along a narrow, east - west striking coastal strip, the Ivory Coast Basin.

AGROMINERALS

Phosphates

During a reconnaissance survey in the coastal Tertiary sediments of Côte d'Ivoire, small occurrences of phosphatic sediments were identified by Dian (1977). The phosphates occur as nodules in unconsolidated Paleocene to Eocene sediments near Eboinda in eastern coastal Côte d'Ivoire. The phosphatic sediments occur at depths of 3.50-9 m. Maximum phosphate content in one of the pits was 30% P_2O_5. However, the grade is commonly much lower. Tagini and Gobert (1981) report not only apatite from this location but also wavellite, crandallite and variscite, all typical phosphates of the weathering environment. This occurrence seems to be of small volume and extent and no further work has been reported.

Other agrominerals

Limestone/dolomite

There are only very few limestone or dolomitic limestone resources in Côte d'Ivoire (Tagini and Gobert 1981). Most of them occur along the coastal strip in Cretaceous to Tertiary sediments at Ebocco, Nzida, Yakoboue and Fresco, some of them under considerable soil cover. Only a few metamorphosed limestones were identified in the Precambrian rocks of Côte d'Ivoire, northwest and southeast of Man and south of Yamousssoukro (Lorenz 1996).

Dolomitic limestones have been tested successfully in oil palm plantations in the south of the country.

Glauconite

During the exploration for phosphates, Dian (1977) reports on glauconitic sediments in the coastal sediments of Côte d'Ivoire.

Agromineral potential

The potential of developing agrominerals in the Côte d'Ivoire is low. It is limited to the narrow coastal strip with its Tertiary sediments, which include small phosphatic lenses, limestones and glauconitic sediments. Precambrian limestone and dolomite resources for amelioration of acid soils seem to be very limited.

References:

Dian KW 1977. Note sur les indices de phosphates d'Eboinda, Octobre 1976 - Mars 1977. Report No. 419, SODEMI.

Lorenz W. 1996. Ivory Coast. In: Bosse H-R, Gwosdz W, Lorenz W, Markwich, Roth W and F Wolff (eds.) Limestone and dolomite resources of Africa. Geol. Jb., D, 176-179.

Tagini B and M Gobert 1981. Carte au 1/4 000 000 et catalogue des gîtes et principaux indices minéraux de la Côte d'Ivoire. Société pour le Développement Minier de la Côte d'Ivoire (SODEMI), Abidjan, 22pp.

Wright JB, Hastings DA, Jones WB and HR Williams 1985. Geology and mineral resources of West Africa. Allen and Unwin, London, UK, 187pp.

Djibouti

Total population (July 2000 estimate): 451,000
Area: 22,000 km^2
Annual population growth rate (2000): 1.45%
Life expectancy at birth (1998): 50.8 years
People not expected to survive to age 40 (1998): 32.8% of total population
GDP per capita (1998): US $1,266

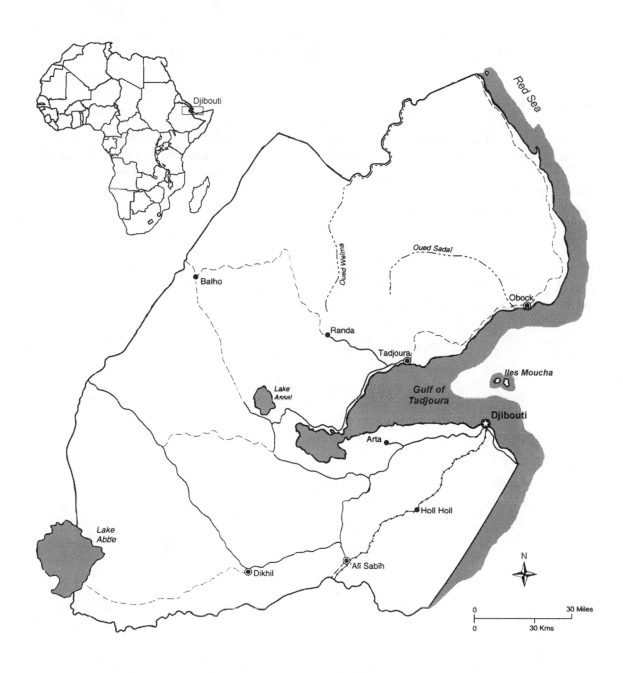

Djibouti is a small country in the Horn of Africa, located between Eritrea, Ethiopia, and Somalia at the southern end of the Red Sea. It consists of the port city of Djibouti and a small hinterland of semi-desert to desert. Annual precipitation ranges from 150 to 350 mm.

The economy of Djibouti is dominated by the service and trade sector. The port of Djibouti is currently the sole maritime entry point of goods into Ethiopia. The share of the agricultural sector is very small.

The mineral industry is also very small, mainly confined to the extraction and use of construction materials and dimension stone.

Geological outline

Most of Djibouti is underlain by Quaternary volcanic rocks. Lower Cretaceous limestones occur in the south of the country at the border with Ethiopia and Somalia and coral reef limestones occur along the coastal area.

Agromineral potential

The potential for agromineral development in this very small and climatically extreme country is very limited. Small occurrences of perlite, pumice and scoria have been reported, but have not been developed. Rock mulching practices using the locally available volcanic scoria and pumice resources as in neighbouring Ethiopia (see chapter Ethiopia, Woldeab et al. 1994) may be tested to see whether evaporation could be reduced substantially.

Reference:

Woldeab A, Assefa A, Yematawork A, Abera S, van Straaten P, Groenevelt P and W Chesworth 1994.
Report on the results of the Ethiopia-Canada Agrogeology Project - Rock Mulch. Unpubl. Report, University of Guelph, Guelph, Canada, 76pp.

Equatorial Guinea

Total population (July 2000 estimate): 474,000
Area: 28,051 km^2
Annual population growth rate (2000): 2.47%
Life expectancy at birth (1998): 50.4 years
People not expected to survive to age 40 (1998): 33.2% of total population
GDP per capita (1998): US $1,817

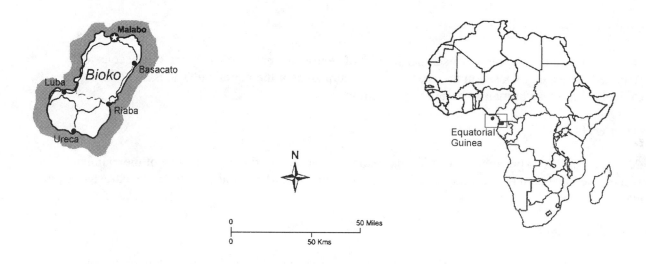

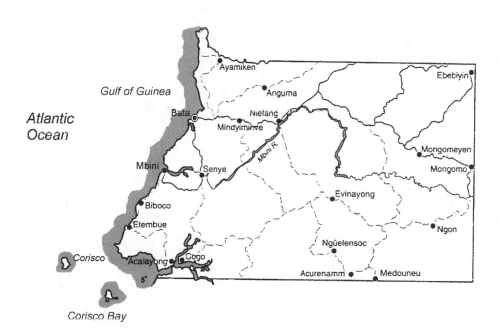

Equatorial Guinea, located at the bend of West Africa, is made up of the island of Bioko in the Atlantic Ocean and the mainland portion (called Rio Muni) located between Cameroon in the north and Gabon in the south.

Equatorial Guinea's economy is one of the fastest growing economies of sub-Saharan Africa as a result of oil discoveries in the early 1990s. The oil sector contributes over 60% to the GDP. At the end of 1999 Equatorial Guinea produced 102,000 barrels per day.

The agricultural sector contributes 20% to the GDP and employs 58% of the labour force. The main food crops are cassava, sweet potatoes, maize, bananas and yams. Equatorial Guinea's agricultural exports are timber and cocoa.

Geological outline

Precambrian metamorphic sequences underlie most of central and eastern Rio Muni. Cretaceous to Tertiary sediments are exposed in the coastal and western zone of the mainland. The island of Bioko is volcanic, having rocks of mainly basaltic composition.

Agrominerals

There are no reports of phosphate or limestone resources exposed in the coastal basin of the mainland. The Cretaceous sediments in the coastal basin include limestones but whether any of them are extracted is not known.

Agromineral potential

The potential of developing local geological resources to improve soils and crop production is limited although liming materials could be used depending on the distribution and extent of acid soils relative to the location and extractability of the limestone resources. The Upper Cretaceous and Tertiary sediments in the coastal areas of the mainland should be investigated for their phosphate potential.

Eritrea

Total population (July 2000 estimate): 4,136,000
Area: 121,320 km^2
Annual population growth rate (2000): 3.86%
Life expectancy at birth (1998): 51.1 years
People not expected to survive to age 40 (1998): 31.4% of the total population
GNP per capita (1998): US $833

Eritrea is located in the Horn of Africa, between the highlands of Ethiopia and the Red Sea. It has a long coastline with the Red Sea.

In 1999, the agricultural sector accounted for 17% of the GDP and provided a livelihood for around 80% of the population. The major food crops are maize, wheat, sorghum, barley and beans. Eritrea exports livestock, sesame seeds and textiles.

The mineral sector of Eritrea is very small. However, there is some potential to develop the known gold and copper resources. At present, Eritrea exports salt and small amounts of marble.

Geological outline

Geologically, Eritrea is largely made up of Tertiary to Recent volcanics and Neoproterozoic terranes (De Souza Filho and Drury 1998). Marine sediments of Mesozoic to Quaternary age are exposed in the coastal area of Eritrea along the Red Sea.

AGROMINERALS

Phosphates

There are no known phosphate resources in Eritrea. Only small bird guano deposits are known from the Dahlak archipelago and other islands in the Red Sea (Hutchinson 1950).

Potassium-salts and gypsum

Enormous reserves of late Tertiary to Pleistocene evaporites including halites, gypsum and potassium salts exist in the Dallol depression located in the Danakil depression, an area located mainly in Ethiopia with a small portion reaching into Eritrea. Previous exploration work, mainly on the Ethiopian side of the Danakil depression, has been compiled by Holwerda and Hutchinson (1968) and Arkin (1969). The latter author concluded that in the whole depression there are at least 160,456,000 short tons of potash ore with 31-34% KCl. Arkin (1969) states that only a small portion of the Danakil depression has been tested for its potash resources. The well-explored areas are located in the Musley and Crescent area, on the Ethiopian side of the border. On the northern side of the Danakil depression some parts of the evaporite sequence, including K-salts and gypsum/anhydrite beds, may continue across the Eritrea/Ethiopia border into Eritrea.

Gypsum deposits occur along the coastal area of eastern Eritrea (Schlede 1989).

Limestone/dolomite

The limestone resources of Eritrea are large. Limestones occur in Quaternary sediments along the coast, and in Mesozoic sediments east of the Danakil depression, in the Danakil Alps. Marble lenses, some of which are dolomitic, are found in Proterozoic rocks of Eritrea (Schlede 1989). The usefulness of agricultural liming material in Eritrea is limited due to the limited extent of acid soils close to the limestone and dolomite resources (Schlede 1989).

Sulphur

Jelenc (1966) reported small sulphur occurrences in the Zariga area, along the road from Dallol to Mersa Fatma.

Agromineral potential

The potential for small-scale agromineral development in Eritrea is difficult to assess due to a very limited database. Known agrominerals are few and seem to be located far from agricultural land. The extent of potash-bearing beds on the Eritrean side of the border, in the northern portion of the Dallol/Danakil depression, is not known at present.

References:

Arkin Y 1969. Potash in Ethiopia. Ministry of Mines, Geological Survey, Unpubl. Report, 28pp.

De Souza Filho CR and SA Drury 1998. A Neoproterozoic supra-subduction terrane in Northern Eritrea, NE Africa. J. Geol. Sci. London, 155:551-556.

Holwerda JG and RW Hutchinson 1968. Potash-bearing evaporites in the Danakil area, Ethiopia. Econ. Geol. 63:124-150.

Hutchinson GE 1950. Survey of existing of biogeochemistry - The geochemistry of vertebrae excretion. Bull. Am. Mus. Nat. History, 96,554 pp.

Jelenc DA 1966. Mineral occurrences of Ethiopia. Ministry of Mines, Addis Ababa, 720pp.

Schlede H 1989. Distribution of acid soils and liming materials in Ethiopia. Note 326. Ethiopian Institute of Geological Surveys. Unpubl. Rep. Ethiopian Institute of Geological Surveys, Addis Ababa, Ethiopia.

Ethiopia

Total population (July 2000 estimate): 64,117,000
Area: 1,127,127 km^2
Annual population growth rate (2000): 2.76%
Life expectancy at birth (1998): 43.4 years
People not expected to survive to age 40 (1998): 42.1% of the total population
GDP per capita (1998): US $574

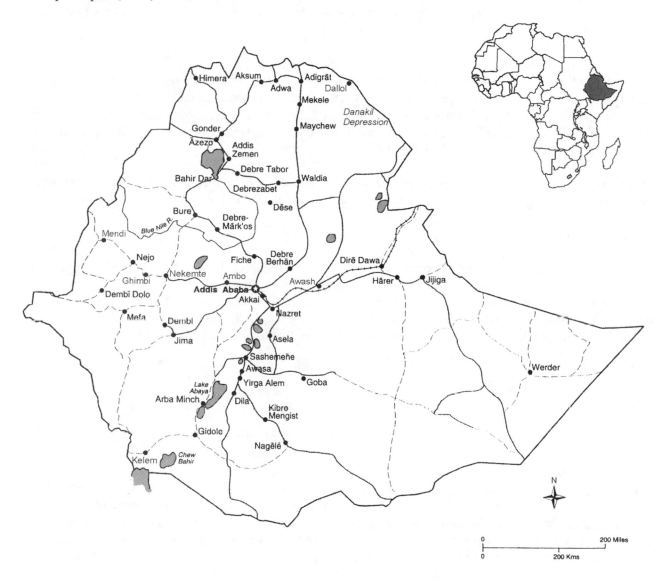

Ethiopia, located in the Horn of Africa, is a largely mountainous country. The central highlands with altitudes between 1,500 and 4,000 m are dissected by numerous rivers, including the Blue Nile. The highlands are split by the Rift Valley, which runs from the Danakil depression close to the Red Sea to the southern part of the country in a south-southwesterly direction.

The economy of Ethiopia is primarily based on agricultural production. The agricultural sector contributes approximately half of the GDP and provides a livelihood to more than 80% of the population. The main food crops are 'teff ' (*eragrostis teff*), which is a small grain cereal crop, wheat, barley, sorghum, millet, yams, potatoes, and beans. The major export crop is coffee.

The mineral potential of Ethiopia lies mainly with the development of gold, potash, thermal energies, and industrial minerals.

Almost 90% of the population of Ethiopia live in the Ethiopian highlands (above 1,500 m), which cover almost half of the country. Animal manure and crop residues, instead of being returned to the land, are largely used as fuel and livestock feed respectively. Due to intensive land use and high population pressure, the land is severely degraded and eroded. In addition, the nutrient status of most soils is decreasing. Between 70 and 75% of the agricultural soils of the highland plateau area of Ethiopia are phosphorus deficient (Duffera and Robarge 1999).

Mining plays a minor role in Ethiopia's economy. Nevertheless, more than 100,000 persons are involved in small-scale mining (mainly gold mining) in Ethiopia (International Labour Organisation 1999).

Geological outline

Geologically, Ethiopia lies at the northern end of the continental part of the Eastern Rift. Voluminous piles of mainly Tertiary volcanic rocks occupy large parts of the country along the Rift Valley. Proterozoic rocks occur in western Ethiopia, and Mesozoic and Tertiary rocks underlie most of the eastern part of the country. The floor of the Rift Valley is filled with relatively young lacustrine sediments and volcanics. Several alkaline plugs are known from Ethiopia, but no carbonatite has been delineated as yet.

AGROMINERALS

Phosphates

Considerable efforts have been made by the Ethiopian Institute of Geological Surveys (EIGS) over the last few decades to discover phosphates in Ethiopia. Assefa (1991) summarized the exploration efforts of the EIGS and showed the potential of finding phosphate accumulations in various geological settings of Ethiopia. Based on paleo-environmental and lithological considerations along with findings from borehole evidence, Assefa (1991) showed that the late Cretaceous (Coniacian-Campanian) Faf Series of eastern Ethiopia has great potential for phosphate accumulations. The Upper Cretaceous represents a phospho-genic period in which many phosphorites have been discovered worldwide. Unfortunately, the Upper Cretaceous sediments do not crop out at the surface. Largely obscured and covered by Paleogene successions, these sediments are only known from boreholes (Assefa 1991).

Sheldon (1984) evaluated the potential of finding phosphates in Ethiopia and concluded that the greatest chance of finding large quantities of sedimentary phosphates are in the eastern part of the country, in Tertiary sedimentary sequences associated with transgressions and regressions in the Somalia-Ogaden embayment. He pointed out that the Auradu sequence in particular has the potential of bearing phosphates as these sediments were deposited under conditions favourable for phosphate accumulation. These characteristics include a favourable paleogeographic setting, cyclic transgressive-regressive sequences, a typical chert-limestone-marl association and deposition during a major phosphogenic time interval, the Eocene.

Sheldon (1984) concluded that other potential phosphorite accumulations could be expected in the black shale-chert-limestone associations of another major phosphogenic period, the Neoproterozoic. In Ethiopia these sequences occur in the Tulu Dimtu meta-sedimentary sequence of Wollega region, in the Adigrat area of Tigre region, and in various other geological formations (Sheldon 1984; Assefa 1991).

Sheldon (1984) and Assefa (1991) also point out that other potential areas for finding phosphates are the carbonatite-peralkaline ring structures of Cenozoic age.

The Bikilal phosphate resource

The only igneous phosphates discovered to date, are at Bikilal, 24 km north-northeast of Ghimbi in Wollega Administrative Province (Abera 1988; Assefa 1991; Abera 1994; Abera *et al.* 1994). The phosphate mineralization is relatively unusual, as it is associated with a Proterozoic layered gabbro-anorthosite intrusion. Low-grade phosphates (3-8% P_2O_5, mean 4.56% P_2O_5) have been encountered in the apatite-magnetite-ilmenite mineralization that is spatially and genetically associated with the intrusive complex (Abera 1988; Assefa 1991). The apatite-magnetite-ilmenite mineralization in hornblendites occurs in a zone about 15 km long and 0.7 to 1.2 km wide. Several apatite-bearing hornblendites have been delineated in steeply dipping bands (Abera 1988). The crystallographic unit-cell a-value of the Bikilal apatites is a = 9.394 Å (Abera *et al.* 1994), indicative of a relatively unreactive fluor-apatite (Abera 1988).

Reported reserve estimates of apatite-bearing material in the Bikilal area, to a depth of 200 m, are 127 million tonnes at 3.5% P_2O_5, 23.8% Fe_2O_3, 7.3% TiO_2 (Yohannes 1994).

The near-surface, low-grade igneous phosphates from Bikilal have been evaluated on their suitability for upgrading through seizing and magnetic separation (Abera 1988; Abera *et al.* 1994). Apatite concentrates up to 36% P_2O_5 were produced using simple processing techniques. However, the recovery rate was low at only 40-58% (Abera *et al.* 1994).

Extraction of P from Unreactive Bikilal Phosphates

Initial agronomic testing of directly applied apatite concentrate from Bikilal using maize as a test crop showed that direct application of Bikilal apatite concentrate was not effective. However, studies by Bekele and Hoefner (1993) showed that Bikilal phosphate concentrate could be effective on Ethiopian soils when using rapeseed (*Brassicus napus* L.) as a crop.

Other phosphates

Small amounts of mitridatite, a very rare Ca-Fe-Mn phosphate mineral with the formula $Ca_6(H_2O)[(Fe^{3+}_{8.2} Mn^{3+}_{0.8})O_6(PO_4)_9] \cdot 3H_2O$ has been found in lacustrine sediments in the Shungura Formation near Kelem north of Lake Turkana, in southwestern Ethiopia (Rogers and Brown 1979). These minerals occur together with hydroxy-apatite, following partial dissolution of carbonate substituted apatite (fish scales and bones). The beds described by Rogers and Brown (1979) are, however, only a few centimetres thick. The lateral extent of these lacustrine phosphatic beds is not known. These phosphate finds are important as they indicate biogenic phosphate mineralization in a lacustrine rift-related environment, similar to that in which the Minjingu phosphate deposit in the Tanzanian rift valley has been found.

A sample of unknown location was provided by Assefa (pers. comm. 1992) for analysis. The red 'soil' sample contained 10% P_2O_5 and elevated Rare Earth Element (REE) concentrations, indicative of a residual soil overlying a phosphate containing carbonatite. So far, however, no carbonatite occurrence has been reported from Ethiopia.

Potash

There are large potash resources in Ethiopia in the extremely hot and arid Danakil depression near Dallol. The potash deposit is part of a Quaternary evaporite sequence that covers an area of about 1,150 km^2, of which only a small portion has been explored. Exploration work by the US-based Ralph M. Parsons Company included drilling of more than 300 boreholes, seismic work and shaft sinking to 100 m depths, as well as approximately 600 m underground openings (Holwerda and Hutchinson 1968). The company delineated two ore bodies in the Dallol area: the Crescent ore body and the Musley ore body. In this area the evaporite sequence is greater than 1,000 m thick and includes large potash reserves. Most of the potassium salt is in the form of sylvite (KCl), but carnallite and kainite are also reported. The main sylvite-bearing zone ranges from 15-40 m in thickness.

The tonnage of recoverable potash product in the Musley ore zone, based on 85 drill holes, is 30,021,000 short tons (Arkin 1969). Since the flooding of the exploration shaft in March 1967, all exploration and development work stopped. According to Arkin (1969), the whole depression contains at least 160,456,000 short tons of ore with 31-34% KCl. Reserve estimates by Abera (1994) exceed 60 million tonnes of recoverable KCl. A 1968 evaluation report by the consulting company MacKay and Schnellmann (quoted in Arkin 1969) confirmed that drill-indicated plus possible reserves of saleable potash product would be on the order of 86 million short tons. The grade of ore and recovery process indicates a 3:1 ratio in tons of ore to product.

For small-scale mining, only the sylvite and carnallite found at the surface near the Black Mountains, less than 1.5 km southwest of Dallol, could be mined. Some 3,578 short tons and 2,500 short tons were mined by small-scale extraction techniques in 1917 and 1927 respectively (Holwerda and Hutchinson 1968).

Limestone/dolomite

As illustrated in Figure 2.6, soil surveys of Ethiopia show that the soils of large areas of western and southwestern Ethiopia are acid, with pH levels below 5.5 (Schlede 1989). The largest volumes of limestone are located, however, in the eastern part of the country. Exceptions are the extensive and thick Mesozoic limestone and gypsum sequences in the Blue Nile River area in Central Ethiopia.

Proterozoic limestone/dolomite deposits in western and southwestern Ethiopia have considerable potential as they are located close to the acid soils. Dolomitic limestones and marbles have been reported from many places in western Ethiopia, including Daletti, near Mendi (Abera 1991). Scientists from the Institute of Agricultural Research carried out successful agronomic experiments with limestone on acid soils of the Nejo area close to Mendi, Wollega Province (Institute of Agricultural Research 1975).

Liming material can be found in Ethiopia within three major geological units:

- in Proterozoic rocks, mainly as marble,
- in Mesozoic sedimentary sequences, mainly as limestone, dolomite, and marl,
- in Cenozoic sediments, as limestones, dolomites, and marls.

Proterozoic liming materials

Proterozoic marbles occur in northern Ethiopia (Tigray), in the west (Gojam, Wollega, Illubabor, Kaffa), southern (Omo, Sidamo) and eastern (Hararghe) parts of Ethiopia. Accounts of these resources are provided by Schlede (1989). A general observation is that these resources occur in areas where strong to moderately acid soils (pH< 5.5) are dominant. Schlede (1989) states that the marble deposits are well distributed over the area of acid soils that require liming materials to improve soil productivity.

Mesozoic liming materials

Mesozoic limestone, dolomitic and marl deposits in western and northern Ethiopia occur in Tigray, in the Danakil Alps and in the Blue Nile (Abbay) valley. They also outcrop over large areas on the Somali plateau. Smaller outcrops of Mesozoic liming materials occur in the central plateau area near Ambo town, in the Didessa valley. Smaller deposits occur in the Kella area south of Addis Ababa.

The Jurassic Antalo Group with sequences of limestone, dolomites and marls occur in the Blue Nile (Abbay) valley and the Mekele area (Tigray). In the Mekele area the Antalo limestone is about 750 m thick (Kazmin 1972).

In general, the Mesozoic limestone, dolomite and marl resources are located further away from areas with strong to moderate acid soils (pH<5.5).

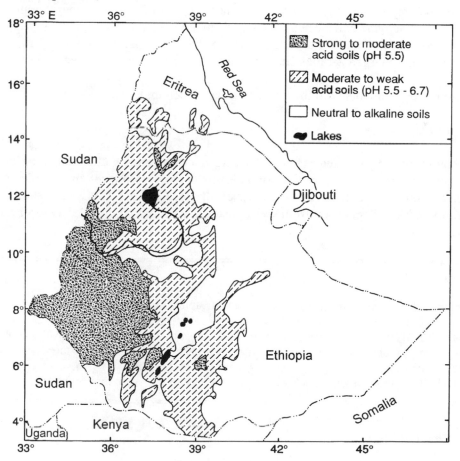

Figure 2.6: Distribution of acid soils in Ethiopia and Eritrea (after Schlede 1989).

Cenozoic liming materials

Cenozoic calcareous sediments occur in three areas of Ethiopia: in eastern Ogaden, in the Danakil Depression and in the lower Omo Valley. The limestone resources from the east of the country are too far from the acid soils of western and southwestern Ethiopia to be of economic interest.

Gypsum/anhydrite/sulphur

There are extensive and thick gypsum and anhydrite deposits in central Ethiopia (in the Blue Nile area), and some deposits of lesser thickness in the Mekele area of northern Ethiopia and in the southeast of the country (Abera 1991).

Native sulphur is reported in sediments of the Danakil depression and also in association with volcanic activities and solfataras in the Awash Valley and the Danakil area. Small-scale extraction was carried out in the Dofan area of the Awash Valley and, in the 1950s, in the Dallol area (Jelenc 1966).

Natural zeolites

Several million tonnes of high-grade zeolite deposits (mordenite and clinoptilolite) were discovered by geologists of the Ethiopia-Canada agrogeology project in rift valley sediments near Nazret and Boru, west of Nazret (unpublished). Zeolites have high cation exchange capacities and, specifically, high ammonium selectivities (Mumpton 1984). There are many applications of zeolites in agriculture and horticulture (van Straaten 1993; Allen and Ming 1995). Among them are applications of zeolites in chicken houses that can reduce the losses of ammonium-nitrogen by ion exchange and adsorption into the channels of zeolites. These ammonium-charged zeolites could be used as an effective slow-release N soil amendment.

No agronomic experiments with these minerals have been undertaken as yet.

Scoria/pumice

Large resources of volcanic scoria and pumice have accumulated within and along the margins of the rift valley. These resources can be used in soil moisture conservation techniques, called rock mulching. Experiences from other parts of the world, especially the Canary Islands, have shown that rock mulch can considerably reduce evaporation from soil surfaces (Fernandez Caldas and Tejedor Salguero 1987; Groenevelt et al. 1989).

Moisture Conservation Using Rock Mulch

Rock mulch field experiments using local scoria and pumice resources from near Nazret were carried out in the framework of the Ethiopia-Canada agrogeology project (Woldeab et al. 1994). The results of field experiments illustrated the effects of scoria and pumice mulches in the Rift Valley of Ethiopia. The application of 3 to 5 cm scoria or pumice mulch on top of the soil surface resulted in effective soil moisture conservation, as well as grain yield increase of maize by as much as 4 times (Woldeab et al. 1994). The main constraints to this system are availability of mulching materials in the close vicinity to soils with moisture stress, and economics.

Agromineral potential

Ethiopia is endowed with a great variety of agrominerals. The only known phosphate resources in Ethiopia, the Bikilal phosphates, are very low-grade igneous phosphates with low solubilities. The mining and upgrading of these low-grade, unreactive phosphates on a large scale would require considerable investment if economic feasibility could be proven. Also small-scale extraction and upgrading of this resource is questionable.

The occurrence of small amounts of lacustrine phosphate in the Shungura Formation in southwestern Ethiopia is of interest. Detailed surveys should be carried out to determine the lateral extent of these phosphatic beds. There is the potential of finding 'Minjingu-type' biogenic phosphates in lacustrine, late Tertiary to Recent lake beds in southern Ethiopia and in rift related sediments.

Exploration efforts to delineate carbonatites should be intensified.

There is reasonable potential for the discovery of nitrates in the rift valley extension of the Lake Turkana rift. In raised beds of old lake sediments in the Kenyan Rift Valley immediately south of the Ethiopia/Kenya border, Owen and Renault (1989) discovered diatomaceous lacustrine silts with up to 7.5% interstitial nitrates (see section on Kenya).

The application of gypsum as a soil amendment for alkaline soils on S-deficient soils and for groundnut production should be agronomically tested. Gypsum deposits should also be tested on the acid soils of western Ethiopia, especially in acid soils with high Al-toxicities.

The extent of the natural zeolites in the Rift Valley should be surveyed, and the zeolites need to be characterized mineralogically and chemically. Practical applications for the natural or modified zeolites of Ethiopia in agriculture and horticulture have to be assessed.

The highest potential for increased crop production using agrominerals rests with dolomitic limestones of Proterozoic age, especially in western Ethiopia. Here the soils are acid and, in places, crop production is impeded by Al-toxicities. Local resources of agricultural limestones and dolomites, as well as gypsum, should be investigated for their potential to ameliorate acid and Al-toxic soils. As in many countries, these resources of 'aglime' and dolomite have largely been overlooked. Research should be carried out to determine cost-effective extraction and low-cost crushing and grinding technologies followed by demonstration of the agronomic effectiveness of liming materials and gypsum on acid soils. Further exploration and testing of their suitability and agronomic effectiveness are needed. In addition, it is important to demonstrate the benefits of using local limestone/dolomite and gypsum to farmers.

References:

Abera S 1988. The evaluation of Bikilal Apatite-Magnetite-Ilmenite deposit with particular reference to apatite as a potential phosphate resource. M.Sc. thesis, University of Hull, UK, 132pp.

Abera S 1994. Review of industrial minerals in Ethiopia. In: Mathers SJ and AJG Notholt (eds.) Industrial minerals in developing countries. AGID report series Geosciences in International Development 18:173-180.

Abera S, Woldeab A, Assefa A, van Straaten P and W Chesworth 1994. Report on the results of the Ethiopia-Canada Agrogeology Project-Igneous phosphates. Report to IDRC, University of Guelph, Guelph, Canada, 49pp.

Allen ER and DW Ming 1995. Recent progress in the use of natural zeolites in agronomy and horticulture. In: Ming DW and FA Mumpton (eds.) Natural zeolites '93: occurrence, properties, use. International Committee on Natural Zeolites, Brockport, New York, USA: 477-490.

Arkin Y 1969. Potash in Ethiopia. Ministry of Mines, Geological Survey. Unpubl. Report, Addis Ababa, Ethiopia, 28pp.

Assefa A 1991. Phosphate exploration in Ethiopia. Fert. Res. 30:155-163.

Bekele T and W Hoefner 1993. Effects of different phosphate fertilizers on yield of barley and rape seed on reddish brown soils of the Ethiopian highlands. Fert. Res. 34:243-250.

Duffera M and WP Robarge 1999. Soil characteristics and management effects on phosphorus sorption by highland plateau soils of Ethiopia. Soil Sci. Soc. Am. J. 63:1455-1462.

Fernandez Caldas E and MK Tejedor Salguero 1987. Mulch farming in Canary Islands. In: Wachira JK and AJG Notholt (eds.) Agrogeology in Africa. Commonwealth Sci. Council, Technical Publ. Series 226:242-256.

Groenevelt PH, van Straaten P, Rasiah V, and J Simpson 1989. Modifications in evaporation parameters by rock mulch. Soil Techn. 2:279-285.

Holwerda JG and RW Hutchinson 1968. Potash-bearing evaporites in the Danakil area, Ethiopia. Econ. Geol. 63:124-150.

Institute of Agricultural Research 1975. Unpublished progress report. Results of research in Nejo substation, 70pp.

International Labour Organization 1999. Social and labour issues in small-scale mines. TMSSM/1999, 99pp.

Jelenc DA 1966. Mineral occurrences of Ethiopia. Ministry of Mines, Addis Ababa, 720pp.

Kazmin V 1972. The Precambrian of Ethiopia and some aspects of the geology of the Mozambique Belt. Geol. Surv. Rep. 23, Addis Ababa, Ethiopia.

Mumpton F.A. 1984. Natural zeolites. In: Pond WG and FA Mumpton (eds.) Zeo-agriculture: Use of natural zeolites in agriculture and aquaculture. Westview Press Boulder, Colorado, 247-254.

Owen RB and RW Renault 1989. Nitrate deposition in the Turkana basin of northern Kenya. J. Afr. Earth Sci. 10:701-706.

Rogers RJ and FH Brown 1979. Authigenic mitridatite from the Shungura Formation, southwestern Ethiopia. Am. Mineralogist 64:169-171.

Schlede H 1989. Distribution of acid soils and liming materials in Ethiopia. Ethiopian Institute of Geological Surveys. Unpub. Rep., Note 326.

Sheldon RP 1984. Phosphate resource potential of Ethiopia based on available geologic data. Unpubl. Rep. UN/DTCD ETH/83-025, United Nations, New York, 45pp.

van Straaten P 1993. Zeolites in agriculture and horticulture: reduction of nitrogen losses. Abstract, Symposium of Geol. Ass. Canada: Industrial minerals in environmental applications. Vancouver, Canada, Nov. 18/19th 1993.

Woldeab A, Assefa A, Yematawork A, Abera S, van Straaten P, Groenevelt P and W Chesworth 1994. Report on the results of the Ethiopia-Canada Agrogeology Project - Rock Mulch. Report, University of Guelph, Guelph, Canada: 76pp.

Yohannes WW 1994. Ethiopia. Mining Annual Review, Mining Journal Ltd. London, p.143.

Gabon

Total population (July 2000 estimate): 1,208,000
Area: 267,667 km^2
Annual population growth rate (2000): 1.08%
Life expectancy at birth (1998): 52.4 years
People not expected to survive to age 40 (1998): 30.7% of total population
GDP per capita (1998): US $6,353

Gabon consists of a plateau landscape that rises from a narrow coastal strip. Several mountain peaks reach 1,500 m. Tropical rainforest covers more than half of the country. The climate is hot and humid.

The economy of Gabon is largely based on the export of crude oil, which made up almost 50% of the GDP in 1999. Gabon is the third-largest oil producer in sub-Saharan Africa (after Nigeria and Angola) with 331,000 barrels per day produced in the year 2000. Gabon's proven oil reserves are 2.5 trillion barrels. The natural gas reserves of Gabon are 1.2 trillion cubic feet.

The main mineral resources of Gabon are manganese and uranium.

Agriculture accounted for only 8% of the GDP in 1999 although almost half of the population engage in agricultural production, mostly on a subsistence basis. The main food crops are cassava, maize and plantains. Gabon exports rubber, palm oil, cocoa beans and valuable timber.

The 1998 Gross Domestic Product per capita in Gabon was US $ 6,353, making Gabon one of the richest countries in sub-Saharan Africa.

Geological outline

Geologically, the country lies in the northwest part of the Congo Craton and more than two-thirds of the country is underlain by Precambrian rocks. The Chaillu and North Gabon granitic domains are of Archean age.

The Paleoproterozoic Francevillian Supergroup contains fluvio-deltaic sedimentary sequences deposited in intracratonic basins (Bertrand-Safarti and Potin 1994). The Francevillian Supergroup is well known for its mineral resources, especially manganese and uranium (Bonhomme *et al.* 1982; Thomas *et al.* 1999). The Mesoproterozoic is restricted to rocks of the Mayombe Supergroup (Thomas *et al.* 1999). The Neoproterozoic is part of the West Congo Basin and is largely made up of sandstones, shales and the calcareous sequence of the 'Schisto-Calcaire.'

The coastal Gabon basin consists of approximately 8,000 m thick Mesozoic-Tertiary marine sequences and upper Cretaceous evaporites.

AGROMINERALS

Phosphates

Two types of phosphate deposits have been discovered in Gabon, sedimentary and igneous. Sedimentary phosphates were discovered during exploratory oil drilling. The best accumulations of phosphates, at the bottom of the Senonian (Coniacan) occur close to salt domes in the Wara na Yeno and Ikassa area at the coast approximately 110 km south-southeast of Port Gentil (Slansky 1986). The phosphate content in these sediments ranges from 8-32% P_2O_5. However, these phosphorites lie at considerable depths, beyond the range of economic extraction.

Late Cretaceous phosphatic lenticular sediments were reported from the southern coast of Gabon. Exposed on the coast and in lagoons, these frequently decalcified and silicified phosphate sediments occur in the striking continuation of the upper Cretaceous (Maastrichtian) Holle Series from the Republic of Congo (Giresse 1980). Only few data are available on this phosphate sequence.

Igneous phosphates were discovered during the construction of the Trans-Gabon railway in the early 1980s. A French – UNDP-assisted mineral inventory programme conducted side-scan radar, airborne magnetics and radiometric surveys of the Precambrian basement and discovered a geophysical anomaly caused by a deeply weathered carbonatite ring complex. Detailed geological, geochemical surveys of the Mabounie ring complex (age 660 ± 3 million years), located 40 km ESE of Lambarene, showed a complex residual phosphate/niobium deposit (Laval *et al.* 1988).

During a US $12.5 million pre-feasibility study of the Mabounie complex, geologists delineated 140 million tonnes of ore at 24% P_2O_5. From this, 100 million tonnes could be excavated by open pit mining (Industrial Minerals 1996) and Niobium (from pyrochlore) could be obtained as by-product. It was estimated that the contained niobium resource could account for 15% of the world market share of niobium. Preliminary capital costs for the mine were estimated at US $600 million.

A cost per tonne of phosphate concentrate (39% P_2O_5) was approximately US $25 per tonne (Industrial Minerals 1996).

Limestone/dolomite

Limestone and dolomite occurrences are known from Precambrian sequences of Gabon and the Cretaceous of the coastal basin. At least four major dolomite occurrences have been recorded, two in the Paleoproterozoic Francevillian System (in the Mounana/Moanda area, and near Lastoursville), and two in the Schisto-Calcaire of the Neoproterozoic (Tchibanga and Ndende areas). The Francevillian dolomites form escarpments and cliffs up to 60-70 m thick, and the reserves of the Schisto-Calcaire are reportedly considerable (Gwosdz 1996).

The Cretaceous (Aptian-Albian) limestones in the coastal basin of Gabon are extensive and several hundred metres thick. The cement plant east of Libreville uses these limestones as source material (capacity 300,000 tonnes per year). The limestones are also used for road aggregate. Whether any of these limestones and dolomites are used for agricultural purposes is not known.

Agromineral potential

The main phosphate deposit of Gabon (Mabounie) occurs in the weathered environment overlying the Mabounie carbonatite complex. The deposit is likely to be mined and processed on a large industrial scale only. The development of this deposit by small-scale mining techniques will be difficult due to the thick overburden of more than 20 m.

Liming materials, especially the dolomites in the Precambrian areas, form a major resource that could be developed by small-scale operations should they occur close to agricultural areas with soil acidity problems.

References:

Bertrand-Safarti J and B Potin 1994. Microfossiliferous stromatolites in the 2000 Ma Franceville Group, Gabon. Precambr. Res. 65:341-356.

Bonhomme MG, Gauthier-Lafaye F and F Weber 1982. An example of Lower Proterozoic sediments: the Francevillian in Gabon. Precambr. Res. 18:87-102.

Giresse P 1980. The Maastrichtian phosphate sequence of the Congo. Soc. Econ. Paleont. Mineral, Spec. Publ. 29:193-205.

Gwosdz W 1996. Gabon. In: Bosse H-R, Gwosdz W, Lorenz W, Markwich, Roth W and F Wolff (eds.) Limestone and dolomite resources of Africa. Geol. Jb., D, 148-152.

Industrial Minerals 1996: Partners required for phosphate development. Ind. Min. March 1996: 13,15.

Laval M, Johan V and B Tourliere 1988. La carbonatite de Mabounie: example de formation d'un gîte residual à pyrochlore. Chron. Rech. Min. 491:125-136.

Slansky M 1986. Geology of sedimentary phosphates. Elsevier Science Publ. New York, 210pp.

Thomas RJ, Chevallier L, Martin J and JF Makanga 1999. Precambrian geology and metallogeny of Gabon. J. Afr. Earth Sci. 28 (Special Abstr. Issue):78-79

Gambia

Total population (July 2000 estimate): 1,367,000
Area: 11,300 km^2
Annual population growth rate (2000): 3.2%
Life expectancy at birth (1998): 47.4 years
People not expected to survive to age 40 (1998): 37.2% of total population
GDP per capita (1998): US $1,453

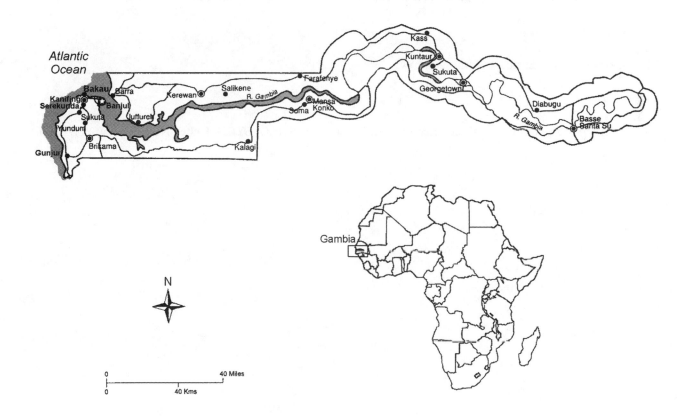

Gambia is a small narrow country along the Gambia River, completely surrounded by Senegal. The economy of this country depends largely on tourism and farming.

Agriculture (mostly subsistence) contributes about 23% of the GDP and engages over 75% of the working population. Groundnuts and groundnut products (groundnut oil and groundnut paste) form the dominant land-based agricultural products. The main food crop is rice, followed by sorghum, millet and maize.

There are no significant mineral resources in Gambia. Of local importance are sand, gravel, clays and shells for domestic construction needs.

AGROMINERALS

No phosphate, limestone or gypsum occurrences have been reported in Gambia.

Agromineral potential

The agromineral potential of Gambia is low.

Reference:

Labonne B 1989. The Gambia - Mission Report. Min. Res. Branch, NRED, DTCD, United Nations, New York, 7pp.

Ghana

Total population (July 2000 estimate): 19,534,000
Area: 238,540 km^2
Annual population growth rate (2000): 1.87%
Life expectancy at birth (1998): 60.4 years
People not expected to survive to age 40 (1998): 20.6% of total population
GDP per capita (1998): US $1,735

The landscape and climate of Ghana are characterized by several zones ranging from a narrow coastal belt with a hot, humid climate in the south to a sequence of rolling hill ranges with wide valleys in the centre of the country to the hot, dry, semi-arid areas of the north.

Ghana is a country with extensive mineral and agricultural resources. The export economy is dominated by the sale of gold, cocoa and timber. The agricultural sector contributes about 36% to the GDP and employs approximately 60% of the labour force. The main food crops are cassava, yams, plantain, taro, rice and maize. The main exports crops are cocoa and coffee.

Ghana is a mining country with gold mining playing an important part in its long history. Ghana is the second largest producer of gold in Africa, with at least twelve formal gold mines, seven of which are large open pit operations. It is the third largest producer of aluminum metal and manganese on the continent. Small amounts of diamonds are also found in Ghana. In 1994, small-scale miners recovered more than 10% of the 53 tonnes of gold produced in Ghana. The International Labour Organization (1999) estimated 50,000-300,000 people to be involved in small-scale gold and diamond mining in Ghana.

Geological outline

The geology of Ghana is dominated by predominantly metavolcanic Paleoproterozoic Birimian sequences and the clastic Tarkwaian in the central west and northern parts of the country. Clastic shallow water sediments of the Neoproterozoic Volta Basin cover the east of the country. A small strip of Paleozoic and Cretaceous to Tertiary sediments occur along the coast and in the extreme southeast of the country.

AGROMINERALS

Phosphates

No major phosphate deposits have been discovered in Ghana as yet (Kesse 1985; Sheldon 1986; Iddrisu 1987) although indications of phosphate mineralization are known from 4 principal geological resources:

1.   Eocene sediments of the Keta Basin, similar to the middle Eocene Hahotoe phosphates in neighbouring Togo,
2.   Devonian sediments of the Sekondi Series, along the coast of Ghana,
3.   Phosphatic sediments in the Neoproterozoic/early Paleozoic middle Voltaian rocks below a prominent carbonate horizon, similar to the types found in neighbouring Burkina Faso, Benin and Niger,
4.   phosphates associated with igneous rocks.

Eocene sediments.

Early indications of phosphate mineralization in Eocene sedimentary beds are based on sludge samples from boreholes drilled during water surveys in southeast Ghana, close to the border with Togo. Some of the sludge samples contained phosphate concentrations ranging from 10-15% P_2O_5 (Annan Yorke 1974). However, no follow-up surveys have been carried out to date (Kesse 1985; Iddrisu 1987).

Sheldon (1986) concluded that these Eocene beds form the most attractive prospect for finding extensive sedimentary phosphates, which could be excavated easily on various scales. He noted that the phosphate-bearing Aflao bed (mean 14.53% P_2O_5) described by Annan Yorke (1974) is most likely the unweathered equivalent of the phosphate ore bed of the Hahotoe deposits in neighbouring Togo. 'The total amount of phosphate in the 20 ft. ore bed at the Hahotoe deposit in Togo (which is currently mined) and the 35 ft. sequence drilled at Aflao (Ghana) are essentially the same' (Sheldon 1986).

Devonian sediments

Devonian sediments of the Sekondi Series occur along the coast of Ghana. Phosphorite nodules containing up to 14.7% P_2O_5 were reported in the Devonian Takoradi shales (Austin and Smit 1965). The phosphatic nodules are believed to be fish coprolites. The occurrence is of limited extent and phosphates are unlikely to be extracted, even by small-scale methods.

Neoproterozoic/early Paleozoic rocks

Neoproterozoic/early Paleozoic rocks in the Volta Basin are similar in stratigraphic position to the phosphate bearing strata in neighbouring Burkina Faso, Benin and Niger. In the Volta Basin of Burkina Faso and Benin these phosphates occur stratigraphically above a widespread tillite horizon and are associated with barites, limestones and oolitic limestones (Trompette *et al.* 1980). In the Volta Basin of Ghana, similar successions with occurrences of tillites and barites have been described (Iddrisu 1987). However, exploration work on phosphates by Ashanti Goldfield Corporation Ltd. in 1975 and by the Ghana Geological Survey was inconclusive (Iddrisu 1987).

Other phosphate occurrences

Minor phosphate occurrences of various origins have been reported by Kesse (1985), Sheldon (1986) and Iddrisu (1987). Small apatite occurrences have been found in pegmatites in the Bole and Anobabo areas and in the nepheline syenite/carbonatite complex of the Kpong area (Sheldon 1986; Iddrisu 1987).

Other agrominerals

Limestone/dolomite

There are several large and many small limestone and dolomite deposits in Ghana. Most of the limestone deposits have been investigated for their potential use in the cement industry. Dolomitic limestone and dolomite occurrences with less than 5% MgO content have not been investigated in detail.

Afenya (1982), Kesse (1975, 1985) and Iddrisu (1987) report dolomitic limestone deposits in a sequence of lower Voltaian sediments near Oterkpolu (0° 05' W; 6°15' N) in the eastern region of Ghana. Iddrisu (1987) reports reserves of 8-10 million tonnes. The resources are currently being worked for the production of terrazzo chips (Kesse 1985). No data on the rate and amounts of disposal or use of carbonate fines and wastes are available. The limestone/dolomite resources in the Buipe area (1°30' W; 9°00' N) represents the largest occurrence of magnesian limestone in northern Ghana. The total reserves are 6 million tonnes of limestone and 138 million tonnes of dolomite (Kesse 1985). The reserves of the Bongo-Da limestone/dolomite beds (0°15'W; 10°22'N) within the lower Voltaian in northern Ghana are 15 million tonnes of calcitic limestone and 20-30 million tonnes of dolomite. The deposits are suitable for lime production (Kesse 1985). The Nauli limestone deposit, made up of an extensive ridge containing several beds of Campanian limestone, occurs in southwestern Ghana (5°02' N; 2° 45'-2° 50' W). This deposit with a strike length of more than 50 km has been investigated for its use as potential raw material for the cement industry. The reserves of these limestone beds are in excess of 23 million tonnes and are easily mineable by open-cast methods (Kesse 1985). Smaller limestone/dolomite deposits are known from the Fo river area in southeast Ghana (15 m thick, in excess of 1.5 million tonnes, low Mg content), and near Daboya (162,000 tonnes limestone, 0.5 million tonnes dolomite) in northern Ghana. Other small limestone occurrences are reported from the Anyaboni and Sadan-Abetifi areas, in the Longoro, Prang and Yeji areas, in the Ashanti Region, and in the Du area of the Upper Eastern Region (Kesse 1985). Calcitic shell deposits (reserves = 700,000 tonnes) are currently collected from the sandbanks of the Volta River near Akuse for the production of lime (Kesse 1985).

Agricultural experiments with calcitic limestone on acid soils of the high rainfall area of SW Ghana resulted not only in increased grain yield of maize but also in improved soil and water conservation (Bonsu 1991). The application of agricultural lime at rates of 1-4 tonnes ha^{-1} improved grain yield in a linear fashion. Bonsu (1991) relates the reduction of soil and water losses to prolific root growth and better soil structure in the limed soils.

Gypsum

There are no economic gypsum deposits in Ghana. Kesse (1985) reported small amounts of gypsum and gypsiferous clays from near Accra and localities in the Western Region, and from the Keta region.

Agromineral potential

So far, no large phosphatic resources have been delineated in Ghana. However, the potential for finding local phosphate resources is considered good. Best indications of good quality phosphatic sediments are in Eocene sediments of the Keta Basin in the extreme southeastern corner of Ghana, in the striking continuation of the Togo phosphate beds. Sheldon (1986) rated the probability of finding and developing phosphate deposits in the Keta area as 'high' and suggested more detailed work.

Local limestone resources are currently used mainly for whitewash purposes. Based on the need for agricultural liming materials on acid soils, these resources should be evaluated on their suitability for small-scale production of ground limestone and dolomite.

References

Afenya PM 1982. Ghana's mineral resources for small-scale mining industries. In: JM Neilson (editor) Strategies for small-scale mining and mineral industries, AGID Rep. 8:24-28.

Annan Yorke 1974. Phosphate evaluation project. Rep. to Director, Geol. Surv.Ghana 1966-67. Unpubl. Rep. 15pp.

Austin WGC and AFJ Smit 1965. Phosphatic nodules from the Sekondi series, Ghana. J. Nigerian Min. Geol. Metall. Soc. 2:47-56.

Bonsu M 1991. Effect of liming on maize production and erosion on an acid soil in SW Ghana. Trop. Agric. (Trinidad) 68:271-273.

Coakley GJ 1995. The mineral industries of Ghana.Minerals Yearbook, Vol. III, United States of the Interior, Geological Survey.

Iddrisu Y 1987. Rock phosphate prospects in Ghana. In: Wachira JK and AJG Notholt (eds.) Agrogeology in Africa. Commonwealth Sci. Council, Technical Publ. Series 226:67-76.

International Labour Organization 1999. Social and labour issues in small-scale mines. TMSSM/1999, 99pp.

Kesse GO 1975. Limestone deposits of Ghana. Ghana Geol. Survey Report No. 75/4, 16pp.

Kesse GO 1985. The mineral and rock resources of Ghana. Balkema, Rotterdam, 610pp.

Sheldon RP 1986. Potential phosphate resource assessment of Ghana. Unpubl. Rep. to United Nations Department of Technical Cooperation for Development (UNDTCD), 33pp.

Trompette R, Affaton P, Joulia F and J Marchand 1980: Stratigraphic and structural controls of Late Precambrian phosphate deposits of the northern Volta Basin in Upper Volta, Niger, and Benin, West Africa. Econ. Geol. 75:62-70.

Guinea

Total population (July 2000 estimate): 7,466,000
Area: 245,857 km^2
Annual population growth rate (2000): 1.95%
Life expectancy at birth (1998): 46.9 years
People not expected to survive to age 40 (1998): 37.8% of total population
GDP per capita (1998): US $1,782

Guinea consists of a coastal plain, a mountain range along the coast and the Guinea Highlands in the interior. The climate is generally tropical with high rainfall in the south and along the coast (up to 4,000 mm precipitation per year) while the northern parts of Guinea receive about 1,200 mm annually.

Guinea's economy is largely founded on agricultural production and the export of bauxite. Additional mineral exports are diamonds and gold, much of which is extracted by the approximately 40,000 artisanal miners (International Labour Organization 1999).

In 1999, the agricultural sector of Guinea accounted for 24% of the GDP. Approximately 80% of the population is involved in agricultural production, mainly at a subsistence level. Main crops are cassava, rice, plantain, citrus and bananas. Export crops include oil palm products, pineapple, cotton and coffee.

Geological outline

The geology of the country is dominated by the Archean Man Craton and the Paleoproterozoic Birimian domain (Wright *et al*. 1985). Neoproterozoic and lower Cambrian sediments with a basal tillite and sandstones, marls and quartzites cover wide parts of northern Guinea (Villeneuve 1989).

AGROMINERALS

Phosphates

No phosphates have been reported from Guinea to date. The nearest phosphates are those of the Neoproterozoic Namel Group in southern Senegal. These rocks continue into northern Guinea.

Limestone/dolomite

Only limited information is available on the distribution, chemical nature and volume of limestone and dolomite resources of Guinea. Limestone deposits occur in the Siguiri area (in the Paleoproterozoic Birimian). Metamorphosed limestone occurrences were reported from the Kankan-Konsankoro area and from the Tougue area. Coulibaly (1992) describes the distribution and volume of limestones in Guinea: the Lebekene limestone occurrences in the Mali area of northern Guinea (12 million tonnes), the Sougeta (Kindia) deposit (10 million tonnes), and the Kourouni (Sigiuri) deposit (8 million tonnes).

Agromineral potential

The potential for agromineral use is difficult to assess without detailed soil and other agricultural data. Potentially, phosphates could be discovered in northern Guinea, in the continuation of the Senegal Namel phosphates. The limestone resources should be investigated for their suitability for acid soils.

References:

Coulibaly S 1992. Industrial minerals of Guinea. Industrial Minerals, May 1992: 141,143.

International Labour Organization 1999. Social and labour issues in small-scale mines. TMSSM/1999, 99pp.

Villeneuve M 1989. The geology of the Madina-Kouta basin (Guinea-Senegal) and its significance for the geodynamic evolution of the western part of the West African Craton during the Upper Proterozoic period. Precambr. Res. 44:305-322.

Wright JB, Hastings DA, Jones WB and HR Williams 1985. Geology and mineral resources of West Africa. Allen and Unwin, London, UK,187pp.

Guinea-Bissau

Total population (July 2000 estimate): 1,286,000
Area: 36,120 km^2
Annual population growth rate (2000): 2.4%
Life expectancy at birth (1998): 44.9 years
People not expected to survive to age 40 (1998): 40.6% of total population
GDP per capita (1998): US $616

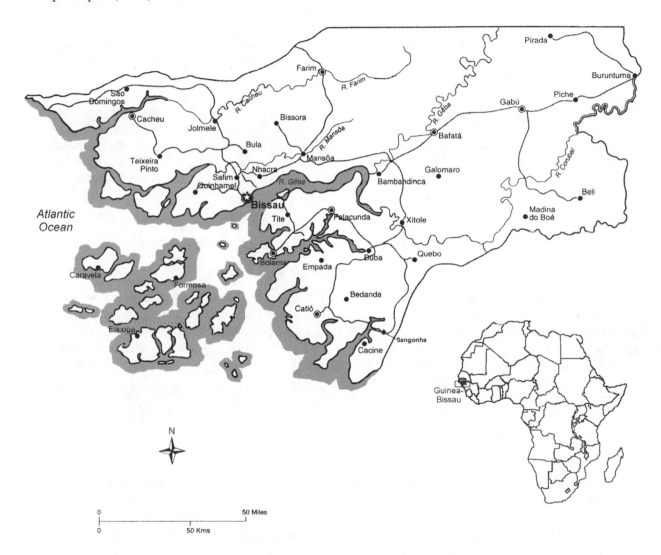

Large parts of Guinea-Bissau consist of low-lying areas with numerous islands, rivers and mangrove swamps. Further inland are savanna and small mountainous areas along the border with Guinea.

Agriculture dominates the economy of Guinea-Bissau. In 1999, the agricultural sector contributed 62% of the GDP and provided a livelihood to more than 80% of the population. Rice is the staple food of the people of Guinea-Bissau, followed by cassava, beans, sweet potatoes, yams and fruits. Cashew nuts, oil palm kernels and groundnuts are the main export crops.

To date, the mining industry of Guinea-Bissau is insignificant, with only some small-scale mining for sand and gravel meeting domestic construction needs. Low-grade bauxite deposits exist in the country but have not been developed.

A major boost to the mining industry came when Champion Mineral Resources Inc., Canada, announced the signing of a memorandum of understanding to develop the extensive phosphate resources of the Farim deposit (Industrial Minerals 2000).

Geological outline

Geologically, Guinea-Bissau can be divided into an eastern zone with predominantly Paleozoic rocks and a western zone with mainly upper Mesozoic to Cenozoic sediments. The sedimentary facies of the Paleozoic are mainly clastic, with carbonates occurring only in the Silurian. The Cretaceous to Cenozoic sediments are mainly of marine origin.

AGROMINERALS

Phosphates

Phosphates in the Farim area (Farim-Saliquinhe) of northern Guinea-Bissau were discovered during oil drilling in the early 1950s. The Directorate of Geology and Mines drilled seven boreholes in the same area in the late 1970s, one of which intersected a 4.90 m thick sandy phosphate layer. Subsequent drilling (in excess of 100 boreholes) outlined a phosphate deposit with reserves of 112 million tonnes at 29.85% P_2O_5, 7.8% SiO_2, and 7.1% $Fe_2O_3 + Al_2O_3$ (Sustrac 1986; Prian 1989). The CaO/P_2O_5 ratio of the phosphate ore is 1.41. The age of the deposit is Eocene (Prian 1989).

The phosphate deposit of Guinea-Bissau represents the southern equivalent of phosphate deposits in Senegal and Mauritania and was deposited at the flanks of the Mauritania-Senegal-Guinea basin (Figure 2.7).

The Saliquinhe phosphate deposit (also known as Farim deposit due to its location close to the town of Farim) formed during middle Eocene in a shallow sheltered bay. The 1-6 m thick phosphate bed (mean thickness 3.2 m) is made up of greyish-whitish unconsolidated phosphates with no calcareous cement. Some limited aluminum phosphates have formed at the top of the deposit due to weathering. The Fe content of the ore is high due to the presence of 1-8% pyrite. Uranium concentrations range from 80-160 mg kg^{-1} and cadmium values of 80 mg kg^{-1} were found in a composite drill hole sample (Prian 1989). Beneficiation tests in France produced a concentrate assaying 37.8% P_2O_5, 1.02% Fe, and 0.1% S.

A major problem for the extraction of the ore is the overburden, which ranges from 26 m near Farim to 50 m in the northern part of the deposit (Prian 1989). The stripping ratio of over 6:1 is high.

A re-evaluation of the resources amounted to 105 million tonnes of phosphorites grading 29.8% P_2O_5 (Industrial Mineral 1997). Three possible ways to develop the deposit have been discussed:

- extract the unprocessed phosphate ore at US $39 per tonne and ship it for processing,
- concentrate the phosphates on-site to at least 32% P_2O_5 and ship it for further processing,
- fully process the phosphates on-site, at US $208 per tonne fertilizer product.

The company decided to develop 32% P_2O_5 concentrates at 750,000 tonnes per year for the first 5 years (Industrial Minerals 2000).

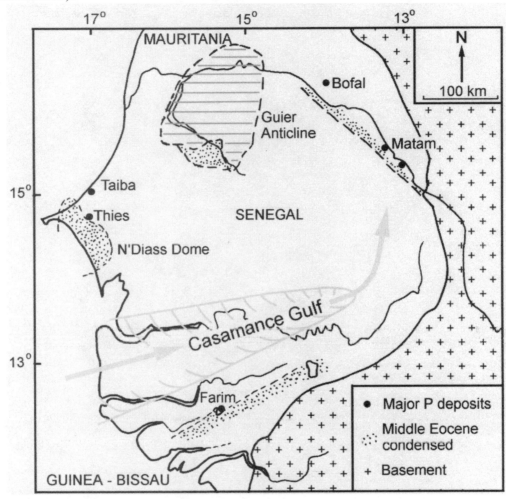

Figure 2.7: Geological setting of the Farim-Saliquinhe phosphate deposit.

Agromineral potential

The Farim deposit is a large sedimentary phosphate deposit with considerable overburden. As such, it does not lend itself to small-scale agromineral development. Agricultural direct application tests with ground Farim phosphates have been conducted in Guinea Bissau on cereal and groundnut crops (Prian 1989), but no results have been reported. The potential for the development of other agromineral resources is unclear due to the paucity of detailed geological and soils information.

References:

Industrial Minerals 1997. New phosphate deposit under evaluation. Oct. 1997, p.19.

Industrial Minerals 2000. Champion to boost phosphate capacity. Jan. 2000, p.10.

Prian JP 1989. The Farim-Saliquinhe Eocene phosphate deposit Guinea Bissau, West Africa. In: Notholt AJG, Sheldon RP and DF Davidson (eds.) Phosphate deposits of the world. Vol. 2. Phosphate rock resources. Cambridge University Press, Cambridge, UK: 277-283.

Sustrac G 1986. BRGM phosphate prospecting methods and results in West Africa. Trans. Instn. Min. Metall. (Sect. A: Min. Industry) 95:A134-A143.

Kenya

Total population (July 2000 estimate): 30,340,000
Area: 582,650 km^2
Annual population growth rate (2000): 1.53%
Life expectancy at birth (1998): 51.3 years
People not expected to survive to age 40 (1998): 30.6% of the total population
GDP per capita (1998): US $980

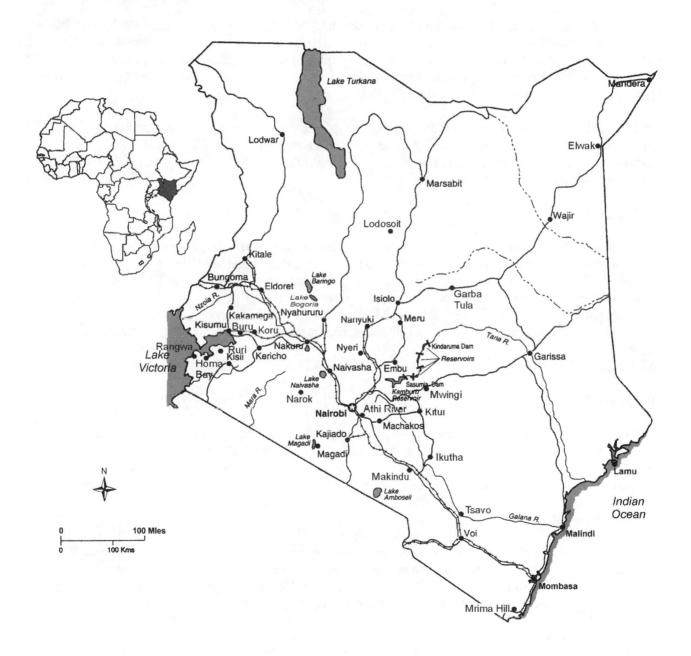

Kenya lies along the equator in East Africa. Most of the country consists of high plateau areas and mountain ranges that rise up to 3,000 m and more. The plateau area is dissected by the Eastern Rift Valley, which is 40-50 km wide and up to 1,000 m lower than the flanking plateaux. The narrow coastal strip along the Indian Ocean is backed by a zone of thornbush-land. Some areas in central Kenya, at the flanks of the Rift Valley, and in western Kenya, close to Lake Victoria, are very densely populated.

The backbones of Kenya's economy are agriculture and tourism. In 1999, the agricultural sector accounted for 23% of the GDP. Large parts of the population make their living from subsistence agriculture. The predominant food crops are maize, rice, wheat, bananas and cassava. The main export crops are coffee and tea.

The mineral industry is small, accounting for only about 1.3% of the GDP in 1993 (Izon 1993). The main minerals of economic significance are soda ash (from Lake Magadi), limestone for the cement industry, and other industrial minerals. Small gold deposits are exploited by small-scale miners in the western part of the country. The International Labour Organization (1999) estimates the number of persons involved in small-scale mining in Kenya to be 30,000 to 40,000.

Increased population density has resulted in increased intensity of crop production and depletion of soil fertility. Per capita food production is decreasing. One of the main biophysical causes of lower food production is decreasing soil fertility, specifically low availability of soil phosphorus and nitrogen (Buresh *et al.* 1997; Sanchez *et al.* 1997; Smithson *et al.* 2001).

Geological outline

The geology of Kenya is characterized by Archean granite/greenstone terrain in western Kenya along Lake Victoria, the Neoproterozoic 'Pan-African' Mozambique Belt, which underlies the central part of the country and Mesozoic to Recent sediments underlying the eastern coastal areas. The Eastern Rift Valley crosses Kenya from north to south and the volcanics associated with rift formation largely obliterate the generally north-south striking Neoproterozoic Mozambique Belt (Schlueter 1997). Rift Valley volcanogenic sediments and lacustrine and alluvial sediments cover large parts of the Eastern Rift.

AGROMINERALS

Phosphates

The phosphate resources of Kenya are limited. They are confined to small guano deposits and small igneous phosphate resources associated with carbonatites (Gaciri 1991). No detailed surveys have been conducted to assess the potential for locating sedimentary phosphates in the Phanerozoic marine sediments and lacustrine sediments in the Rift Valley of Kenya as yet.

Igneous phosphates

The principal igneous phosphate occurrences are related to carbonatites and iron-rich dike systems. The main carbonatite related phosphate occurrences are found at Mrima Hill in the southeast of the country, and on the carbonatite south and east of Homa Bay in western Kenya. The only phosphate occurrence of uncertain origin is the intrusive vein-type iron deposit at Ikutha in central-southeast Kenya.

1.   The Mrima Hill carbonatite.

Mrima Hill is located in the Coast Province of Kenya, some 78 km south of Mombasa at 4° 29'10" S; 39° 15' 10" E. The hill rises approximately 250 m out of the seaward-sloping plain. Geologically, Mrima Hill is an elliptical carbonatite plug approximately 2 km across. A thick blanket of unconsolidated, deeply weathered material covers the hill. This residual soil, in places more than 100 m deep, was explored mainly for niobium (Nb) and Rare Earth Elements (REE) (Coetzee and Edwards 1959; Hussein 1995).

Coetzee and Edwards (1959) and Hussein (1995) also carried out detailed geological investigations of the weathering processes that affected this carbonatite, and economic studies. Anglo-American reported 41.8 million short tons of 0.67% Nb_2O_5 in weathered rocks from the surface to a depth of 30 feet. Phosphates at Mrima Hill occur mainly in the form of monazite (a Cerium-Lanthanum phosphate mineral) and the complex barium phosphate mineral gorceixite. Only very minor amounts of apatite have been reported from Mrima Hill and no occurrences of secondary calcium-phosphates, such as francolite, are reported. Based on the investigations of Hussein (1995) and other geoscientists it can be concluded that no economic residual accumulations of apatites for agricultural use are associated with this carbonatite.

2.   The Rangwa carbonatite complex.

The Rangwa carbonatite complex on the eastern shores of Lake Victoria has been the subject of many investigations, including studies on its phosphate potential. Le Bas (1977) reports of two types of carbonatite rocks in the Rangwa carbonatitic complex: 1) the Ekiojanga carbonatite and breccia, and 2) the Kinyamungu carbonatite and breccia with up to 20% apatite (approximately 8% P_2O_5) in some breccias. Le Bas (1977) also describes a 'dyke of carbonated collophane rock' (probably francolite) in the southwestern part of the complex. No details regarding the exact location or thickness of this phosphate-rich dyke is given.

Idman (1985) and Idman and Mulaha (1991) concentrated their efforts on finding phosphate mineralization in the inner ring carbonatite rock suite of the Kinyamungu carbonatite. They found boulders made up of 'pure apatite rock,' some of which was 'crypto-crystalline,' possibly francolite. Subsequent mapping and drilling in the primary carbonatite, intersected carbonatites with only slightly elevated phosphate contents (39 m with 3.87% P_2O_5 in DH 1, and 27 m with 5.37% P_2O_5 in DH 7). No sizeable accumulations of phosphates have been discovered in this environment as yet. Idman and Mulaha (1991) carried out a systematic soil survey with 50 m intervals and, at selected sites, pitting. The results of only one pit (out of 44) encountered highly weathered, yellowish earthy residual soils with 24.46% P_2O_5 over an interval of 1 m. All other samples proved to contain very low P_2O_5 concentrations.

Based on their intensive exploration work Idman and Mulaha (1991) concluded that the chances of finding extensive phosphate mineralization in the fine-grained Kinyamungu carbonatite are very low. The accumulation of phosphates in the fine-grained Kinyamungu carbonatite is limited to a narrow zone (100 x 300 m) with low grades of primary phosphates (3-4% P_2O_5). Also the phosphate concentrations in the eluvial and alluvial deposits of the Nyakirangacha Valley were clearly too low for economic extraction.

A prospector sent one phosphate rock sample to the International Fertilizer Development Center (IFDC) for analysis (IFDC, 1986). The total P_2O_5 content of the sample was found to be high (25.3%). The mineralogical investigation by IFDC (1986) showed that the phosphate is a francolite with a unit-cell a-value of 9.329 Å. The neutral ammonium citrate solubility (AOAC method) of the francolite is very high with 3.6% (IFDC, 1986; Van Kauwenbergh 1991). The exact location of this specific sample is unknown, but it is believed to originate from the Rangwa carbonatite complex.

Prins (1973) analyzed another sample of apatite, probably from primary calcium-carbonatite (soevite) of the Rangwa carbonatite. The refractive index of the Rangwa apatite was $\omega = 1.630$ and the unit-cell a-value measured 9.380 Å, indicative of fluor-apatite.

3.   The Homa Bay, Ruri and Buru Hill carbonatites.

Pulfrey (1950) described small and insignificant phosphate occurrences at the Homa Bay carbonatite complex and at the Ruri carbonatite complexes south of the Kavirondo Gulf in western Kenya. At the Buru Hill carbonatite, east of Kisumu, Japanese exploration companies were looking for Rare Earth Elements (REE) and niobium. They found only small amounts of these elements and very low-grade phosphates in the primary and weathered rocks. Follow-up work by Finnish and Kenyan geologists indicated low and sporadic concentrations of apatite in parts of these carbonatite complexes. In addition, grade and volume are too low to be of any economic interest, even from a small-scale mining point of view (van Straaten 1997).

4.   The Koru carbonatite.

The Koru carbonatite, 55 km east of Kisumu, is estimated to contain 65 million tonnes of cement grade limestone (Kortman *et al.* 1991). It was considered in the past as a possible source for cement production, but is used at present for the production of lime for road construction, agriculture, the sugar processing industry, and, in some instances, for the gold mining industry (for cyanide treatment of ores). Homa Lime Co. Ltd. currently mines the Koru carbonatite for lime production at a rate of approximately 25,000 tonnes per annum. The mined carbonatite material contains a small amount of phosphate (1.5-1.9% P_2O_5).

5.   The Ikutha vein-type iron ore/phosphate occurrence.

The phosphate mineralization at Ikutha (2° 8'20" S; 38° 11'40" E) is associated with the intrusive vein-type Ikutha iron ore deposit. The volume of the minor mineral apatite proved to be very small. Detailed geological and geophysical investigations and drilling by a Finnish project (Kuivasaari 1991) show ore reserves of about 80,000 tonnes containing magnetite concentrate (66% Fe_2O_3) and 31,000 tonnes of 35% P_2O_5 apatite concentrate. The Ikutha iron ore deposit does not constitute an economic phosphate resource.

Other agrominerals

Limestone/dolomite/travertine/calcrete

Bosse (1996) compiled data of limestone, dolomite, travertine and calcrete occurrences and deposits from existing geological maps of Kenya. More than 27 major 'crystalline limestone' occurrences are reported from meta-sedimentary gneiss sequence of the Mozambique Belt in Kenya. Marble and dolomite marble horizons occur in the southeast of the country near Voi, at sites close to the main Nairobi-Mombasa road, near Kitui, at Kajiado south of Nairobi, and near Mwingi, Isiolo and Garba Tula. Some of these extensive marbles occur in remote areas far from farming areas and are thus of little practical use. A major Precambrian marble to be exploited for lime production occurs near Kajiado in central Kenya.

Mesozoic to Quaternary limestones and coral reef limestones occur in the coastal basin. Porous coral limestones are mined and calcined south of Mombasa for the production of lime by Homa Lime Co. A thick limestone bed is quarried at Bamburi near Mombasa and provides limestone feed for the Bamburi cement industry.

Other carbonate resources include carbonatites (Homa, Koru-Legetet, Rangwa), calcrete and travertine. As mentioned before, some 25,000 tonnes of lime are produced annually from the Koru carbonatite in western Kenya.

Calcrete resources in the Athi River Quarry, SE of Nairobi are exploited as a raw material for the Athi River Cement Plant. Five additional small travertine occurrences are reported, some of which are used for small-scale lime production (Bosse 1996). The combined rate of Kenya's cement production exceeds 1.3 million tonnes per year, a large portion of which is exported to neighbouring countries.

Gypsum

Several gypsum occurrences are reported from the eastern part of the country and two occurrences from central Kenya. Impure gypsum is reported from Garissa consisting of pinkish gypsum in clays. Indications of large volumes of gypsum in soft earthy gypsum/clay aggregates (approximately 2,000 million short tons) are located near El Wak at the Somali border (Walsh 1970). Good quality gypsum occurs in the Kajiado area in central Kenya and has been used for the Athi cement industry. Some of the gypsum used for the Bamburi cement industry near Mombasa is mined at Roka, 37 km southwest of Malindi (Theuri 1994).

Nitrates

Owen and Renault (1989) describe an occurrence of natural sodium nitrate (nitratine) accumulation in the remote semi-arid area of Lake Turkana in northern Kenya. Here, nitrates are widely distributed in the Galana Boi Formation, which covers an area of approximately 1.2 x 0.5 km. In this area the thickness of the Galana Boi Formation ranges between 10 and 32 m. These sediments represent part of a series of stranded raised Holocene sediments that surround modern Lake Turkana. Nitrates occur as interstitial nitratine ($NaNO_3$) in diatomaceous lacustrine silts. The sodium nitrate content ranges from 1.1-7.5% by weight. (In comparison, most of the sodium nitrates exploited in Chile from 'caliche' deposits have grades of 7-10% nitrate.) Owen and Renault (1989) point out prospective areas for further investigations and suggest that the Suguta Valley south of Lake Turkana and much of the southern part of the Ethiopian Rift should be investigated for potential nitrate deposits.

Guano

Small bat guano deposits are reported from several caves in Kenya. Randel and Johnston (1991) describe guano accumulations in the lava tunnels of the Suswa Volcano in the central part of the Rift Valley. The guano occurs as a loose, fine, brown powder on the tunnel floors. The nitrogen content of four samples from these accumulations varies from 7-12.5% and the P_2O_5 content varies from 7.0-13.3%. Other cave deposits are known from the Chyului Hills near Makindu, and from the Amala area, north of Narok. Analytical results from guano samples from Amala gave P_2O_5 values of 7.07 and 3.28% for the powder and chunky, massive samples respectively. The total nitrogen contents of the samples were 3.82 and 4.5% respectively. The volume of the Amala guano is not known (van Straaten 1997).

Vermiculite

Four small vermiculite deposits have been worked in Kenya. One of the vermiculite deposits is located at Kinyiki, half way between Nairobi and Mombasa. This vermiculite mineralization, associated with an ultramafic dunite body, was exploited in the past. However, the volume was small and mining ceased. A vermiculite deposit that has been mined intermittently is the Wasin Mine near Lodosoit, approximately 30 km west of the main Nanyuki-Isiolo-Marsabit road in northern Kenya. The vermiculite mineralization is associated with an altered sheared mafic rock (Walsh 1970; Mason and Theuri 1980). Between 1972 and 1998 some 72,000 tonnes of vermiculite were produced from the Wasin mine. Peak production was reached in 1987 when 9,220 tonnes were produced at Wasin. Most of the vermiculite products are used in the local building industry. Only minor use of vermiculite is made in the horticultural industry of Kenya.

Natural zeolites

Analcime and natrolite concentrations up to 40% have been described from siltstones in the Lake Bogoria basin in the Kenyan Rift Valley (Renault 1993). Ego (2000) describes clinoptilolite and analcime in the Miocene Ngorora Formation in the Kenya Rift Valley. The zeolites are interpreted as reaction products of volcanic glass with saline, alkaline waters in closed basins.

No massive zeolite beds have been reported from Kenya as yet. Based on experiences from other parts of the world it seems likely, however, that large high-grade zeolite deposits could have formed in this relatively young volcanic area with predominantly alkaline pore waters.

Pumice

Large deposits of pumice have been found in the Rift Valley in the Naivasha area, southeast of Longonot and as valley fillings in the Njorowa Gorge, all in the Rift Valley (Walsh 1970). Other deposits are found in the Sultan Hamud area. The pumice occurs as terrestrial bands and as lacustrine deposits. The pumice deposits are commonly composed only of pumice without foreign rocks. Local firms have been extracting pumice as source of building materials. No use has been made as yet for horticultural purposes.

Agromineral potential

The nitrate deposit at Lake Turkana warrants detailed geological investigations including studies of the size and volume of the deposit. Additional exploration should be carried out in the Suguta Valley south of Lake Turkana.

There is potential for the discovery of sedimentary phosphates in coastal sediments. Late Cretaceous to early Tertiary sedimentary sequences, especially those associated with transgressive phases and located at local embayments should be investigated (see chapter on Ethiopia).

Phosphate exploration should also be conducted in the Eastern Rift Valley of Kenya. There are considerable chances of finding lacustrine and biogenic phosphate accumulations in Rift Valley sediments, similar to the ones at Minjingu in Tanzania. Residual igneous phosphates can be expected in an area that covers the Ekiojanga carbonatite and breccia in the Rangwe complex of western Kenya. Efforts should be made to delineate and assess the grade and extent of the 'dyke of carbonated collophane rock' in the southwestern part of the Rangwa carbonatite complex.

The carbonate resources of Kenya are significant and additional agricultural trials should be carried out to evaluate the agronomic effectiveness and economics of the liming materials on acid soils. The efficacy of liming materials from the Koru deposit, mined and processed by Homa Lime Co. Ltd., should be tested on acid soils in western Kenya.

The potential for finding substantial volumes of zeolites in the Rift Valley is high. The potential use of these materials for agriculture is described in Pond and Mumpton (1984).

References:

Bosse H-R 1996. Kenya. In: Bosse H-R, Gwosdz W, Lorenz W, Markwich, Roth W and F Wolff (eds.) Limestone and dolomite resources of Africa. Geol. Jb., D, 102:180-199.

Buresh RJ, Smithson PC and DT Hellums 1997. Building soil phosphorus capital in Africa. In: Buresh RJ, Sanchez PA and F Calhoun (eds.) Replenishing soil fertility in Africa. Soil Sci. Soc. Amer. Special Publ. 51:111-149.

Coetzee GL and CB Edwards 1959. The Mrima Hill carbonatite, Coast Province of Kenya. Transact. Geol. Soc. South Afr. 62:373-395.

Ego JK 2000. Zeolite mineralisation in the Neogene paleolakes of the Ngorora Formation, Kenya Rift Valley. Special Abstract Issue. 18th Coll. African Geology, Graz, Austria. J. Afr. Earth Sci. 30:25-26.

Gaciri SJ 1991. Agromineral resources of Kenya. Fert. Res. 30:165-166.

Hussein SS 1995. The Mrima Hill carbonatite, Kenya: Mineralogy, geochemistry and supergene alteration. Unpubl. M.Sc. Thesis, ITC, Delft, Netherlands, 109pp.

Idman H 1985. The phosphate-investigations in Western Kenya. Annual Report for 1984, Mines and Geological Department, Nairobi, 71pp.

Idman H and T Mulaha 1991. Assessment of phosphate and niobium in carbonatitic and alkaline silicate complexes of South Nyanza, Kenya. Mines and Geol. Dep., Geol. Memoir 8, 30pp.

International Fertilizer Development Centre 1986. Cursory characterization of a phosphate ore sample from Northern Kenya. IFDC Unpubl. Rep., 12pp.

International Labour Organization 1999. Social and labour issues in small-scale mines. TMSSM/1999, 99pp.

Izon D 1993. The mineral industry of Kenya. In: Mineral Industries of Africa. United States Department of the Interior, Bureau of Mines - 1993 International Review:77-79.

Kortman C, Githinji I, Alviola R., Mulaha T. and K Nzau 1991. Assessment of Western Kenya limestone deposits for cement manufacture. Koru and Songhor deposits. Mines and Geol. Dept., Geol. Memoir 5, 30pp.

Kuivasaari T 1991. Assessment of phosphate in the Ikutha iron ore deposit, Kenya. Mines and Geol. Dep., Geol. Memoir 7, 29pp.

Le Bas 1977. Carbonatite-nephelinite volcanism. An African case history. John Wiley & Sons Ltd., UK, 347pp.

Mason JE and FG Theuri 1980. Industrial mineral development in Kenya. 4th Industrial Minerals Intern. Congress, Atlanta, USA 1980, 18pp.

Owen RB and RW Renault 1989. Nitrate deposition in the Turkana basin of northern Kenya. J. Afr. Earth Sci. 10:701-706.

Pond WG and FA Mumpton (editors) 1984. Zeo-Agriculture: Use of natural zeolites in agriculture and aquaculture. Westview Press, Boulder, Colorado, USA, 296pp.

Prins P 1973. Apatite from African carbonatites. Lithos 6:133-144.

Pulfrey W 1950. Ijolitic rocks near Homa Bay, Western Kenya. Quart. J. Geol. Soc. CV:373-402.

Randel RP and RW Johnston 1991. Geology of the Suswa area. Ministry of Environm. and Natural Res., Mines and Geol. Dept. Report 97:41pp.

Renault RW 1993. Zeolitic diagenesis of late Quaternary fluviolacustrine sediments and associated calcrete formation in the Lake Bogoria Basin, Kenya Rift Valley. Sedimentology 40:271-301.

Sanchez PA, Shepherd KD, Soule MJ, Place FM, Buresh R J, Izac AMN, Mokwunye AU, Kwesiga FR, Ndiritu CG and PL Woomer 1997. Soil fertility replenishment in Africa: An investment in natural resource capital. In: Buresh RJ, Sanchez PA and F Calhoun (eds.) Replenishing soil fertility in Africa. Soil Sci. Soc. Amer. Special Publ. 51:1-46.

Schlueter T 1997. Geology of East Africa. Gebrueder Borntraeger, Berlin-Stuttgart, Germany, 484pp.

Smithson P, Jama B, Delve R, van Straaten P and R Buresh 2001. East African phosphate resources and their agronomic performance. Presentation July 2001, Kuala Lumpur, Malaysia.

Theuri FG 1994. The Kenyan industrial minerals sector. In: Mathers SJ and AJG Notholt (eds.) Industrial Minerals in Developing Countries. AGID Geosciences in International Development 18:167-172.

Van Kauwenbergh SJ 1991. Overview of phosphate deposits in East and Southeast Africa. Fert. Res. 30:127-150.

van Straaten P 1997 Geological phosphate resources in Central East Africa, Trip report June 23-July 21 1997, Report, University of Guelph, Canada, 49pp.

Walsh J 1970. Minerals of Kenya. Geol. Surv. Kenya, Bull. 11, 82pp.

Lesotho

Total population (July 2000 estimate): 2,143,000
Area: 30,355 km^2
Annual population growth rate (2000): 1.65%
Life expectancy at birth (1998): 55.2 years
People not expected to survive to age 40 (1998): 26% of the total population
GDP per capita (1998): US $1,626

Lesotho is a small, densely populated country in southern Africa, completely surrounded by the Republic of South Africa. About 75% of Lesotho is mountainous, with altitudes reaching over 3,000 m. The majority of the population, however, lives in the 'lowlands' at around 1,500 m.

The economy of Lesotho is largely based on agriculture, income from migrant labourers, tourism and natural resource utilization (water, diamonds).

In 1999, agriculture contributed about 18% of the GDP. Some 85% of Lesotho's population lives in rural areas and farming is mainly at the subsistence level. The main food crops are maize, sorghum, wheat and beans. The performance of the agricultural sector in Lesotho continues to decline, largely because of reduction in the area that is suitable for cultivation. Climatic variations, soil degradation and soil erosion are other causes for this decline. The deterioration of soil quality and quantity is one of the primary concerns along with water resource management issues.

The mineral sector of Lesotho is very small. The main mineral commodity extracted in Lesotho is diamonds, mainly from alluvial sources. The source rocks for diamonds in Lesotho, kimberlites, are currently being re-investigated on their resource potential. Small but uneconomic uranium occurrences are also reported from Lesotho. Sand and clays, as well as flagstones, are utilized for the local building industry.

Geological outline

The rocks exposed in Lesotho are almost entirely of Triassic and Jurassic age, belonging to the Karoo Supergroup (Schmitz and Rooyani 1987). The Karoo sediments were largely deposited in continental environments. Large parts of Lesotho are made up of basalt flows of the Drakensberg Group. The kimberlite pipes and dykes occurring in northern Lesotho are of lower Cretaceous age.

AGROMINERALS

Phosphates

Small amounts of phosphates have been found at several locations in Lesotho, mainly in nodular form in the lower Elliot Formation of the Karoo Supergroup. At one site, two diffuse bands and lenses of pale coloured nodular phosphatic sediments, 10-20 cm thick and 5-10 m long, were observed. The nodules are slightly radioactive (470-800 ppm U_3O_8) and contain 15-24% P_2O_5 (Reed 1978; UNDP 1984). In places, the nodules contain reptile bones.

The quality and quantity of theses phosphate occurrences have not been studied in detail but appear to be very small and of poor quality.

Limestone

Small amounts of limestones occur in the lowlands of Lesotho. Nodular limestones and irregular lenses of limestone have been described in the Elliot and Clarens Formations of the Stormberg Group (upper Triassic-lower Jurassic).

Natural zeolites

Only very small volumes of natural zeolites have been found in Lesotho. Zeolites occur in vesicles in the Lesotho basalts. Their volume is too small to be of any economic interest. There are, however, considerable volumes of vitreous tuffs and tuffaceous sediments in the Elliot and Clarens Formations and some of these vitreous tuffs could be zeolitic.

Agromineral potential

The potential of finding extensive phosphate deposits in Lesotho is very low. Also the potential of developing some of the local limestones for agricultural purposes is low. However, the chances of finding zeolite accumulations in the vitrous tuffs and tuffaceous sediments of the Elliot and Clarens Formations are regarded as good.

References:

Reed JJ 1978. Radioactive occurrences in Lesotho. Special Report JR/6, UNDP, Project LES 73-021- Exploration for minerals, Phase II, Lesotho, 12pp.

Schmitz G and F Rooyani 1987. Lesotho, geology, geomorphology, soils. National University of Lesotho, 204pp.

United Nations Development Programme 1984. Exploration for diamonds (Phase I), exploration for minerals (Phase II). Technical Report, United Nations, New York, 252pp.

Liberia

Total population (July 2000 estimate): 3,164,000
Area: 111,370 km^2
Annual population growth rate (2000): 1.94%
Life expectancy at birth (1999): 51 years
GDP per capita (1999 estimate): US $1,000

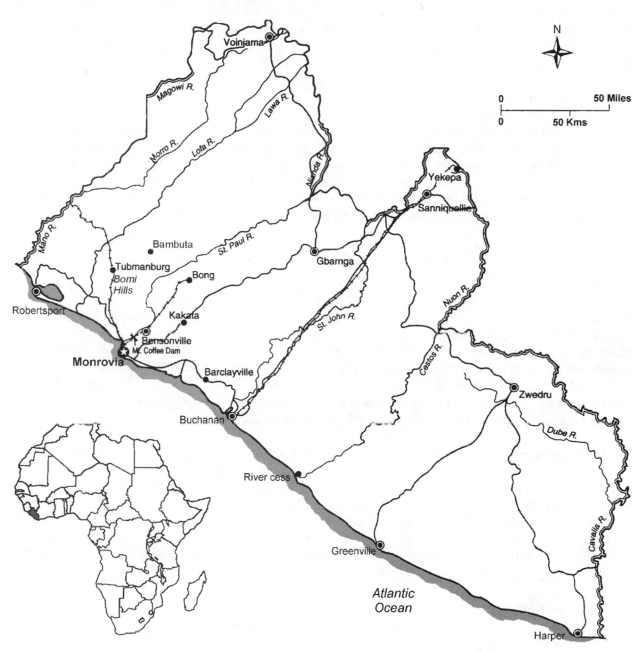

Liberia, located between Côte d'Ivoire, Guinea and Sierra Leone, has a 580 km long, marshy and lagoon-studded Atlantic coastline. The hinterland is made up of ill-defined and dissected plateaux. The climate is humid/tropical with high rainfall, and high temperatures.

The export economy of Liberia was, until recently, dominated by sales of agricultural products (timber, rubber and coffee), iron ore, diamonds and gold. But agricultural production and mining activities have been adversely affected by the civil war that started in 1989. Artisanal miners continued with the extraction of diamonds during the civil unrest.

Agriculture in Liberia is primarily subsistence in nature and, in time of peace, contributed up to 50% of the GDP. Approximately 70% of the labour force was engaged in agricultural activities. The main food crops are rice, cassava, sugarcane and bananas. Historically, the main export crops were rubber, palm oil and cocoa beans.

Geological outline

The geology of Liberia is dominated by Precambrian rock formations of the West African Craton. Metamorphosed rocks of the Liberian Province underlie the western two-thirds of Liberia (Hurley et al. 1971), metamorphites and granites of the Paleoproterozoic Eburnian Province dominate the eastern part of Liberia. The iron ore deposits of the Bong Range occur in the Liberian Province. A narrow belt of supracrustal rocks affected by the Neoproterozoic to lower Cambrian Pan-African event strike parallel to the coastline. Unmetamorphosed Paleozoic to Recent sediments occur along the coast.

AGROMINERALS

Phosphates

There are two small known phosphate deposits in Liberia. The deposit at the Bomi iron ore deposit, 60 km north of Monrovia, is composed of grey to cream coloured phosphatic rocks superficially resembling calcareous tufa. Secondary Fe-phosphate, mainly phosphosiderite and strengite, fill cavities and form cements between iron ore fragments. A sample from the leucophosphite ($KFe_2[PO_4]_2OH(H_2O)_2$) at Bomi contained 33.46% P_2O_5 and 36.85% Fe_2O_3, as well as 7.86% K_2O. Axelrod et al. (1952) interpreted this occurrence as a reaction product of bat excreta with iron oxides. There is an abundance of bat guano in the caves. No figures exist on volume and grade of the Bomi phosphate resources.

The Bambuta deposit is located 70 km north-northeast of Monrovia, 25 km east of Bomi Hill iron mine ($6°$ 56' N; $10°$ 33' W). Results of a diamond drilling program and mapping have shown a minimum reserve of 1 million tonnes of phosphate rock at 32% P_2O_5, or 1.5 million tonnes of ore grading 28% P_2O_5 (Rosenblum and Srivastava 1979). The phosphorus bearing minerals are mainly members of the variscite-strengite series (secondary Al-Fe phosphates). Like at Bomi, the phosphates are associated with an iron ore deposit. The genesis of this deposit remains unclear although Rosenblum and Srivastava (1979) discuss the possibilities of a metasedimentary-metasomatic origin or, alternatively, origin as a result of phosphate precipitation from guano-derived solutions.

Other agrominerals

Major sources of limestone and dolomites are unknown in Liberia (Nair and Dorbor 1990). The geology of the country is generally unfavourable for the formation of limestones and dolomites. Lime products are made from local deposits of marine shells on the beaches of eastern Liberia.

No other agrominerals are reported from Liberia.

Agromineral potential

Apart from the occurrences of phosphates there are no major agrogeological resources reported in the country. In general, the nature of the geology of Liberia is not favourable for the formation of rocks and minerals that can be used for soil fertility improvement.

References:

Axelrod JM, Carron MK, Milton C and TP Thayer 1952. Phosphate mineralization at Bomi Hill and Bambuta, Liberia, West Africa. Am. Miner. 37:883-909.

Hurley PM, Leo GW, White RW and HW Fairbairn 1971. Liberian age province (about 2,700 m.y.) and adjacent provinces in Liberia and Sierra Leone. Geol. Soc. Am. Bull. 82:3483-3490.

Nair AM and JK Dorbor 1990. Industrial minerals of Liberia. Ind. Miner., March 1990:137.

Rosenblum S and SP Srivastava 1979. The Bambuta phosphate deposit, Liberia - a reconnaissance report. US Geol. Surv. Bull. 1480, 26pp.

Madagascar

Total population (July 2000 estimate): 15,506,000
Area: 587,040 km^2
Annual population growth rate (2000): 3.02%
Life expectancy at birth (1998): 57.9 years
People not expected to survive to age 40 (1998): 21.8% of total population
GDP per capita (1998): US $756

Madagascar is the largest island-nation and fourth largest island in the world. Madagascar is comprised of at least three contrasting north-south striking landscapes. The central plateau forms the central 'spine' of the country with elevations between 750 and 1,500 m. Several massifs reach as high as 2,800 m. To the east of the highlands lies the narrow coastal strip with tropical rainforests. To the west are low plateaux and wide plains of savannah and forest. The southern part of Madagascar is arid.

The economy of Madagascar is largely based on agricultural production, which accounts for about 30% of the GDP and provides the livelihood for more than 80% of the population. The principal food crops are rice, cassava, sweet potatoes, potatoes, bananas, maize and beans. Cotton, sugarcane and livestock are other agricultural commodities. The main agricultural export crops are coffee, vanilla, cloves, and sugar.

Intensive farming practices, combined with heavy population pressure and uncontrolled deforestation, have caused serious problems of soil erosion and soil nutrient depletion. The central highlands, where agricultural production is intensive, have the highest rate of soil degradation. Forest clearing in the eastern coastal strip has caused severe land degradation and erosion. Approximately 150,000 hectares of forest are cut down every year due to population increase and rice cultivation.

The geological natural resource bases of Madagascar are graphite, chromite, coal, bauxite and salt. The International Labour Organization (1999) estimated that 5,000-20,000 people are involved in small-scale mining in Madagascar.

Geological outline

Geologically, Madagascar can be divided into two main zones, the Precambrian basement complex in the eastern part of the country, and the sedimentary cover formations in the west. The Precambrian is subdivided into Archean, medium to high-grade metamorphic rocks such as gneisses, migmatites, mica schists and amphibolites, and Proterozoic metasediments (Windley *et al.* 1994; Tucker *et al.* 1999). Karoo sediments and Jurassic to Tertiary sediments, mainly marine in origin, cover the basement rocks in the west of the country.

AGROMINERALS

Phosphates

Sedimentary phosphates of largely unknown extent and quality occur in Cretaceous and Tertiary sediments of the Mahajanga (Majunga) Basin of northwest Madagascar. Phosphatic nodules occurring in lower Cretaceous marls are described from Ambato-Boeni (Lacroix 1922; Besairie 1966), and in the area of Anjiajia, 3 km west of Ankilahila, as well as near Maevarano, all in the Mahajanga Basin (Lacroix 1922; Besairie 1966). Some of the phosphate nodules contain 16-23% P_2O_5, and are in the form of 'collophanite' (Lacroix 1922; Besairie 1966). Phosphates also occur in upper Cretaceous sediments near Marovoay, and south of Soalara, as well as near Sitampiky. Reported concentrations are 'less than 20% P_2O_5' (Besairie and Collingnon 1972, quoted in Notholt *et al.* 1989) and 9.6% P_2O_5 (Lacroix 1922; Besairie 1966). Phosphatic concentrations are also reported from the Antonibe Peninsula where they occur at the base of Palaeocene sediments. Low-grade phosphatic sediments occur in lacustrine environments at Lake Alaotra, and in Pliocene marls near Antanifotsy (Besairie and Collingnon 1972, quoted in Notholt *et al.* 1989).

Igneous apatites are reported from phlogopite-bearing pyroxenites in the south of the country, near Betroka and Bekily. Here, phlogopite mica has been mined since 1913, with an annual production of approximately 300-400 tonnes. The total pyroxenite rock mined (also containing diopside, and apatite as accessory minerals) is approximately 6,000 tonnes per year (Murdock 1963). Only a few of the phlogopite mines report apatite in the 'wastes,' but in some of the pegmatoid veins apatite 'is actually predominant' (Murdock 1963, p. 127).

Guano

Considerable amounts of bird guano have accumulated on coral limestone in the Mozambique Channel. Murdock (1963) describes the guano deposit of the French island of Juan de Nova (17° 03'S; 42° 45'E), 175 km northwest of Maintirano and 420 km from Mahajanga/ Majunga (Hutchinson 1950). The size of the deposit is 5.4 km by 1.5 km. Analyses of the bird guano showed 29.1% P_2O_5, 44 % CaO, 8.5% H_2O. Mining on this island was conducted by hand on a contractual basis, with typical production of 1 tonne per person per day. The guano 'ore' was mechanically crushed. The guano production started in 1922 and lasted until 1940 with a total output of 122,316 tonnes and a maximum annual production of 13,400 tonnes in 1929. Guano production was taken up again in 1956 and until 1960, the average annual production was 6,071 tonnes. The guano fertilizer product was mainly shipped to Mauritius and South Africa (Murdock 1963).

The Malagasy guano deposits of the Barren Islands, 10-20 km from the western coast of Madagascar (Lacroix 1922; Hutchinson 1950; Troung et al.1981) are currently considered for extraction. The government of Madagascar has given permission to GEMEX (50% Malagasy, 50% French and South African) to develop the Barren Island guano deposits with estimated reserves of 613,000 tonnes. Over half of these deposits (312,000 tonnes) are located on the island of Andrano (Support and Supervision Team 1997).

Lacroix (1922) described the guano-related phosphates as 'collophanite,' a fine-grained concretionary fibrous apatite with the composition: 35.66% P_2O_5, 49.64% CaO, 2.45% CO_2, 6.44% H_2O^+ and 3.49% H_2O^-. Chemical and mineralogical analyses by Troung et al. (1981) showed that the phosphates of the bird guano islands in the Mozambique Channel also contain various amounts of aragonite. The crystallographic unit-cell a-value for the phosphates from the island of Andrano was determined as a = 9.451 Å (Troung et al. 1981). These phosphates have a very high solubility (15.84% citrate AOAC solubility) and contain generally less than 0.15% F (Troung et al. 1981).

Mining of bird guano from the Barren Islands is expected to have severe environmental impacts on the coral reefs and marine life surrounding the islands. In a report prepared for the World Bank, the Support and Supervision Team (1997) recommended that a strict and sound environmental management system be put in place to reduce the ecological damage caused by guano mining from the islands, or alternatively consider a buy-out option.

The application of guano from Barren Islands to maize (which accounts for only 13% of the area under cereals) on Malagasy soils showed considerably higher agronomic responses and economic benefits than on paddy rice (Support and Supervision Team 1997).

In addition to bird guano deposits there are several small bat guano deposits in caves of the calcareous zone of Madagascar, near Amboarana (Hutchinson 1950), Andoraharo (Jourdan 1962), and Toliara in southwestern Madagascar. The bat guanos also have high phosphate solubilities (20-28% citrate AOAC solubilities) and F concentrations of less than 0.1% (Truong et al. 1981). Like the bird guano deposits, these phosphates are considered suitable for direct application in agriculture (Truong et al. 1981).

Other agrominerals

Limestone/dolomite/marble

There are large carbonate reserves in Madagascar. Precambrian marbles and dolomitic marbles occur at several localities in central and eastern Madagascar. Gwosdz (1996) describes numerous Precambrian marble deposits in the following areas:

- near Ambatondrazaka, northeast of Antananarivo,
- to the southeast of Antananarivo,
- south of Antsirabe,
- near Ambatofinandrahana,
- northwest and south of Fianarantsoa,
- southwest of Ihosy,
- northwest of Betroka,
- near Miandrivazo,
- southwest of Maevatanana.

Numerous marble resources, including the marbles of the Ambatondrazaka area and the dolomitic marbles of Diavonaomby (south of Fianarantsoa), have been exploited for quicklime manufacture (Gwosdz 1996).

Mesozoic and Tertiary sediments underlie large areas in the western part of the country. Reserves of limestones are considerable in the Antsiranana area, in the Antsohiyi area, at Narinda Bay. Abundant Cretaceous limestones and marls are reported at Amboania close to Mahajanga (Majunga) and near Soalara, 25 km south of Toliara. Relatively small Jurassic limestone deposits have been mined for quicklime production on the Bemaraha plateau along the road from Miandrivazo to the west coast.

How much of the limestone/dolomite resources of Madagascar are currently used for soil improvement is not known.

Gypsum

Small gypsum lenses, up to 3 m thick and 10-85 m long, approximately 100,000 tonnes in size, occur on the banks of the Ankay River, 20 km north of Mahazoma. The gypsum could replace a small fraction of the imported gypsum for the local cement industry (Murdock 1963).

Glauconite

Glauconite occurs 'in abundance' in lower Cretaceous (Neocomian) sands and sandstones within the Analavelona massif, northeast of Toliara (Murdock 1963). In the Menarandroy Valley, west of Betioky, rich glauconite beds occur in Hauterive (lower Cretaceous) sediments, where certain weathered zones consist of 'quasi-pure' glauconite (Besairie 1966).

Agromineral potential

The potential for development of the agromineral resources in Madagascar is good. However, additional soil data are needed to identify nutrient deficiencies and the distribution of low pH soils. The size and chemical/mineralogical characteristics of the local sedimentary phosphate rock deposits in the Mahajanga Basin are largely unknown. A geological survey to identify, characterize and quantify the local sedimentary phosphate resources is urgently needed. The data obtained to date are only indications and need verification and assessment. Exploration work for additional sedimentary phosphates, especially in association with minerals commonly associated with sedimentary phosphate deposits, (attapulgite) and glauconite, should be initiated.

One of the clay minerals that is commonly underlying sedimentary phosphates in sub-Saharan Africa (for instance in Niger, Nigeria, Senegal, Togo) is the fibrous clay mineral palygorskite (attapulgite). And in Madagascar a large Eocene 'bentonitic' clay deposit, made up of 60% illite and 40% palygorskite (attapulgite), occurs on the Eocene limestone plateau to the west of Ejeda (Murdock 1963). The Eocene is a time period in which many phosphate deposits have been discovered in other parts of sub-Saharan Africa.

The general, preliminary assessment of known phosphates and phosphate indicator minerals shows that there is a good potential of finding sizeable sedimentary phosphate resources in Madagascar.

The mining of guano deposits on the offshore islands of Madagascar should be carefully monitored to reduce environmental damage. The possibility of erecting artificial roosting platforms like in Namibia (see chapter Namibia) to 'harvest' guano in a sustainable and environmentally controlled manner should be evaluated.

There are substantial reserves of limestone and dolomite, as well as glauconite, in Madagascar. Their suitability for use on the local soils and crops needs further agronomic testing.

References:

Besairie H 1966. Gîtes Minéraux de Madagascar. Annls. Geol. Madagascar 34, 822 pp.

Besairie H and M Collignon 1972. Géologie de Madagascar. I. Les Terrains sédimentaires. Annls. Géol. Madagascar 35: 82, 200-202, 296, 323-324. Quoted in Notholt *et al.* 1989.

Chantraine J and L Radelli 1970. Tectono-minerogenetic units of the basement of Madagascar. Econ. Geol. 65:690-699.

Gwosdz W 1996. Madagascar. In: Bosse H-R, Gwosdz W, Lorenz W, Markwich, Roth W and F Wolff (eds.) Limestone and dolomite resources of Africa. Geol. Jb., D, 102:216-228.

Hutchinson GE 1950. Survey of existing of biogeochemistry - The geochemistry of vertebrae excretion. Bull. Am. Mus. Nat. History, 96, 554 pp.

International Labour Organization 1999. Social and labour issues in small-scale mines. TMSSM/1999, 99pp.

Jourdan E 1962. Reconnaissance aux grottes à guano d'Andoharano. Institut Agronomique Malgache, Bull. 3, 15pp.

Lacroix A 1922. Géologie, Minéralogie descriptive - phosphates, In: Minéralogie de Madagascar. Vol. 1 Paris, France: 343-364.

Murdock TG 1963. Mineral Resources of the Malagasy Republic. U.S. Bureau of Mines, Inf. Circ. 8196, 147pp.

Notholt AJG, Sheldon RP and DF Davidson 1989. Africa - Introduction. In: Notholt AJG, Sheldon RP and DF Davidson (eds.) Phosphate deposits of the world, Vol. 2 - Phosphate rock resources, Cambridge University Press, Cambridge, UK:164-170.

Pichot J, Truong B and A Traore 1981. Influence du chaulage du sol sur la solubilisation et l'éfficacité des phosphates naturels tricalciques d'Afrique de l'Ouest. Etude en milieu controlé sur un sol ferralitique de Madagascar. Agronomie Tropicale XXXVII-1:56-67.

Support and Supervison Team IFDC/CIRAD/ICRAF/NORAGRIC 1997. PR initiative case studies: Synthesis report. An assessment of phosphate rock as a capital investment: Evidence from Burkina Faso, Madagascar, and Zimbabwe. Report prepared for The World Bank, Washington, D.C., 21pp.

Truong B, Beunard P, Diekola K and J Pichot 1981. Caractérisation et comparaison des phosphates naturels de Madagascar en vue de leur utilisation directe en agriculture. Agromie Tropicale XXXVII-1:9-16.

Tucker RD, Ashwal LD, Handke MJ, Hamilton MA, le Grange M and RA Rambesolon 1999. U-Pb geochronology and isotope geochemistry of the Archean and Proterozoic rocks of North-Central Madagascar. J. Geol. 107:135-153.

Windley BF, Razafiniparany A, Razakamanana T and D Ackermand 1994. Tectonic framework of the Precambrian of Madagascar and its Gondwana connections: a review and reappraisal. Geol. Rundsch. 83:642-659.

Malawi

Total population (July 2000 estimate): 10,386,000
Area: 118,480 km^2
Annual population growth rate (2000): 1.61%
Life expectancy at birth (1998): 39.5 years
People not expected to survive to age 40 (1998): 47.5% of total population
GDP per capita (1998): US $523

Malawi is a landlocked country in southeastern Africa. The country consists of three major geographical zones:

- The rift valley floor area along Lake Malawi in the north and centre of the country, and continuing into the Shire valley in the south,
- The plateau region at altitudes between 750 and 1,400 m, with gentle slopes and broad valleys,
- The predominantly mountainous areas, mainly in the north of the country.

Agriculture is the dominant sector of Malawi's economy. In 1999, agriculture accounted for 38% of the GDP. More than 80% of the population is living in rural areas and is engaged in agriculture. Smallholder agriculture (average farm size less than 2 hectares) provides most of the food crops maize, sorghum, millet, pulses, rice, root crops and fruit. Estate agriculture provides more than 90% of the total value of exports, especially tobacco, tea, sugar, coffee and groundnuts.

So far, the mining sector has played only a minor role in the economy of Malawi. In recent years, the contribution of the mining sector to the GDP rose from 1% in 1994 to 3% in 1996. This is largely due to increased production of coal, cement, lime and gemstones (Malunga 1997).

Geological outline

The 'Basement Complex,' composed of Precambrian metamorphic and igneous rocks, underlies most of Malawi. The Precambrian of Malawi consists of various Proterozoic lithologies and structures: paragneisses, quartzites and marbles of the Neoproterozoic Mozambique Belt, rock sequences of the Mesoproterozoic Irumide Belt, including granulite facies rocks in southern Malawi (Daly 1986), and northwest-striking rocks of the Paleoproterozoic Ubendian Belt in northern Malawi (Fitches 1970; Ray 1974).

Sedimentary rocks and basalts of the Permian to Jurassic Karoo System occur in the far north and far south of the country. Several carbonatite intrusions are known from southern and south-central Malawi. Quaternary to Recent alluvial and lacustrine sediments are found along the shores of Lake Malawi and in the Shire Valley.

AGROMINERALS

Phosphates

The phosphate resources of Malawi are mainly of igneous origin, occurring in association with carbonatites and mica pyroxenites. The Tundulu carbonatite complex at the southern end of Lake Chilwa, close to the border with Mozambique, has been studied by many geoscientists, among them Garson (1962, 1966), Appleton *et al.* (1991), and Notholt (1994). The *in-situ* phosphate resources of this complex are made up of apatite-rich rock and apatite soevite (Garson 1962, 1966). The apatite-rich rocks form an arcuate, 30 to 100 m wide zone around Nathace Hill. This hill forms the centre of the Tundulu carbonatite ring complex. The apatite-rich rock is a pearly white 'sugary' rock type, which in places is massive to 'layered.' The refractive indices of the apatite are $R.I._{\omega} = 1.632\text{-}1.634$ and $R.I._{\varepsilon} = 1.627\text{-}1.629$ indicating a fairly pure fluor-apatite (Garson 1966). The crystallographic unit-cell a-value of the Tundulu apatite is a = 9.3574 Å (Appleton *et al.* 1991). The neutral ammonium citrate (NAC) solubility (2nd extraction) of the apatite is 1.6% P_2O_5, which is relatively high in comparison to other igneous apatites from carbonatite complexes, for instance Dorowa, Zimbabwe (0.8% P_2O_5) and Sukulu, Uganda (1.2% P_2O_5). It is, however, low in comparison to sedimentary phosphates, which commonly have NAC solubilities in excess of 3% P_2O_5.

The phosphate rock resources at Tundulu are estimated to be in excess of 0.8 million tonnes with a grade of >20% P_2O_5 to a depth of 30 m. In addition, Garson (1962) indicated another 1 million tonnes of apatite-bearing soevite with more than 10% P_2O_5. Drilling work undertaken by the Geological Survey of Malawi in the 1970s indicated phosphate resources of 900,000 tonnes at 22% P_2O_5. According to Garson (1962), the total P_2O_5 content of the deposit is 260,000 tonnes (0.8 million tonnes of phosphate ore at 20% P_2O_5 = 160,000 tonnes P_2O_5, plus 1 million tonnes of ore at 10% P_2O_5 = 100,000 tonnes P_2O_5). Some parts of the Tundulu carbonatite ring complex could conceivably be mined selectively to provide high-grade phosphate ores.

Direct Application of Tundulu Phosphate Rock

Various international and national institutions and researchers have tested the suitability of the Tundulu phosphate rock (Tundulu PR) for agricultural applications, including researchers from Malawi-British projects (Appleton *et al.* 1991, Appleton 1994), from the Malawi-German project (Mueller *et al.* 1993) and for the Rockefeller Foundation (Wendt and Jones 1997). The researchers concluded that the application of relatively unreactive Tundulu PR could be attractive only for use in P-deficient acid soils of Malawi. Initial agronomic testing with Tundulu PR using acid-tolerant perennial tea as a test crop (Mueller *et al.* 1993) indicates positive results, similar to the results of tea research in India and Sri Lanka (Golden *et al.* 1981).

In addition, Wendt and Jones (1997) demonstrated that on P-deficient acid soils, direct application of the unreactive Tundulu PR could also effectively increase the yield of the staple food maize. The researchers found that Tundulu PR was more effective when band-applied compared to the traditional point application and demonstrated that application of Tundulu PR at low application rates (20 kg P_2O_5 per hectare) on acid P-deficient soils can have positive agronomic effectiveness.

The low-cost application of Tundulu PR in composting systems has been planned by various scientists (Weil and Mughogo, pers. comm.1992), but has not been tested as yet.

Other phosphate resources

Two other carbonatite complexes, the Kangankunde carbonatite and the Chilwa Island carbonatite, contain only small amounts of primary apatite. The P_2O_5 concentration in residual and eluvial phosphate accumulations range from 1.32 to 8.9% P_2O_5 with an average of 2.5% P_2O_5. No quantitative resource estimates of the residual and eluvial deposits have been made (Chisale and Kaphwiyo 1987). Other eluvial phosphate accumulations are reported from the Chingale meta-pyroxenite (8.7 million tonnes at 3.7% P_2O_5), the Bilira meta-pyroxenite (mean 1.42% P_2O_5), and the Ordovician Mlindi ultrapotassic pyroxenite to syenite (Blomfield 1952; Chisale and Kaphwiyao 1987; Laval and Hottin 1992). From the above pyroxenite complexes only the Mlindi complex (Figure 2.8) has some potential for the extraction of phosphates.

At Mlindi, two areas with apatite rich residual soils were delineated overlying the meta-pyroxenite. Chisale and Kaphwiyo (1987) estimated probable reserves of 2.4 million tonnes of residual soils with grades of 7% to 14% P_2O_5. In terms of P_2O_5 tonnage, the Mlindi residual phosphate deposit is about the same size as the Tundulu complex. The Mlindi residual soils of 2.4 million tonnes at 7% P_2O_5 contain 168,000 tonnes P_2O_5, or 2.4 million tonnes at an average grade of 10% P_2O_5, which translates into 240,000 tonnes P_2O_5. In addition to phosphates, there are considerable amounts of K-containing minerals associated with the Mlindi complex, especially biotite.

A prospector produced a local soil amendment made up of 40% ground biotite-apatite rock from the weathered biotite-pyroxenite, 20% finely ground hand-picked apatite, and 40% ground dolomitic limestone from the vicinity. This material was supplied to various government experimental stations (Blomfield and Garson 1965), but no results from these tests have been obtained.

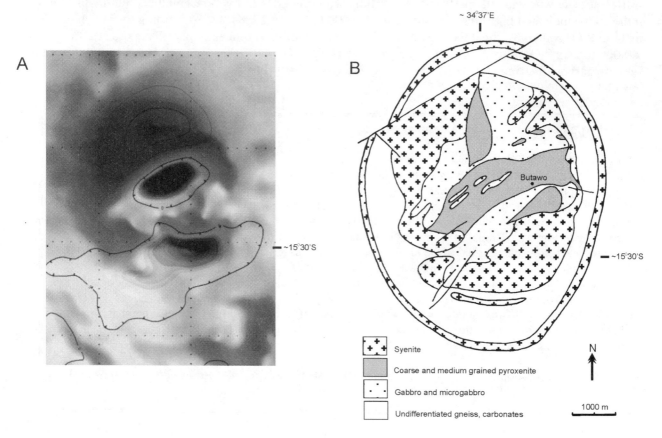

Figure 2.8: A. Aeromagnetic field of the Mlindi ring structure, **B.** Simplified geology of the Mlindi complex (after Laval and Hottin 1992).

Phosphate-enriched lacustrine sediments from Lake Malawi have also attracted considerable interest. Kalindekafe (1991) reported phosphatic sand crusts, phosphatic muds and some phosphatic nodules in Recent sediments of Lake Malawi. The main phosphate minerals in these sediments are apatite, vivianite and anapanite. Vivianite is found in lake muds under reducing environments. The suggested origin of these phosphates is the 're-phosphatization of fish bones' (Kalindekafe 1991). The same author reports the accumulation of bird (cormorant) guano on some islands in Lake Malawi. On Boadzulu Island, large populations of cormorants thriving on fish have caused some 'guanization' (Kalindekafe, pers. comm., August 2001). It is noteworthy that the Minjingu phosphate deposit in northern Tanzania, although of older age, was probably formed by a similar mechanism of biogenic accumulation.

The utilization of the P-accumulations on the islands on Lake Malawi are constrained by their small volume (Kalindekafe, pers. comm. 2001).

Other agrominerals

Limestone/dolomite

There are many occurrences of limestone and dolomite reported from Malawi. Charsley (1972) lists over 90 occurrences. Most of Malawi's Precambrian crystalline limestone and dolomite occurrences are concentrated in the southern region between Blantyre and Lilongwe. Several outcrops of lenticular, coarse-grained Precambrian marbles are known from areas north and east of Kasungu in central Malawi. The limestones in the north of the country occur mainly in the Karoo basin (Charsley 1972). Other carbonates occur in the Chilwa Island carbonatite, at Tundulu, and near Karonga in the north of the country. Secondary limestones, such as travertine and tufa, are known from numerous locations in Malawi (Charsley 1972; Bosse 1996).

The main use of limestone and/or calcitic marble is in the cement industry. The Portland Cement Company of Malawi works the largest known calcitic marble deposit, Changalumi, 13 km west of Zomba. Estimated reserves are 100 million tonnes (Bosse 1996).

Limestone and calcitic marble as well as dolomitic limestone can be also used for the production of lime. In the early 1990s, lime consumption in Malawi consisted of 3,200 tonnes for the sugar industry and 3,500 tonnes for construction and agriculture (Spiropoulos 1991). In 1994, lime consumption was 10,521 tonnes, and the government projected a 10% annual increase in lime demand (MET-CHEM 1997). In the 1980s, marble for use as lime was quarried in the Chenkumbi Hills, some 10 km east of Balaka. Here, the marble reserves are estimated at 3.7 million tonnes (Spiropoulos 1991). The marble was calcined to lime by small-scale operators with a workforce of 600 people in 1988. Production from this deposit ranged from 1,000-2,000 tonnes per year. An experimental vertical-shaft kiln at Chenkumbi produced up to 2.8 tonnes of lime per day (Spiropolous 1991) with a fuelwood consumption of 800 kg per tonne of lime. The fuel-wood consumption of this new kiln is low in comparison to traditional lime operations that consume approximately 1,500 kg fuelwood per tonne of lime. However, for various reasons, the operation ceased in 1992 (MET-CHEM 1997).

Other small-scale mining of carbonate material is reported from the Lirangwe area, some 40 km north of Blantyre. In 1990 about 3,000 tonnes of dolomite was produced for use as soil improver and as filler for fertilizers (Bosse 1996).

In the late 1990s, MET-CHEM of Canada carried out a technical and economic evaluation of a potential mining operation and lime production unit using the Bwanje Valley limestone deposit at the southern end of Lake Malawi (MET-CHEM 1997). Based on drilling results the overall resource base is estimated at 12.3 million tonnes of calcitic ore and 3.7 million tonnes of dolomitic ore (MET-CHEM 1997). The Malawi Development Corporation contracted Boliden Contech of Sweden to conduct a study of the Bwanje Valley limestone resources for production of agricultural lime and chemical lime for the sugar industry.

It is apparent that there are many limestone/dolomite occurrences in Malawi that could be mined and crushed/ground by small-scale methods for agricultural applications. The best potential areas for agricultural lime/dolomite application are areas with acid soils (pH < 5), mainly located in northern (south of Mzuzu and west of Nkhata Bay) and southern regions. Finely ground sedimentary dolomitic limestones such as those found in the Uliwa area of Karonga in the north, and the Chuzi area southwest of Chikwakwa, are preferred agricultural limestone materials (Charsley 1972).

The growth of the lime industry is largely dependent on the development of the economic growth of the building industry and the agricultural sector, including the agro-processing industries, for instance, the sugar cane refining industry.

Gypsum

Small gypsum occurrences are known from several seasonally flooded shallow valleys (dambos) in the northern part of Malawi. Geologists from the Geological Survey of Malawi investigated the Kasangadzi Dambo, approximately 5 km northwest of Mponela in central Malawi (Chapuma, no date) and described a gypsum horizon with an average thickness of 0.9 m overlain by 0.5-1.0 m thick sticky black cotton soils (vertisols). No reserve estimates are given. However, mining of these gypsum resources is regarded as difficult due to flooding and the hardness/stickiness of these gypsum-bearing soils.

Malawi imports most of its gypsum requirements (approximately 6,000 tones per year). Gypsum is used mainly for the cement industry. However, some of the gypsum imported from Zimbabwe is also used by groundnut farmers in Malawi. The imported Zimbabwean gypsum is a 'waste product' from phosphate processing (phospho-gypsum).

Sulphur Deficiencies and Gypsum in Malawi

The sulphur contained in gypsum can be an effective agromineral resource to reduce S deficiencies in Malawi soils. The sulphur requirements of maize (*Zea mays* L.) in Malawi soils have been assessed by Weil and Mughogo (2000). They showed that small applications of sulphur (5-6 kg S per hectare), in the form of gypsum, decreased S deficiencies in maize crops and increased yield in some parts of Malawi.

Potassium silicates

Potassium deficiencies have been recognized in many continuously cultivated soils of Malawi (Mueller *et al.* 1993). According to Gwosdz *et al.* (1996) 59,000 km^2 of Malawi's soils are K-deficient, representing more than 60% of the land area.

K occurs in many silicate rocks in varying concentrations. The highest K$_2$O is found in micas (phlogopite, biotite, muscovite) and K-feldspars. The fastest release rate of K is from phlogopite and biotite, the slowest release rate is from muscovite and feldspar. So far no evaluations have been made of phlogopite- or biotite-rich resources in Malawi, such as those found in association with the Mlindi ultrapotassic pyroxenite (Figure 2.8). Instead, British, German and Malawian geoscientists have evaluated the feldspar deposits of Malawi as a potential K-source (Appleton 1994; Gwosdz *et al.* 1996). Gwosdz *et al.* (1996) made an inventory of feldspar resources in Malawi, concentrating on pegmatites, nepheline-syenites, and K-feldspar-rich rocks associated with carbonatites. The findings indicate that most pegmatite bodies are too small to be economically viable. The only K-feldspar concentrations of large enough volume are those of the Chilwa Island carbonatite (>30 million tonnes of feldspathic rock), and at Tundulu (5 million tonnes of feldspathic breccia with K$_2$O contents ranging from 4.3-13%). However, the feldspathic breccia of Tundulu also has a high MnO content (up to 2%), a potentially toxic concentration for plants. The potassium release from K-feldspars is known to be very slow and the feldspars were seen as potential slow release K-fertilizers only, to be potentially applied to K-deficient soils, near to sites that contain K-rich mineral resources.

Vermiculite

Vermiculite is found at several places in southern Malawi, the best-known resource being that of Feremu (Mwanza District) with approximately 2.5 million tonnes at 10% vermiculite. The vermiculite deposit was mined by the company British Plaster Board from 1981-1983, but was abandoned due to the heterogeneity of the material. Hoffmann (1991) reported the cation exchange capacity of the Feremu vermiculite as 24.1 cmol$^+$/kg for the original unground vermiculite and 85.3 cmol$^+$/kg in the ground state. The exchangeable Mg^{2+} concentration was 20.2 and 71.8 cmol$^+$/kg for the raw and ground state respectively.

Agromineral potential

The potential for development of Malawi's agrominerals by small-scale methods is considered good. The phosphate resources of Malawi are relatively small, with two deposits (Tundulu and Mlindi) with near surface resources of approximately 200,000-250,000 tonnes of P_2O_5 each. The mineability of both residual phosphate resources is good and suitable for small-scale operations. To increase the P-release rates from the low reactivity igneous apatites from Tundulu and Mlindi, biological and other modification techniques should be tested.

In addition, greater efforts should be put towards the development of limestone and dolomite resources in Malawi. Small-scale operations with intermediate crushing and grinding technologies are warranted in areas where acid soils limit crop production. Liming trials with only ground but not calcined limestone or dolomite should be undertaken on various soils and crops in Malawi.

It will be useful to continue testing K-Mg-Ca silicates in the nutrient-deficient soils of Malawi. Instead of using the relatively insoluble K-feldspars as a K-source, the use of phlogopite or biotite resources should be tested. An example of such a resource is the low-grade 'ultrapotassic' mica-pyroxenite of Mlindi where rock analyses of coarse-grained pyroxenite indicate 3-4% K_2O (from phlogopite/biotite), 12-17% CaO, 15-17% MgO, and up to 5.6% P_2O_5 (Laval and Hottin 1992). These K resources should be tested on crops with high K-demands, like root crops and fruits.

The natural resource base of gypsum is very limited. The relatively inexpensive gypsum 'waste' (phosphogypsum) from Zimbabwe and some of the local resources should be tested on S-deficient soils.

Vermiculites from Feremu have only limited use for field crop production, but should be tested for use in plant and tree nurseries of Malawi, as well as in the floricultural sector.

References:

Appleton JD 1994. Direct-application fertilizers and soil amendments - appropriate technology for developing countries? In: Mathers SJ and AJG Notholt (eds.) Industrial minerals in developing countries. AGID Report Series Geosciences in International Development 18:223-256.

Appleton JD, Styles MT, Chisale RTK, Hardcastle PD, Sitaube LA and JK Syers 1991. Potential use of phosphate resources from African carbonatites as low-cost direct-application fertilizers. In: DA Stow and DJC Laming (eds.) Geoscience in Development, AGID Report 14, Balkema, Rotterdam, Netherlands:181-190.

Bloomfield K 1952. A note on the concurrence of apatite in the Mlindi ring, Neno district. A. Rep. Geol. Surv. Nyasaland, 22-23.

Blomfield KB and MS Garson 1965. The geology of the Kirk Range - Lisungwe Valley area. Bull. Geol. Surv. Malawi 17, 234pp.

Bosse H-R 1996. Malawi. In: Bosse H-R, Gwosdz W, Lorenz W, Markwich, Roth W and F Wolff (eds.) Limestone and dolomite resources of Africa. Geol. Jb., D, 102:228-269.

Carter GS and JD Bennett 1973. The geology and mineral resources of Malawi. Bull. Geol. Surv. Malawi, 6, 62pp.

Chapuma MF no date. Report on gypsum exploration and preliminary reserve calculation at Kasangadzi dambo. Malawi geol. Surv. Report MFC/3/T, 5pp.

Charsley TJ 1972. The limestone resources of Malawi. Memoir Geol. Survey Malawi 6, 128pp.

Chisale RTK and CE Kaphwiyo 1987. Rock phosphate resources of Malawi - a review. In: Wachira JK and AJG Notholt (eds.) Agrogeology in Africa. Commonwealth Sci. Council, Technical Publ. Series 226:77-83.

Daly MC 1986. The intracratonic Irumide Belt of Zambia and its bearing on collision orogeny during the Proterozoic of Africa. In: Coward MP and AC Ries (eds.) Collision Tectonics. Geol. Soc. Spec. Publ. 19:321-328.

Fitches WR 1970. A part of the Ubendian Orogenic Belt in northern Malawi and Zambia. Geol. Rdsch. 59:444-458.

Garson MS 1962. The Tundulu ring complex in southern Nyasaland. Memoir Nyasaland Geol. Surv. 2, 248pp.

Garson MS 1966. Carbonatites in Malawi. In: Tuttle OF and J Gittins (eds.) Carbonatites, Interscience Publishers, New York, 33-71.

Golden DC, Weed SB, Sivasubramaniam and P Nalliah 1981. Studies on the performance of two phosphatic fertilizers on tea soils with respect to the P-adsorption, mineralogy and plant species using ^{32}P-labelled fertilizer. Tea Quarterly 50/2:50-60.

Gwosdz W, Mshali RSM and T Atcama 1996. On feldspar occurrences in Malawi. Techn. Cooperation Proj. 89.2028.2, Malawi-Fed. Rep. Germany, Zomba/Hannover, 82pp.

Hoffmann R 1991. Present and potential utilization of agrominerals in Malawi. Techn. Cooperation Proj. 89.2028.2, Malawi-Fed. Rep. Germany, Zomba/Hannover, 49pp.

Kalindekafe LSN 1991. Terrigenous and authigenic mineralisation in Lake Malawi sediments. M.Sc. thesis Chancellor College, University of Malawi, 294pp.

Laval M and AM Hottin 1992. The Mlindi ring structure. An example of an ultrapotassic pyroxenite to syenite differentiated complex. Geol. Rdsch. 81:737-757.

Lowell K and RR Weil 1995. Pyrite enhancement of phosphorus availability from African phosphate rocks: A laboratory study. Soil Sci. Soc. Am. J. 59:1645-1654.

Malunga GWO 1997. Malawi. Mining Annual Review, Mining Journal Ltd. London, p.149

McClellan GH and AJG Notholt 1986. Phosphate deposits of sub-Saharan Africa. In: Mokwunye AU and PLG Vlek (eds.) Management of nitrogen and phosphorus fertilizers in sub-Saharan Africa. Martinus Nijhoff, Dordrecht, Netherlands:173-224.

MET-CHEM 1997. Summary of the Bwanje Valley limestone feasibility study. Unpubl. Report, 25pp.

Mueller HW, Jones RB, Wendt J and J Kumwenda 1993. Results from the field trials with agrominerals in Malawi. Techn. Cooperation Proj. 89.2028.2, Malawi-Fed. Rep. Germany, Zomba and Chitedze, 9pp.

Notholt AJG 1994. Phosphate rock in developing countries. In: Mathers SJ and AJG Notholt (eds.) Industrial minerals in developing countries. AGID Report Series: Geosciences in International Development 18:193-222.

Ray GE 1974. The structural and metamorphic geology of northern Malawi. J. Geol. Soc. London 130:427-440.

Spiropoulos J 1991. Small-scale industries - Their role in rural development. In: Stow DA and DJC Laming (eds.) Geoscience in Development, AGID Report 14, Balkema, Rotterdam, 197-208.

Weil RR and SK Mughogo 2000. Sulfur nutrition of maize in four regions of Malawi. Agron. J. 92:649-656.

Wendt JW and RB Jones 1997. Evaluation of the efficacy of Malawi Tundulu phosphate rock for maize production. Nutr. Cycl. Agroecosystems 48:161-170.

Mali

Total population (July 2000 estimate): 10,686,000
Area: 1,241,232 km^2
Annual population growth rate (2000): 2.98%
Life expectancy at birth (1998): 53.7 years
People not expected to survive to age 40 (1998): 33.1% of total population
GDP per capita (1998): US $681

Mali is a landlocked country in central West Africa. The Sahara desert and some mountainous areas occupy the northern part of the country. The Niger River Valley in the centre of the country crosses Mali and provides essential water and nutrient resources. Only in the extreme south is rainfall sufficient to cultivate crops without irrigation. The vegetation ranges from desert plants in the north to tall grass and savannas in the south. Annual rainfall in the north is below 200 mm; in the south, close to the border with Côte d'Ivoire, it reaches 1300 mm.

Mali's soil fertility is generally poor. Characteristically, the soils are mainly sandy, the soil organic matter is very low and soil pH values range from 4.3-6.3. One of the major limiting factors for agriculture is the low phosphorus status of the soils. The lack of precipitation is another major constraint to sustainable crop production in large parts of Mali.

The economy of Mali is mainly based on agricultural production and stock rearing. In 1999, the agricultural sector accounted for 48% of the GDP. Some 85% of the population is involved in livestock raising, crop production and fishing. The major crop production systems vary with the available soil moisture. Rotation of groundnut and pearl millet is prominent in the centre of the country with annual precipitation varying between 500 and 800 mm. Rotation of maize-cotton is common in the southern sub-humid to humid rainfall zone (> 1000 mm). The northern limit of the major cash crop of Mali, rainfed cotton, is dictated by the line of 700 mm annual precipitation.

Mali's mineral resource development plays an increasingly important role in the economy of the country. Gold is the main mineral commodity for export. In 1995, gold made up 95% of Mali's mineral production. With the opening of the Sadiola gold mine in 1997, Mali became Africa's fourth largest gold producer, behind South Africa, Ghana and Zimbabwe. In addition, considerable amounts of gold, found near the surface, is mined by artisanal miners. The International Labour Organization (1999) estimated the number of people involved in small-scale mining at 100,000.

Geological outline

The geology of Mali includes a wide range of rock types. Archean and Paleoproterozoic rocks underlie large parts of western and central Mali, and sediments of the intracratonic Taoudenni Basin occupy large parts of central and north Mali. The Taoudenni Basin is mainly composed of Neoproterozoic to lower Cambrian, and Phanerozoic platform sediments. The Neoproterozoic to lower Cambrian contains a sequence of tillites, limestone (with barite), and chert, a sequence known in other parts of West Africa as 'triad.' Precambrian rocks, deformed during the Neoproterozoic Pan-African collision event, as well as Cretaceous and Tertiary sediments, underlie parts of northern and eastern Mali. Devonian and Carboniferous sediments are found in areas around Taoudenni in the north of the country.

AGROMINERALS

Phosphates

Mali hosts voluminous high-grade Tertiary sedimentary phosphates. These up to 2.2 m thick phosphorites are located in eastern Mali. They extend for more than 400 km between Asselar to Telatai and the Niger border (Pascal and Traore 1989). The best-known phosphate deposits, of Eocene (Lutetian) age, occur in the Tilemsi River Valley (Figure 2.9).

The phosphorite deposit on the east bank of the (dry) Tilemsi River Valley has been studied in detail by many geoscientists. Technical and economic studies were undertaken by Kloeckner Industrie (1969), by the German Technical Cooperation (GTZ 1977), and by the International Fertilizer Development Center (IFDC 1977).

The best-studied area of phosphate rocks in the Tilemsi area is that of Tamaguilel (17° 40' N; 0° 15' E) (Figure 2.9). Here, the unconsolidated phosphatic sediments consist mainly of fish and reptile bone debris as well as coprolites. Detailed mineralogical investigations have identified the phosphate mineral as francolite with crystallographic unit-cell a-value of 9.331 Å, indicating a relatively highly reactive PR. Indeed, the neutral ammonium citrate solubility of Tilemsi PR is high at 4.2% P_2O_5 (McClellan and Notholt 1986), making it suitable as direct application phosphate fertilizer.

The mean grade of the phosphatic layers at Tamaguilel is 27% P_2O_5. The phosphatic ore is not calcareous. In places the phosphates contain relatively high Fe-concentrations: up to 8% Fe_2O_3 in the Tamaguilel area, up to 20-30% in the Telatai area. Some parts of the phosphatic layers are also high in manganese.

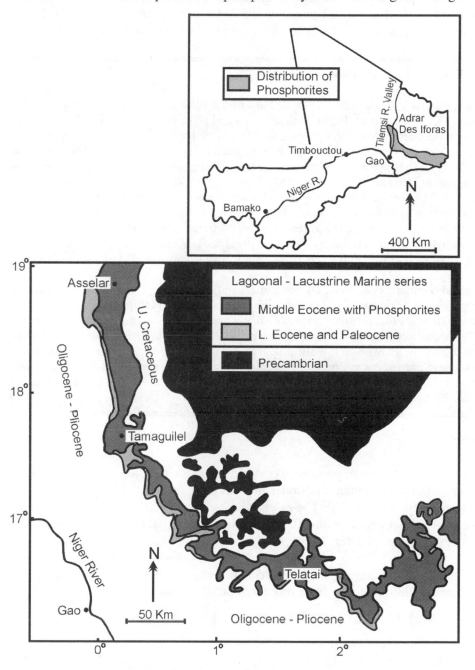

Figure 2.9: General geological setting of the phosphate mineralization of Eastern Mali (after Pascal and Traore 1989).

The surface area of Tilemsi PR is the highest of the PRs of West Africa reported by Truong and Montange (1998): 26.4 m^2 g^{-1} for the 0.5 mm fraction, and 34.2 m^2 g^{-1} for the 0.1 mm fraction. The P uptake rate from applied Tilemsi PR and the agronomic effectiveness is correspondingly very high (Truong and Montange 1998).

Phosphate reserves are in excess of 20 million tonnes, with some 12 million tonnes at 25% P_2O_5 at Tamaguilel alone. Approximately 10 million tonnes at the Tamaguilel deposit are located beneath 15 m of overburden (Sustrac 1986).

The deposit is located in a remote area and the infrastructure is not well developed as yet. A crushing and bagging plant was built at Bourem in December 1980 and continued producing phosphate at a rate of 1,000-3,000 tonnes per year until 1995. The mill has a processing capacity up to 30,000 tonnes per year.

Direct Application of Tilemsi Phosphate Rock

Tilemsi phosphate rock (Tilemsi PR) was tested as direct application phosphate fertilizer already in the early 1970s (Pieri 1973; Thibaut *et al.* 1980). Between 1982 and 1986, experiments with Tilemsi PR were carried out at 10 experimental stations in Mali in collaboration between the Institut d'Economie Rural (IER), the International Fertilizer Development Center (IFDC) and the International Development Research Centre (IDRC) (Diamond *et al.* 1989). The results show that the relative agronomic effectiveness (RAE) of directly applied ground Tilemsi PR varied from crop to crop (for instance 64-100% for groundnuts, 71-76% for millet, 64-100% for sorghum and 73-98% for maize). The average RAE of Tilemsi PR when compared to TSP was 78%. This means that Tilemsi PR was 78% as effective in increasing crop yields as TSP. Management practices can influence the effectiveness of Tilemsi PR. Banding of Tilemsi PR was less effective tha nicorporating (Chien and menon 1995). Timing of application of Tilemsi PR was tested by Hellums (1991) on flooded rice. Tilemsi PR performed well when applied 2 weeks before flooding, but was largely ineffective when applied at or after flooding.

Agronomic and economic evaluations by Bationo *et al.* (1997) clearly show that crop yields using Tilemsi PR in direct application are comparable to those of recommended imported fertilizers for cotton or cereal crops. Direct application of Tilemsi PR is relatively profitable in comparison with recommended imported fertilizers (Bationo *et al.* 1997), specifically in areas with sufficient rainfall. The researchers recommend conducting a technical and economical feasibility study of small-scale production of compacted fertilizers in Mali using Tilemsi PR as the P source. Initial tests carried out in Zimbabwe in 2001 proved that the Tilemsi PR is amenable to blending with more soluble P+N fertilizers and can be effectively pelletized using locally produced appropriate technology (van Straaten, unpublished).

Other phosphates

Of minor importance are the small phosphate occurrences in the middle Devonian limestones and in small carbonatite plugs. Middle Devonian limestones in areas north and east of Taoudenni reportedly contain local oolitic phosphates (Wolff 1996). The extent of these phosphatic limestones is not known, although phosphatic rocks of similar age (Devonian/lower Carboniferous) have also been documented from the Agades region of Niger (see chapter on Niger).

Other rocks containing small amounts of phosphate minerals are the carbonatites north of Tessalit (Sauvage and Savard 1985), but they have no economic significance.

Other agrominerals

Limestone/dolomite

The limestone and dolomite resources of Mali are extensive. Several large limestone and dolomite deposits occur in the western part of the country, close to the towns of Kayes, Diamou and Bafoulabe. The Gangotery deposit, near Bafoulabe, reportedly contains 7 million tonnes of limestone. It has been exploited for the cement industry located in Diamou since 1969 (Wolff 1996). Large dolomite occurrences are located some 80 km from Dioila (6°25' W; 12° 4' N), and in the centre of the country, near Goundam and Tomboctou, there are several large limestone to dolomitic limestone deposits. The dolomitic marbles and dolomites near Hombori and Douentza appear to be very extensive. The very small carbonate occurrences associated with carbonatites northwest of Tessalit (Sauvage and Savard 1985) are found in very remote locations and have no practical significance.

Gypsum

Gypsum reserves exceeding 2 million tonnes (Keita 1994), with an annual production of 700 tonnes per year (van Oss 1993), occur in northern Mali, near Tessalit. Also, gypsum has been described from salt lakes near Taoudenni. Gypsum ($CaSO_4 \cdot 2H_2O$), bassanite ($CaSO_4 \cdot H_2O$) and anhydrite ($CaSO_4$) have been reported from the Taoudenni-Arogott basin in northern Mali by Mees (1998).

Potash

A small sylvite (KCl) deposit has been reported from the salt depression of Taoudenni in the far north of Mali (Johnson 1995). Unconfirmed reports of Ivanov (1969) speak of potash salts reaching 180 million short tons. The author reported these large resources from an unspecified location 'between Timbuktu and Taoudenni.'

Agromineral potential

The potential for further development of the Tilemsi phosphate resource is very good, despite the remote location of the deposits. The phosphates are of excellent quality and suitable for small-scale processing and application on P-deficient soils. One of the disadvantages for handling the PRs is the powdery nature of the Tilemsi PR. This may be overcome by appropriate pelletizing techniques and might increase the marketability of the final P products. Technical studies for small-scale, low-cost crushing/grinding and production of compacted or pelletized Tilemsi PR fertilizers need to be conducted. Additionally, biological modification techniques and blending of Tilemsi PR with biological 'waste' products should be envisaged.

References:

Bationo AS, Ayuk E, Ballo D and M Kone 1997. Agronomic and economic evaluation of Tilemsi phosphate rock in different agroecological zones of Mali. Nutr. Cycling Agroecosyst. 48:179-189.

Diamond RB, Henao J, Parish DH, Rosseau P, Traore F, Sanogo Z, Gakou A, Bagayoko M and M Kone 1989. Final Summary Report to IDRC. Phosphate fertilizers (IFDC/West Africa), 28pp.

Chien SH and RG Menon 1995. Factors affecting the agronomic effectiveness of phosphate rock for direct application. Fert. Res. 41:227-234.

GTZ 1977. Etude préliminaire. Exploitation des gisement de phosphate près de Bourem, Tilemsi (Mali). Projet 77.2173.1. Unpublished report, 66pp.

Hellums DT 1991. Factors affecting the efficiency of non-conventional phosphate fertilizers in lowland and upland cropping systems. Ph.D. Thesis Auburn University, Auburn AL, USA.

International Fertilizer Development Center (IFDC) 1977. West Africa fertilizer study. Vol. III, Mali, 56pp.

International Labour Organization 1999. Social and labour issues in small-scale mines. TMSSM/1999, 99pp.

Ivanov AA 1969. Developed and undeveloped potash deposits in Africa. Lithol. Miner. Resources 2:187-195.

Johnson AKC 1995. Inventory and mining of local mineral resources in West Africa. In: Gerner H and AU Mokwunye (eds.) Use of phosphate rock for sustainable agriculture in West Africa. IFDC, Miscellaneous Fert. Studies, 11:21-40.

Keita ND 1994. Mali. Mining Annual Review 1994, Mining Journal Ltd. London, p.152.

Kloeckner Industrie Anlagen 1969. Etude économique et technique en vue de l'exploitation d'un gisement de phosphates dans la région de Bourem (Mali). Rapport final, Duisburg, Germany, 4 vols., 666pp.

McClellan GH and AJG Notholt 1986. Phosphate deposits of sub-Saharan Africa. In: Mokwunye AU and PLG Vlek (eds.) Management of nitrogen and phosphorus fertilizers in sub-Saharan Africa. Martinus Nijhoff, Dordrecht, Netherlands:173-224.

Mees F 1998. The alteration of glauberite in lacustrine deposits of the Taoudenni-Agorgott basin, northern Mali. Sed. Geol. 117:193-205.

Pascal M and H Traore 1989. Eocene Tilemsi phosphorite deposits, eastern Mali. In: Notholt AJG, Sheldon RP and DF (eds.) Phosphate deposits of the world. Vol 2. Phosphate rock resources, Cambridge University Press, Cambridge, UK:226-232.

Pieri C 1973. La fumure des céréales de culture sèche en République du Mali. Premier essai de synthèse. Agronomie Tropical 28:751-766.

Sauvage JF and R Savard 1985. Les complexes alcalins soussatures à carbonatites de la région d'In Imanal (Sahara Malien): une présentation. J. Afr. Earth Sci. 3:143-149.

Sustrac G 1986. BRGM phosphate prospecting methods and results in West Africa. Trans. Instn. Min. Metall. (Sect. A: Min. Industry) 95:A134-A143.

Thibaut F, Traore FM, Pieri C and J Pidrot 1980. L'utilisation agricole des phosphates naturels de Tilemsi (Mali). Synthèse des résultats de la recherche agronomique sur les cultures vivrières et oliogineuses. Agronomie tropicale 35:240-249.

Truong B and D Montagne 1998. The African experience with phosphate rock, including Djebel Onk, and case studies in Brazil and Vietnam. In: Johnston AE and JK Syers (eds.) Nutrient management for sustainable crop production in Asia. CAB International, UK: 133-148.

van Oss HG 1993. The mineral industry of Mali. Minerals Yearbook, Vol.III, US Department of the Interior, Bureau of Mines, 96-99.

Wolff F 1996. Mali. In: Bosse H-R, Gwosdz W, Lorenz W, Markwich, Roth W and F Wolff (eds.) Limestone and dolomite resources of Africa. Geol. Jb., D, 102:269-297.

Mauritania

Total population (July 2000 estimate): 2,668,000
Area: 1,030,700 km^2
Annual population growth rate (2000): 2.94%
Life expectancy at birth (1998): 53.9 years
People not expected to survive to age 40 (1998): 28.7% of the total population
GDP per capita (1998): US $1,563

Mauritania is an arid country in West Africa with 750 km of Atlantic coastline. Vast areas to the north of the Senegal River are occupied by extensive sand dune plains of the Sahara Desert. Mountainous areas occur in the northeastern part of the country. Most of the country receives less than 200 mm of precipitation per year. The only agricultural area with productive soils lies along the Senegal River valley at the border with Senegal.

Mauritania's harsh physical and climatic conditions constrain its agricultural potential. Only a few areas are suitable for crop production and these are mainly located in the narrow strip along the Senegal River and scattered oases. Crops produced are rice, sorghum and millet.

The mineral sector produces iron ore and gypsum. The iron ore industry is the main source of foreign exchange accounting for 12% of the GDP and some 40% of all exports in1999.

Agricultural production of cereals, as well as livestock and fish, make up approximately one third of Mauritania's GDP. The main agricultural export products of Mauritania are fish and fish products.

Geological outline

Geologically, Mauritania can be divided into four major domains:

- The Archean Reguibat Shield in the north of the country, which strikes into Western Sahara and Algeria,
- The north-south striking Mauritanide Belt, folded and thrusted during the Variscan orogeny,
- The Taoudenni Basin with predominantly continental sediments of Neoproterozoic to Phanerozoic age, covering most of central and southern Mauritania,
- The Senegal Basin with mainly marine sediments of Jurassic to Tertiary age.

AGROMINERALS

Phosphates

Several phosphate deposits and occurrences are known from Mauritania. Relatively small Paleozoic (Cambrian and Devonian) nodular deposits occur in remote areas of the north, in the Zemmour Noir area near Bir Moghrein. Phosphorites of greater extent and volume are found in Eocene deposits near the Senegal River (McClellan and Notholt 1986). The economically most important phosphorites are the transgressive Eocene deposits of Bofal and Loubboira, west of Kaedi (Boujo and Jiddu 1989). The Sive, Bofal and Loubboira phosphates form a continuation of the phosphates of Matam on the Senegalese side of the border. At Boufal and Loubboira the almost horizontal phosphate beds are 1.7-2.0 m thick, have an average grade of 22% P_2O_5, are highly siliceous and contain bone fragments, fish teeth and coprolites (Boujo and Jiddu 1989). The mineable phosphate beds are free of carbonates. These phosphorites, overlain by dolomites and yellow clays followed by sandstones, could be mined by open-cast methods. However, the stripping ratio of waste to ore is relatively high at 6.6:1.

Probable reserves of the deposits of Bofal and Loubboira are: 70 million tonnes at Bofal, and 24 million tonnes at Loubboira. Memady (1997) estimated the phosphate resources of the whole area as exceeding 135 million tonnes. The trace element concentrations of uranium and cadmium are low (U = 80 ppm, Cd = 12 ppm) (Boujo and Jiddu 1989).

Other agrominerals

Limestone/dolomite

There are several extensive limestone and dolomite resources in Mauritania (Wolff 1996). Thick stromatolitic limestones and dolomitic limestones occur at the northern margin of the Taoudenni Basin. One of the carbonate horizons overlies the Neoproterozoic tillite horizon that has been identified throughout large parts of the Taoudenni Basin as part of the 'triad' (Wright *et al*. 1985). Quaternary and sub-Recent carbonate deposits and shell occurrences have been investigated around the capital Nouakchott with reserves of 5.3-8.4 million tonnes (Wolff 1996). However, these resources are of little practical agronomic importance for a country with low agricultural production and Mauritania's soil characteristics.

Gypsum

Large gypsum deposits occur at Sebkha N'Dremcha, approximately 50 km northeast of Nouakchott. Here, several hundred million tonnes of gypsum occur and are extracted at a rate of several thousand tonnes per year by the Arab Company for Inchiri Mines (SAMIN) for plaster production (Memady 1997).

Agromineral potential

Mauritania is endowed with large volume, good grade sedimentary phosphate rocks. Rapid development of phosphates or gypsum for domestic agricultural production is, at present, unlikely, partially due to climatic constraints and the remote location of the resources.

References:

Boujo A and El Houssein Ould Jiddou 1989. The Eocene phosphorite deposits of Bofal and Loubboira, Mauritania. In: Notholt AJG, Sheldon RP and DF Davidson (eds.) Phosphate deposits of the world. Vol. 2. Phosphate rock resources. Cambridge Univ. Press, Cambridge, UK:207-213.

McClellan GH and AJG Notholt 1986. Phosphate deposits of sub-Saharan Africa. In: Mokwunye AU and PLG Vlek (eds.) Management of nitrogen and phosphorus fertilizers in sub-Saharan Africa. Martinus Nijhoff, Dordrecht, Netherlands:173-224.

Memady M 1997. Mauritania. Mining Annual Review 1997, Mining Journal Ltd. London, 157-158.

Wolff F 1996. Mauritania. In: Bosse H-R, Gwosdz W, Lorenz W, Markwich, Roth W and F Wolff (eds.) Limestone and dolomite resources of Africa. Geol. Jb., D, 278-286.

Wright JB, Hastings DA, Jones WB and HR Williams 1985. Geology and mineral resources of West Africa. Allen and Unwin, London, 187pp.

Mauritius

Total population (July 2000 estimate): 1,179,000
Area: 1,860 km^2
Annual population growth rate (2000): 0.89%
Life expectancy at birth (1998): 71.6 years
People not expected to survive to age 40 (1998): 4.8% of the total population
GDP per capita (1998): US $8,312

a = Agalega Islands
c = Cargados, Carajos and Shoais

b = Mauritius
d = Rodrigues

The volcanic islands of Mauritius are located about 800 km east of Madagascar in the Indian Ocean. Mauritius consists of the main island of Mauritius, the much smaller island of Rodrigues and two smaller groups of islands and reefs to the north and northeast of the main island. All islands are of volcanic origin and are surrounded by coral reefs. The climate is subtropical.

Mauritius has one of the strongest economies in Africa. It is largely based on sugar cane production, textile manufacturing, tourism, and an emerging electronic information and technology sector. More than 80% of the cultivated land is used for sugar production. Agricultural production is mainly from estates; there is no subsistence farming on Mauritius. The agricultural sector contributes 6% of the GDP.

The mineral industry of Mauritius is negligible. The main minerals being quarried are basalts for construction purposes (1 million tonnes per year) with smaller amounts of lime (7,000 tonnes per year) being produced from local coral limestone and coral sand (US Bureau of Mines 1995). Potentially important are the polymetallic nodules that occur on the ocean floor at about 4,000 m depth around Mauritius. They contain more than 15% of both iron and manganese and more than 0.35% cobalt (Coakley 1995). The oil company Texaco explored offshore areas at shallower depth for oil in the 1970s.

Geological outline

Geologically, the islands are made up of volcanic rocks between 7.8 million (early Pliocene) and 0.2 million years of age (McDougall and Chamalaun 1969). The 'old' volcanics are mainly olivine basalts and agglomerates with intrusive trachyte and trachyandesitic plugs. The 'young' volcanics are mainly olivine-bearing flood basalts (Simpson 1950; McDougall and Chamalaun 1969).

AGROMINERALS

Only small phosphate (bird guano) resources from the islands of Cargados, Rodrigues and Agalega are reported from Mauritius (Hutchinson 1950). On Cargados, some 3,000-4,000 short tons of guano with phosphate contents of 18% P_2O_5 were produced annually between 1910 and 1922 (Hutchinson 1950). Whether any of the small guano deposits are still exploited is not known.

Other potential 'agrominerals' available in this island country are crushed basaltic rocks, calcareous coral sands, and raised coral reef deposits (Wright 1968).

Application of Crushed Basalt

Crushed basaltic rock was tested in long-term experiments as early as 1937 and later in the 1940s and 1950s at the Sugar Cane Research Station of Mauritius. Basaltic rock powder was applied to depleted soils of Mauritius for the main long-term crop, sugar cane. With application rates ranging from 10-90 tonnes of crushed basaltic rocks per acre, significantly higher yields could be achieved (D'Hotman de Villiers 1937, 1961). Whether the application of these large tonnages of crushed basaltic rocks on Mauritius was only a long-term research project or whether this type of rock application is still practiced is not known.

Coral sands and raised reef deposits are currently used for the construction industry (Wright 1968). Environmental concerns are being raised over the extraction of coastal sand and its impact on coastal lagoons.

It is unknown whether any of these calcareous rocks are used for agricultural purposes.

Agromineral potential

In general, the potential of developing Mauritius' agrominerals and rocks for agricultural purposes is regarded as low. Long-term testing of large tonnages of crushed rock fines, waste products from basalt quarries, should be continued to study the long-term effects of these materials on sugar cane soils.

References:

Coakley GJ 1995. The mineral industries of the islands of Comoros, Mauritius, Reunion, and Seychelles. Minerals Yearbook, vol. III, United States of the Interior, Geological Survey, 47-48.

D'Hotman de Villiers O 1937. Rev. Agric. de l'Ile Maurice 1937:89-92.

D'Hotman de Villiers O 1947. Results of studies on the rejuvenation of our exhausted soils of the humid regions through the incorporation of basalt dust. Rev. Agric. Maurice 26:160.

D'Hotman de Villiers O 1961. Soil rejuvenation with crushed basalt in Mauritius. Intern. Sugar J. 63:363-364.

Hutchinson GE 1950. Survey of existing of biogeochemistry - The geochemistry of vertebrae excretion. Bull. Amer. Mus. Nat. History, 96:554 pp.

Martin-Leake 1948. Soil rejuvenation in Mauritius. Intern. Sugar J. 50:90-91.

McDougall I and FG Chamalaun 1969. Isotopic dating and geomagnetic polarity studies on volcanic rocks from Mauritius, Indian Ocean. Geol. Soc. Am. Bull. 80:1419-1442.

Simpson ESW 1950. The geology and mineral resources of Mauritius. Colon. Geol. Miner. Resour. Vol. 1 No. 3:217-235.

US Bureau of Mines 1995. Mineral Industries of Africa: Islands of Comoros, Mauritius, Reunion, and Seychelles.

Wright PC 1968. Reports on the raw materials available for cement and brick manufacture in Mauritius, together with the results of mineral reconnaissance and radiometric surveys, 22nd May - 18th July, 1967. Institute of Geological Sciences, London, Report No. 76, 54pp.

Mozambique

Total population (July 2000 estimate): 19,105,000
Area: 801,590 km^2
Annual population growth rate (2000): 1.47%
Life expectancy at birth (1998): 43.8 years
People not expected to survive to age 40 (1998): 41.9% of total population
GDP per capita (1998): US $782

Mozambique, located in southeast Africa, has a 2,500 km coastline with the Indian Ocean and a wide coastal plain that varies in width from 150 to 600 km. The major part of the country consists of undulating plateaux. Mountainous areas occur along the border with Zimbabwe.

Mozambique is a country with a large natural resource potential. At present, the economy is largely based on agriculture, fisheries, tourism and transport. Years of civil war, droughts and floods have severely impeded the development of Mozambique. However, over the last few years Mozambique has made a successful economic recovery, and yet, according to UN statistics, 38% of the population still lives on less than US $1 per day.

The agricultural sector of Mozambique accounts for about one third of the GDP. Over 80% of farmers work their small-holdings on a subsistence basis, with an average cultivated area of less than 2 hectares. Main food crops are cassava, maize, sorghum and rice. Export crops include cotton, copra, cashew nuts and sugar, mostly cultivated by smallholder farmers and commercial farmers.

Only small parts of the mineral resource capital of Mozambique are currently been utilized. With the end of the civil war, increasing amounts of gold, gemstones, marble and graphite, as well as coal, are being mined. World-class titanium-rich sands were discovered inland, near Xai-Xai, about 250 km north of Maputo. Small-scale mining for gold has attracted many thousand artisanal miners. The International Labour Organization (1999) estimates the number of people involved in small-scale mining in Mozambique at 100,000 to 700,000.

Geological outline

Precambrian rocks underlie approximately half of Mozambique, mainly in the north and northwest of the country. They can be divided into three major structural units: Archean granite-greenstone terrane, Mesoproterozoic rocks of the Lurio Belt (Kibaran Orogeny) and the Neoproterozoic Mozambique Belt. Large parts of these Precambrian rocks were rejuvenated during the Neoproterozoic-early Cambrian Pan-African thermo-tectonic event (Bigioggero *et al.* 1989; Pinna *et al.* 1993). Karoo sediments occur in small areas of north and northwestern Mozambique. Karoo volcanics are exposed in the Lebombo Mountains, close to the border with South Africa. Mesozoic to Cenozoic sediments underlie large parts of southern and central Mozambique. Several carbonatite complexes have been delineated in Mozambique.

AGROMINERALS

Phosphates

Apart from numerous small guano deposits, there are large phosphate deposits of metamorphic, igneous and residual phosphates in Mozambique (Figure 2.10), and there are strong indications of sedimentary Tertiary phosphates in Mozambique (Davidson 1986).

1.   Metamorphic phosphate deposits

- Evate. This large and probably metamorphic phosphate deposit lies within the Monapo structure, 100 km east of Nampula and close to the port of Nacala. The Evate apatite-magnetite-biotite mineralization occurs in the oval shaped 970 ± 23 million years old Monapo structure, composed of a metasedimentary sequence of biotite and graphitic gneisses with two separate marble horizons. The Evate marble deposit is 3 km long and 850 m wide. The phosphate-mineralized zones, 5-100 m thick, occur within the marble horizons. The phosphate-rich zones contain fluor-apatite as well as magnetite, forsterite, phlogopite, graphite and minor diopside (Cilek 1989; Manhica 1991). Preliminary reserve estimates indicate a resource of 155,413,000 tonnes of apatite ore at 9.32% P_2O_5, 5.76% Fe and 1.12%

TiO_2 (Manhica 1991; Ministry of Mineral Resources and Energy 1997). The reserves were calculated to a depth of 100 m above sea level. With approximately 14.5 million tonnes of P_2O_5 this is one of the largest phosphate deposits in east-central Africa.

The Evate apatite deposit is capped by a blanket of residual soil, 3-38 m thick, containing 4-64% apatite. The phosphate reserves of the residual apatite, calculated by Davidson (1986), reach 1.5 million tonnes of apatite concentrate. On a P_2O_5 basis, this would add another 525,000 tonnes P_2O_5 to the Evate deposit. The magnetite- and apatite-rich residual soils might lend themselves to simple beneficiation and concentration of apatite and magnetite.

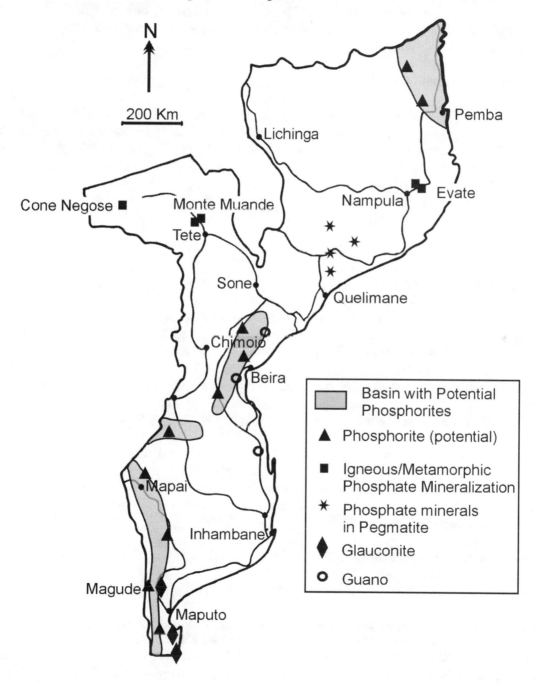

Figure 2.10: Location of phosphate occurrences and deposits in Mozambique (after Cilek 1989).

- Monte Muande. Iron and phosphate mineralization associated with Precambrian marbles is reported from Monte Muande, 30 km northwest of Tete (Staff 1984; Davidson 1986; Cilek 1989). Apatite and magnetite concentrations occur in strata-bound bodies within the foliation of the marble, close to the contact zone, with an intrusive gabbro and pyroxenite. The apatite-magnetite mineralization is localized in three beds. Low-grade phosphates occur mainly in the central bed. The genesis of this deposit is unclear. Cilek (1989) and Manhica (1991) suggest a 'pneumatolitic' type of mineralization, associated with the intrusion of a gabbro into a banded gneiss and marble sequence.

  Residual iron and phosphate accumulations cover the mineralized marble area. The mean iron concentration in these residual soils is 45.22%, and the mean phosphorus content is 5.01% P_2O_5 (Manhica 1991). Reserve calculations based on borehole data indicate 200,000 tonnes of P_2O_5 in the mineralized body (Davidson 1986).

2.   Igneous phosphate deposits

Cone Negose. This Mesozoic volcanic type carbonatite, with vents and dikes cutting Karoo sediments, outcrops at Monte Negose in Tete Province, 80 km southwest of Fingoe. Phosphate enrichment (together with barite) occurs in late stage carbonatite rock (Manhica 1991). No estimates on phosphate grade and tonnage are available.

Phosphate mineralization is also reported from pegmatites in the area between Nampula and Quelimane (Cilek 1989), but their volume and economic potential is low.

3.   Sedimentary phosphate deposits.

Slightly phosphatic (0.7-3.1% P_2O_5) and glauconitic (50%) sandstone beds of upper Cretaceous age (?) have been reported by de Freitas (1959) and Manhica (1991) from Magude, 29 km north-northwest of Maputo on the left bank of the Inkomati River. On the basis of their high glauconite content and their slight P_2O_5 content these 25-50 m thick beds were investigated for their potential use as a direct application fertilizer (Notholt 1994).

The Rovuma Basin in north-northeast Mozambique bears some similarities to the lower Cretaceous phosphatic beds of the Mahajanga (Majunga) Basin in Madagascar and the possibility of finding phosphorites of similar age in this area has been suggested by Notholt (1994).

Based on paleogeographic investigations, studies of existing borehole data and geological and geophysical information, Davidson (1986) concluded that an extensive phosphorite deposit might be present in the southern Mozambique Basin. The glauconite-bearing Eocene Cheringoma Formation, which contains fossil fish and teeth beds, is seen as an excellent potential source rock for phosphorites in the southern basin of Mozambique.

Other agrominerals

Guano

Manhica (1991) reports guano deposits from several localities of Mozambique. The largest guano accumulations are found in caves of the Cheringoma Plateau area. Estimated reserves are 600,000 tonnes (5.14% P_2O_5, 2.74% NO_3, and 1.37% K_2O). Reserves of 132,700 tonnes are also reported from the Buzi area (3.88% P_2O_5, 3.26% NO_3, 1.52% K_2O). Nunes (1961) reports the existence of bat guano in caves of the Jofane formation near Vilanculos with estimated reserves of 22,000 tonnes at 8 to 13% P_2O_5. More recent data from Manhica (1991) indicate 30,000 tonnes with 3.32% P_2O_5, 5.22% NO_3 and 2.95% K_2O

from this area. Between 1953 and 1960 some 6,000 tonnes of guano were excavated from the Vilanculos caves and 1,000 tonnes from the Buzi area (Manhica 1991).

Limestone/dolomite

There are three types of limestone/dolomite resources in Mozambique: sedimentary, metamorphic and igneous.

Sedimentary limestones occur extensively in the Cretaceous and Tertiary basin of Mozambique. The Eocene limestones of Salamanga, south of Maputo, are used in the cement industry. Extremely large deposits (several hundred million tonnes) of Eocene limestone occur along the Cheringoma Plateau south of Inhaminga. Other large limestone formations include the Miocene Jofane Formation, Pliocene-Pleistocene limestones near Nacala, and small Miocene occurrences along the coast between the Tanzanian border and Pemba.

Metamorphic limestone and dolomite resources are mainly found in the Precambrian of northern and central Mozambique (Figure 2.11). Proterozoic marbles and dolomitic limestones and dolomites are found in the following areas:

- approximately 50 km north of Lichinga in the Serra Geci area (Pinna *et al.* 1993),
- near Montepuez,
- near Canxixe,
- north and northwest of Tete (in the Massamba and in the Monte Muande area),
- in the Monapo structure (see phosphates),
- at the Lurio River near Namapa,
- near Chire at the border with Malawi,
- between Massanga and Mungari,
- near Fingoe.

Some of the marbles are being used for the production of lime (Lurio-Namapa; at Malula, north of Lichinga; and in parts of the Monapo structure).

The main igneous limestone/dolomite resources are found at Monte Muambe and Monte Xiluvo. Monte Muambe lies some 30 km southeast of Tete, and is not to be confused with the Monte Muande magnetite-apatite deposit, 30 km northwest of Tete. The almost circular Monte Muambe carbonatite complex is 6.5 km in diameter and contains economic quantities of fluorite (Markwich 1996). The central core of the complex is composed of carbonate rock (Gittins 1966).

The Monte Xiluvo carbonatite complex, which lies close to the Beira-Mutare railway line, consists of a circular ring of hills about 5 km in diameter. The central plug is made up of carbonatite (Gittins 1966). A quarry supplying carbonates for the construction industry has been in operation for many years at this location (Cilek 1989). Some of the more apatite-rich carbonatites have been proposed for use in agriculture (Manhica 1991).

In addition to the above named carbonate resources there are numerous lacustrine limestones and coral limestones along the coast of Mozambique. A compilation of limestone/dolomite resources is listed in Cilek (1989) and Markwich (1996).

Figure 2.11: Distribution of limestone and dolomite deposits in Mozambique (after Cilek 1989).

Gypsum/anhydrite

Cilek (1989) describes several gypsum and anhydrite occurrences from oil and gas exploration boreholes in the coastal zone of Mozambique. The most extensive gypsum and anhydrite deposits are of Oligocene/ Miocene age and occur in the evaporite sequence of the Temane Formation. Most extensive are the 10-15 m thick gypsum and anhydrite beds south of the Save River and Nova Mambone. The reserves of gypsum and anhydrite exceed 250 million tonnes (Cilek 1989). Unfortunately these beds occur at depth of 150-200 m, but might occur closer to the surface in other places (Cilek 1989).

Glauconite

Many of the Cretaceous and Tertiary sediments from Mozambique contain glauconite, specifically the Grudja and Cheringoma Formations (Flores 1973) with some beds containing up to 50% glauconite (Manhica 1991). Their potential agronomic usefulness as soil amendments is based on their elevated potassium and phosphorus contents.

Perlite

Perlite, a volcanic glass that will expand at 800-1,100° C to a lightweight foamy rock material used in the construction and horticultural industry, occurs in the Lebombo Mountains in Mozambique and neighbouring South Africa. In the Lebombo Mountains, perlite is found in association with obsidian and bentonite deposits of the Karoo Supergroup. The perlite resources of Mozambique are largely confined to the deposits around Muguene, west of Maputo. At Muguene South, the reserves of perlite are 100,000 tonnes in the proven reserve category and 400,000 tonnes probable reserves. At Muguene North, the reserves of vitrified volcanic glass are 250,000 tonnes in the proven category and 1 million tonnes probable reserves (Cilek 1989). The bulk density of the expanded perlite from Muguene is 6.84 lb/cubic foot (0.109 g/cm $^{-3}$) which indicates low expansion properties and low quality. A small furnace was operated at Muguene and produced small amounts of perlite in the 1960s.

Extensive obsidian resources with potential perlite properties were discovered in the 1980s near Ressano Garcia, along the Maputo-South Africa highway. However, technical tests of this glassy volcanic material revealed that they had no expansion properties and were therefore unsuitable for the horticultural industry (Cilek 1989). In general, the known perlite resources of Mozambique are small and of low suitability for horticultural industries.

Natural zeolites

The Lebombo volcanics at the border with South Africa are made up of a sequence of extrusives and tuffs. Altered rhyolitic tuffs and perlites of the Lebombo Mountains in the adjacent areas of South Africa are the source for commercial zeolite extraction (Pratley, pers. comm., 1985).

Agromineral potential

The potential for developing Mozambique's geological resources for long-term sustainable agricultural needs is good. There are several extensive phosphate deposits of sedimentary, metamorphic and igneous origin, which could be used for small-scale agromineral development. The very extensive phosphate deposit of Evate (with more than 155 million tonnes of phosphate-bearing ore) and other deposits should not only be investigated for large-scale phosphate extraction, but also on their potential for small-to medium-scale development. The extensive glauconite-bearing Eocene Cheringoma Formation with fossil fish and teeth beds is seen as an excellent indication of finding phosphorite resources in the southern basin of Mozambique and detailed exploration on this target is strongly recommended.

Limestone/dolomite resources are scattered throughout the country and increased efforts should be placed on testing individual resources as to their agronomic efficacy as liming materials, especially on acid soils. Some of these resources are already developed for industrial purposes and their agricultural potential should be assessed. Appropriate and adapted limestone/dolomite crushing and grinding technologies can be developed to provide liming materials to farmers cultivating acid soils.

Glauconitic and slightly phosphatic sandstones of upper Cretaceous age near Maputo should be investigated with regard to their potential use as low-grade slow release 'petrofertilizers.' Their application could be especially interesting for crops with high K requirements like bananas and for perennial crops like coconut.

Exploration for natural zeolites in the Lebombo Mountains near the South African border should occur.

The idea of erecting artificial roosting platforms for sea birds to produce guano, like in Namibia, should be studied.

References:

Bigioggero B, Cadoppi P, Costa M, Omenetto P and R Sacchi 1989. Late Proterozoic granites of Zambezia (Mozambique). IGCP 255 Newsletter, Bull 2:5-7.

Cilek GC 1989. Industrial Minerals of Mozambique. Ministry of Natural Resources, NGIM, Maputo, 326pp.

Davidson DF 1986. Phosphate resources of Mozambique based on available data. Final report to UN/DTCD, INT/80-R45. United Nations, New York, 30pp.

de Freitas AJ 1959. A Geologia e o desenvolvimento Economico e Social de Mocambique, pp 139-140, 146-147.

Flores G 1973. The Cretaceous and Tertiary sedimentary basins of Mozambique and Zululand. In: G. Blant (editor): Sedimentary basins of the African coasts. Union Internationale des sciences géologiques, Assoc. African Geol. Surv. 1973:81-111.

Gittins J 1966. Summaries and bibliographies of carbonatite complexes. In: Tuttle OF and J Gittins (eds.) Carbonatites. Interscience Publ. New York, 417-570.

International Labour Organization (ILO) 1999. Social and labour issues in small-scale mines. TMSSM/1999, 99pp.

Manhica A 1991. Phosphates and apatite of Mozambique. Fert. Res. 30:167-175.

Markwich H 1996. Mozambique. In: Bosse H-R, Gwosdz W, Lorenz W, Markwich, Roth W and F Wolff (eds.) Limestone and dolomite resources of Africa. Geol. Jb., D, 297-309.

Ministry of Mineral Resources and Energy 1997. Mineral resources development and investment opportunities. Maputo, Mozambique, 36pp.

Notholt AJG 1994. Phosphate rock in developing countries: a review of geology, resources and development. In: Mathers SJ and AJG Notholt (eds.) Industrial minerals in developing countries. AGID Report Series Geosciences in International Development 18:193-222.

Nunes AF 1961. Os fosfatos naturais de Mozambique: Boletim dos Instituto de Investigacao Scientifica de Mozambique:17-30.

Pinna P, Jourde G, Calvez JY, Mroz JP and JM Marques 1993. The Mozambique Belt in northern Mozambique: Neoproterozoic (110-850 Ma) crustal growth and tectogenesis, and superimposed Pan-Africa (800-550 Ma) tectonism. Precambr. Res. 62:1-59.

Staff 1984. On geological investigation of magnetite and apatite mineralization at Monte Muanda, Tete Province. Geological Institute, Belgrade, 214pp.

Namibia

Total population (July 2000 estimate): 1,771,000
Area: 825,418 km^2
Annual population growth rate (2000): 1.57 %
Life expectancy at birth (1998): 50.1 years
People not expected to survive to age 40 (1998): 33.5% of total population
GDP per capita (1998): US $5,176

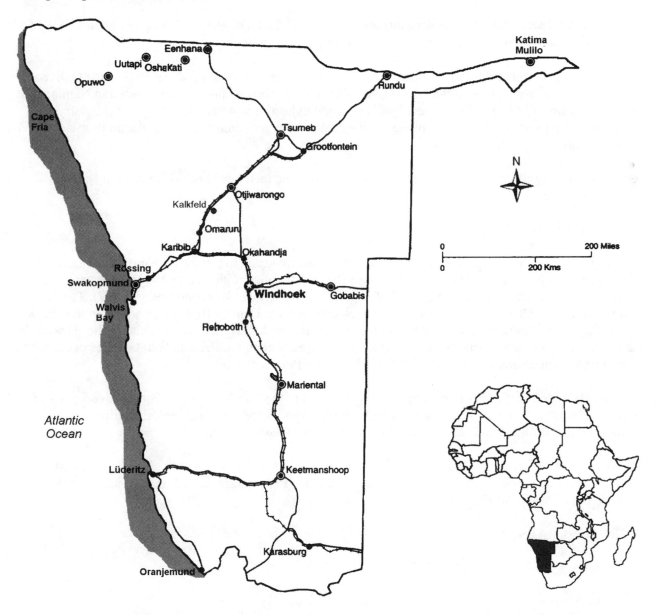

Namibia is a sparsely populated country in southerwestern Africa with a long Atlantic coastline. Desert conditions prevail in a strip along the Atlantic seaboard (the Namib Desert) and throughout the eastern and north-eastern part of the country in the Kalahari Desert. The interior of Namibia consists largely of dissected plateaux and mountainous areas with a semi-arid climate. The north-central portion of Namibia bordering Angola is agriculturally more intensively used than the rest of the country. Here, in the 'Ovamboland' of Namibia, lives approximately 46% of the total population. Annual precipitation in this area reaches 450-550 mm. Crop production is largely subsistence based with millet, sorghum and maize being the main food crops.

The main agricultural activity in the rest of the country is livestock ranching on extensive farms.

The agricultural sector of Namibia accounts for only 12% of the GDP and employs an estimated 38% of the working population. The offshore fishery is gaining in economic importance.

Economically, the mineral sector continues to be a major factor, contributing about 56% of the GDP and employing an estimated 23% of the labour force. The main mineral commodities extracted in Namibia are diamonds, followed by uranium, copper, gold and some industrial minerals including salt (Ministry of Mines and Energy 1992). By far the highest value comes from gem-quality alluvial diamonds mined offshore along the Atlantic coast.

In recent years significant natural gas reserves (3 trillion cubic feet) have been delineated in Namibia's offshore areas.

Geological outline

The geology of Namibia can be divided into several geotectonic and lithologic domains. The oldest domain belongs to the Paleoproterozoic Vaalian to lower Mokolian, followed by the Mesoproterozoic middle to upper Mokolian rocks (Republic of Namibia - Ministry of Mines and Energy 1992). The sedimentary and volcanogenic succession of the Neoproterozoic Damara Belt comprises more than 60% of Namibia's rock outcrops. This northeast - southwest striking belt is folded and metamorphosed with the metamorphic grade progressively increasing towards the axial centre of the fold belt. Granites occur in the central part of the Damara Belt (Martin 1965; Martin and Porada 1977).

A relatively undeformed syn- to post-orogenic succession of the Cambrian Nama Group covers parts of southern Namibia. The terrestrial Kalahari Beds of Tertiary to Recent age are predominantly unconsolidated aeolian sand dunes and occupy large parts of eastern Namibia.

Pan-African and early Cretaceous alkaline ring complexes and carbonatites occur along a north-east trending structural zone, a continental expression of an extensive transform fault that offsets the Mid-Atlantic ridge (Marsh 1972).

AGROMINERALS

Phosphates

Three main types of phosphates can be distinguished in Namibia:

- Phosphates associated with alkaline complexes and carbonatites,
- Phosphates of biogenic sedimentary origin,
- Phosphates in guano.

Phosphates associated with alkaline complexes and carbonatites.

Low-grade phosphates are associated with several of the alkaline and carbonatite complexes in Namibia (McManus and Schneider 1994; Pirajno 1994). These alkaline complexes are aligned along a northeast striking linear zone over a distance of approximately 370 km (Figure 2.12). An extension of this zone is found in Brazil (Marsh 1972).

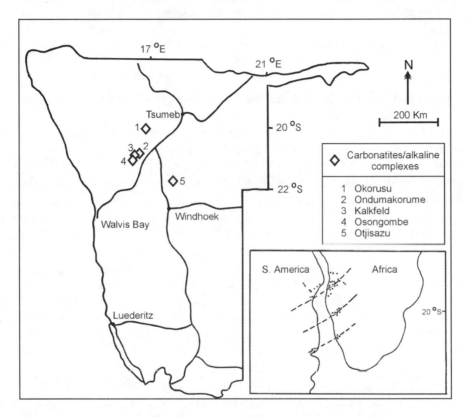

Figure 2.12: Location of carbonatites and alkaline complexes in Namibia with insert showing correlation with similar South American complexes (insert after Marsh, 1972).

The average P_2O_5 content in these alkaline and carbonatite complexes of this zone are as follows:

- Okorusu complex, in the Otjiwarongo District: 3-4% P_2O_5,
- Ondumakorume complex, northeast of Kalkfeld: 7% P_2O_5,
- Kalkfeld complex, 11 km northwest of the village of Kalkfeld: 6.7% P_2O_5,
- Osongombe complex, southwest of Kalkfeld: 6.5% P_2O_5,
- Otjisazu complex, southeast of Kalkfeld, in the Okahandja District: 3-9% P_2O_5,
- and smaller phosphate occurrences in other complexes (McManus and Schneider 1994).

The apatite-bearing part of the Otjisazu pyroxenite complex contains indicated reserves of at least 35 million tonnes of ore at 3-9% P_2O_5 to a depth of 30 m (Schneider and Schreuder 1992).

Sedimentary offshore phosphates

So far, no onshore sedimentary phosphates have been discovered in Namibia but there are considerable offshore deposits of pelletal phosphorite south of the of the Kunene River mouth. The resources are estimated at 174 million tonnes of sediment with P_2O_5 values varying from 1 to 4.6%, at depths of 150-250 m. The offshore phosphatic sediments between Walvis Bay and Luederitz contain 1,430 million tonnes of P_2O_5 with grades exceeding 4.6% P_2O_5 (Schneider and Schreuder 1992). However, the mining of these low-grade phosphate sediments at considerable depth of the ocean is too costly to be economically feasible.

Guano

The only phosphates mined in Namibia at present are those from guano deposits. Bird guano has been extracted since the 1800s (Hutchinson 1950) from 13 small offshore islands along the Atlantic coast. Production between 1844 and 1991 was 869,332 tonnes, averaging approximately 6,000 tonnes per year. A typical analysis of Namibia's offshore guano is 21-29% P_2O_5 and 20-40% N.

A unique development in guano 'mining' started in 1931 with the erection of artificial roosting platforms for birds along the coast of Namibia. Until 1991 the total production of guano from these platforms was 130,275 tonnes, averaging about 2,150 tonnes per year. Most of the guano 'harvested' from these artificial islands is exported to Europe.

Small tonnages of cave (bat) guano have been recovered from caves near Karibib, and from caves on a farm in the Windhoek District (Farm Arnhem 222). Leached parts of the Arnhem bat guano deposits contain only 3% P_2O_5, while unexposed bat guano contains up to 10% P_2O_5. Recovery of bat guano from the Arnhem deposits peaked between 1928 and 1940 and the total yield from these deposits was 2,914 tonnes (Schneider and Schreuder 1992).

Gypsum

Surficially, gypsum-enriched sands and gravel have been found in the coastal Namib belt. Several million tonnes of gypsum-bearing sands grading between 30-90% gypsum have been located close to Swakopmund and Walvis Bay coastal area (Schneider and Genis 1992a; McManus and Schneider 1994). 2,623 tonnes of gypsum was produced between 1967 and 1970 in the Tumas area, 40 km east-northeast of Walvis Bay. The grade of this hard and massive gypsum layer, 30-90 cm thick, is generally more than 90%. The total reserves in the Tumas area amount to more than 4 million tonnes (Schneider and Schreuder 1992).

Limestone/dolomite

Limestone and dolomitic limestone resources of Namibia are enormous and Gwosdz (1996) has compiled the limestone and dolomite resources of Namibia from 22 localities. The carbonates are located mainly in the metasedimentary succession of the Damara Supergroup but carbonates from carbonatites, and from calcrete crusts are also reported.

Nitrates

The coastal Namib Desert, at the east-side of the cold nutrient-rich Benguela Stream geographically and climatically resembles the Atacama Desert in Chile, the world's only nitrate-producing area. However, so far only small amounts of soda nitre ($NaNO_3$) have been found in this area.

The main occurrences of nitrates are in secondary environments where leached nitrate has been accumulated, for instance in sheltered cliffs, in talus at the foot of cliffs and in encrustations of secondary nitrate on various rocks (Schneider and Genis 1992b).

Agromineral potential

The best potential use of locally available, effective 'agrominerals' for Namibia's small crop production sector is limited to guano. In addition, exploration to find nitrate resources in the coastal zone of Namibia should be intensified. Many climatic, geographical and environmental conditions are similar to the areas of the Atacama Desert in Chile, where the largest naturally occurring nitrate deposits of the world are found and mined.

References:

Gwosdz W 1996. Namibia. In: Bosse H-R, Gwosdz W, Lorenz W, Markwich, Roth W and F Wolff 1996 (eds.) Limestone and dolomite resources of Africa. Geol. Jb., D, 102:310-320.

Hutchinson GE 1950. Survey of existing of biogeochemistry - The geochemistry of vertebrae excretion. Bull. Am. Mus. Nat. History, 96:554 pp.

Marsh JS 1972. Relationships between transform directions and alkaline igneous rock lineaments in Africa and South America. Earth Planet. Lett., 18:317-323.

Martin H 1965. The Precambrian geology of South West Africa and Namaqualand. Precambrian Research Unit, University of Cape Town, 159pp.

Martin H and H Porada 1977. The intracratonic branch of the Damara orogen in South West Africa. Precambr. Res., 5:311-357.

McManus MNC and GIC Schneider 1994. Namibia: industrial minerals. In: Mathers SJ and AJG Notholt (eds.) Industrial minerals in developing countries. AGID Report Series Geosciences in International Development 18:111-134.

Pirajno F 1994. Mineral resources of anorogenic alkaline complexes in Namibia: A review. Austral. J. Earth Sci., 41:157-168.

Republic of Namibia - Ministry of Mines and Energy, Geological Survey 1992. The mineral resources of Namibia.

Schneider GIC and G Genis 1992a. Gypsum. In: Ministry of Mines and Energy, Geological Survey 1992. The mineral resources of Namibia: 6.18-1

Schneider GIC and G Genis 1992b. Nitrate. In: Ministry of Mines and Energy, Geological Survey 1992. The mineral resources of Namibia: 6.18-1.

Schneider GIC and CP Schreuder 1992. Phosphate. In: Ministry of Mines and Energy, Geological Survey 1992. The mineral resources of Namibia: 6.18- 1-11.

Niger

Total population (July 2000 estimate): 10,076,000
Area: 1,267,000 km^2
Annual population growth rate (2000): 2.75%
Life expectancy at birth (1998): 48.9 years
People not expected to survive to age 40 (1998): 35.2% of total population
GDP per capita (1998): US $739

Landlocked arid Niger occupies a large expanse of central West Africa at the edge of the Sahara Desert. Northern Niger is occupied by the Air Mountains and extensions of the Hoggar Mountains from Algeria. The Niger River crosses the southwest corner of the country. The climate is hot and dry. More than half of the country receive less than 250 mm precipitation per year. Only in the extreme south, at the border with Nigeria, Benin and Burkina Faso, does the annual rate of precipitation exceed 600 mm.

Niger is one of the poorest countries in the world and droughts and famines are recurrent problems affecting the country. Niger's agriculture is based on livestock rearing and crop production. In 1999, the agricultural sector accounted for 41% of the GDP. Ninety percent of the population lives in rural areas and is engaged in agricultural practices. Population growth and subsequent increased demand for food production creates a strong pressure on the fragile agricultural resources of Niger.

Agriculture consists largely of a subsistence-oriented, rainfed crop production system, combined with livestock rearing and other commercial activities. Low precipitation is the main limiting factor for crop production, although the decline in soil fertility in the sandy acid soils with low organic matter is another. The main soil-limiting nutrients are nitrogen and phosphorus. Food crops are millet, sorghum, cowpeas and cassava. Agricultural exports are mainly livestock, cowpeas and onions.

The main mineral commodities produced in Niger are uranium and gold. The uranium reserves in the north of the country were estimated by the OECD/Nuclear Energy Agency as the fifth largest in the world (OECD/NEA 1980). The combined uranium production in 1999 was 2,916 tonnes (Mining Annual Review 2000). Small amounts of coal are also produced. Recent mineral exploration efforts focus on gold mineralization in the western part of Niger. Small-scale mining of precious minerals employs some 15,000 people (International Labour Organization 1999).

Petroleum exploration resulted in the discovery of a 300 million barrel resource (Mining Annual Reveiw 2000).

Geological outline

Precambrian rocks underlie large parts of Niger but Quaternary and Neogene continental weathering products and sand dunes conceal most of the Precambrian rocks. Paleoproterozoic rocks are exposed in an area to the west of the capital city Niamey. They form a continuation of the Birimian rocks from Burkina Faso (Wright *et al.* 1985; Pons *et al.* 1995). Other Precambrian rocks occur in the Air Massif in the north of the country. Neoproterozoic sequences crop out some 100 km south of Niamey along the border with Benin and Burkina Faso, in a continuation of the Volta Basin.

Paleozoic platform sediments of marine and continental origin occupy parts of northeastern Niger and the Agadez Basin west of the Air Massif. Cretaceous marine and epicontinental sediments of the Ilullemeden Basin occur in the central part of Niger. Tertiary sediments cover parts of the southwest, east of Niamey.

Volcanic activities, with associated lavas, tuffs and ash deposition, have taken place intermittently from the Devonian to the Quaternary.

AGROMINERALS

Phosphates

Phosphate mineralization has been found in at least three different geological environments in Niger. The best known phosphates are the Eocene phosphorites of Tahoua and the Neoproterozoic phosphorites of Tapoa.

The Upper Cretaceous to Eocene phosphorites near Tahoua.

Phosphate nodules occur in flat-lying upper Cretaceous to Eocene sediments near Tahoua, 375 km northeast of Niamey. Initial geological and geophysical assessments were carried out in valley outcrops east and southeast of the village of I-n-Akker (or Aneker), some 63 km north-northwest of Tahoua (Dumas 1971), and in the Kao area. Initial geological surveys carried out in cooperation with a Canadian company (Watts, Griffis and McQuat) indicate that the phosphates occur as discrete nodules in various layers of Paleocene (or possibly Eocene) argillites - 'La series argileuse.' These phosphate-bearing argillites lie below the Tertiary 'continental Terminal' and rest on Paleocene calcareous sediments (Dumas 1971). The nodules are very fine-grained, hard, cream-coloured, spherical or disc-shaped, break with a conchoidal fracture, and stick to the tongue. Nodule size ranges from less than 1 cm to 'baguette-size,' up to 75 cm length. The P_2O_5 concentration in the nodules ranges from 19-27 % with a mean of 23.7% P_2O_5 (63 samples). Associated minerals in the nodules are limonite and goethite, quartz and kaolinite (Dumas 1971). The clay in which the nodules are embedded is palygorskite (attapulgite) and the percentage of nodules in the clay matrix varies but is usually less than 4%. The thickness of the shale beds in which the nodules occur in the I-n-Akker area is 6.5 m.

Elevated radioactivity coincides with the nodule-bearing argillite bed. Detailed investigations show however, that the elevated radioactivity is largely confined to the clays and not to the phosphate nodules. The results of chemical analyses of 14 phosphate samples show that the U_3O_8 concentration in the phosphate nodules is less than 100 mg/kg (Dumas 1971).

The total tonnage of the Tahoua phosphate resource, as reported by Johnson (1995), is 7.5 million tonnes phosphate rock (concentrate), grading 32% P_2O_5. Truong and Montange (1998), quoting *La Chronicle de la Recherche Minière 484* (1986), BRGM – Orléans, estimated the reserves of Tahoua at 5 million tonnes with an average grade of 25% P_2O_5.

Hanon (1990) describes another extensive low-grade Upper Cretaceous to Eocene phosphate resource to the south and southeast of Tahoua towards the border with Nigeria. Detailed mapping was carried out by members of a joint Niger-Belgium cooperative project to the south of Tahoua (Hanon 1990). The sediments are gently inclined to the southwest and capped by a ferruginous Upper Eocene formation.

Phosphatic nodules are reported from various stratigraphic horizons within the Upper Cretaceous to Eocene sedimentary sequence. Phosphate nodules in the 'Formation de Farim Doutchi' of upper Cretaceous (Maastrichtian) age are relatively rare (Hanon 1990) but elevated phosphate concentrations are apparent in the upper 'Formation d'In Wagar,' the top bed of the Maastrichtian (Upper Cretaceous). This bed contains bone debris of fishes and reptiles as well as coprolites.

However, the main phosphate nodule horizons occur in the overlying Paleocene and Lower Eocene 'Formation de Garadaoua' where phosphatic nodules reach sizes of 20-50 cm. The phosphate nodules occur in clay-rich horizons with palygorskite (attapulgite) as main clay mineral. From their very thin-layered appearance these clay beds are also known as 'schistes-carton' or 'schistes papyraces' (Hanon 1990). Weathered out and eroded phosphatic nodules are scattered on valley bottoms. Accumulations of phosphatic nodules of the Paleocene to Lower Eocene occur in the region of Tamaske (35-40 km east-southeast of Tahoua) and at the confluence of the Keita and Ode Rivers (Hanon 1990).

The phosphate-bearing beds north and south of Tahoua can be correlated with phosphate-bearing beds of neighbouring Nigeria and Mali (Hanon 1990) and are part of a large phosphate province that cuts through central West Africa.

The chemical analyses of the phosphates from the Tahoua concentrate (from I-n-Akker) are high in P_2O_5 (27.7%) but also relatively high in Fe_2O_3 (13%) (Bationo 1990; Bationo et al. 1998). The iron likely originates from the iron oxides goethite and limonite in the nodules. The crystallographic data of the phosphate provided by Pichot et al. (1981) and Roesch and Pichot (1985) suggest that the Tahoua phosphate is a francolite with a relatively low reactivity (unit-cell a-value = 9.351 Å). In contrast, the crystallographic data provided by Mokwunye (1995) indicate a francolite with unit-cell a-value of 9.331 Å and a molar PO_4/CO_3 ratio of 4.88, indicating much higher reactivity. The neutral ammonium citrate (NAC) solubility data range from 1.9-3.6% P_2O_5 illustrating the great variability of the phosphate materials. Truong and Montange (1998) rank the reactivity of Tahoua PR as 'medium.' The surface area of the Tahoua francolites is high, 14.7 m^2 per gram for the 0.5 mm fraction and 19.1 m^2 per gram for the 0.1 mm fraction (Truong and Fayard 1995).

Phosphate nodules from the exposed and weathered shale beds in the I-n-Akker and Kao area north of Tahoua were extracted in the 1970s and 1980s from trenches with shovels and pickaxes and the nodules were hand picked. Approximately 1,000 tonnes of phosphate rock per year were produced from 1979 to 1984 in this very dry and remote area.

The phosphate nodules were transported to Tahoua and milled at a plant with a capacity of 10,000 tonnes per year. Most of the phosphates mined and processed between 1979 and 1984 were used for direct application trials (Van Kauwenbergh et al. 1991). Costs of production, including excavation, milling and transport, were US $66.67 per tonne of phosphate concentrate (Dahoui 1995). With transportation to the farming areas, administrative costs and margins, the total cost of Tahoua phosphate rock (Tahoua PR) was US $125.71 per tonne (Dahoui 1995).

Agronomic Testing of Tahoua Phosphate Rock

Scientists from national and international institutions have tested Tahoua PR over many years on various soils, in various agroecological zones, and in various farming systems. Agronomic test work included studies by Roesch and Pichot (1985), Bationo et al. (1990, 1998) and Mahamane et al. (1997). The results show that Tahoua PR proved 82-91% as effective as single superphosphate (SSP) for millet production on sandy soils in Niger in both the initial and subsequent seasons (Bationo et al. 1990). The effectiveness of Tahoua PR proved better in agroecological zones with higher precipitation. Tahoua PR also proved more effective on millet than on cowpea (Mahamane et al. 1997; Bationo et al. 1998).

As part of a GTZ supported project, a team of agronomists and agro-economists from Niger and Germany carried out detailed economic analyses and agronomic research in Niger (Lamers et al. 1999). These researchers concluded that the application of medium quantities of Tahoua PR (39 kg Tahoua PR/ha) in favourable ecological settings seems one of the more promising fertilizer application strategies, along with other measures (Lamers et al. 1999).

Agroeconomic evaluations show that the value-to-cost ratio (VCR) of directly applied Tahoua PR is higher than that of SSP. It is interesting to note that the highest yields were not necessarily the most cost effective and beneficial options for the farmer. The highest VCR was reached with Tahoua PR application followed by additional hillside pocket application of 3 kg P per hectare superphosphate (Bationo et al. 1998). The profitability of fertilizer applications varied according to rainfall zones and on location specific conditions (Lamers et al. 1999).

Scientists from the International Crops Research in the Semi-Arid Tropics (ICRISAT) conducted on-farm evaluations of soil fertility options in Niger. Their work indicates that the most cost-effective technology is Tahoua PR applied on millet-cowpea crop rotation in favourable ecological settings.

Phosphorites of Possible Upper Cretaceous Age.

Nearly horizontal layers of possible 'Upper Cretaceous' phosphorites have been reported from boreholes at Aschia Tinamou northeast of Zinder and 45 km west-southwest of the Massif de Termet, north of Goure (Greigert and Pougnet 1967). Unfortunately these layers have no surface outcrops and information on extent and grade are very limited. The association of phosphorites with palygorskite (attapulgite) clays suggests a favourable environment for phosphate accumulations (McClellan and Notholt 1986). The age of these phosphates is not clear.

Upper Devonian to early Carboniferous phosphorites.

Few details have been reported on the Lower Carboniferous 'gypsiferous phosphate nodules' in the black shales of the Talak Formation in northern Niger, north of Agadez (18°45' N; 7°50' E). The Talak Formation overlies the glaciogenic Devonian to early Carboniferous Teragh Sandstone (Hambrey and Kluyver 1981). The phosphates occur within the sequence of black fossiliferous argillites of the Talak Shale Formation, which also contains Lumachelles (*Productus, Spinifer*), bryozoans and lingulas (Hambrey and Kluyver 1981). No data on the sedimentology, thickness of the phosphatic beds or composition and mineralogy of these 'gypsiferous phosphates' are provided.

The Neoproterozoic Tapoa (Parc W) phosphorite deposit.

By far the largest phosphorite resource in West Africa is located at Tapoa, close to the border with Benin (12°29' N; 2°25' E) (Figure 2.5). This Neoproterozoic phosphate deposit, approximately 135 km south-southeast of Niamey in the Parc Nationaux du 'W,' also called Parc West, can be geologically correlated with the phosphorite deposits of Kodjari in Burkina Faso and Mekrou Bend in Benin. The phosphatic beds are intercalated with shales and siltstones. The flat-lying, 30-40 m thick sedimentary succession is largely covered by thick sandstones. The grade of the phosphorite sequence ranges from 18-35% P_2O_5 (Trompette 1986) with reserve estimates ranging from 100-500 million tonnes of phosphorite containing 23% P_2O_5. Similarly, Truong and Montange (1998) quoted the estimated reserves of Tapoa at 200 million tonnes with a grade of 23% P_2O_5. According to the Mining Annual Review (1995), the phosphate resources are approximately 400 to 500 million tonnes.

Lucas *et al.* (1986) characterized coarse phosphorite samples from Parc West. X-ray diffraction analysis of the apatite indicated a crystallographic unit-cell a-value of 9.354 Å. The refractive index is 1.627. McClellan and Saavedra (1986) determined the a-value of 9.364 Å, with a mean refractive index of 1.624. The agronomic potential based on measurements of the molar PO_4/CO_3 ratio (15.2) and the mineralogical parameters are indicative of a low carbonate-substituted francolite and thus a phosphate rock with low reactivity. The measured neutral ammonium citrate (NAC) solubility of Parc West PR ranges from 1.4-2.8% P_2O_5 (Mokwunye 1995), lower than many other sedimentary phosphates. However, the iron and aluminum contents of these rocks are low (2.9% Fe_2O_3), making them more suitable for modification techniques like partial acidulation.

Bationo *et al.* (1990) demonstrated the higher efficacy of directly applied finely ground Tahoua PR *vis-à-vis* Parc West PR, reflecting the higher reactivity of Tahoua PR. However, partial acidulation (PAPR), was successful for the iron-poor Parc West PR and less effective for the iron-rich Tahoua PR (Bationo *et al.* 1990). This was consistent with the findings of Hammond *et al.* (1989), who indicated that the $Fe_2O_3 + Al_2O_3$ content of PR can significantly influence the agronomic effectiveness of PAPR.

In general, the agronomic effectiveness of Parc West PR is low when applied directly to the soils due to the inherent mineralogical constraints but can be upgraded by partial acidulation or other modification techniques (Bationo *et al.* 1995).

Limestone/dolomite

Large resources of Precambrian marbles occur in remote parts southwest of the Air Massif (Gwosdz 1996). Thin lenses of Precambrian dolomite are reported from an area close to the border with Mali, near Firgoun. Cretaceous limestones occur in several locations in central Niger, specifically east of Tanout (near Damergou), and around Tchi-n-Salantine and southeast of the Air Massif. Paleocene limestones near Malbaza are utilized for the production of cement (Gwosdz 1996).

Gypsum

Johnson (1995) reports several gypsum deposits in Niger, the largest of which is at I-n-Aridal with 28 million tonnes. No further information on quantity, quality and extractability of the gypsum deposits and occurrences of Niger are reported.

Agromineral potential

Niger's agromineral potential, especially for phosphates, is good. The country is well endowed with large phosphate resources. Nodules with 18-35% P_2O_5 from the flat lying Paleocene-Eocene sediments in large areas north and south of Tahoua are of good quality and have good potential for direct application.

From a large-scale mining point of view, however, the resource is probably uneconomic. Appropriate small- to medium-scale mining and processing techniques including selective mining, breaking up of the clay-rich matrix and screening with a trommel to concentrate the nodules should be tested. In addition, grinding and pelletizing equipment as well as biological modification techniques should be envisaged to increase the usefulness of these valuable resources for the local market.

The enormous Precambrian-Cambrian resources of relatively unreactive phosphates from the Parc West deposit (Tapoa) have to be evaluated in more detail to determine their potential as modified phosphate fertilizers. The choice of appropriate phosphate modification technologies will largely depend on the market and end use of these resources.

Other agrominerals have only limited potential for enhancing Niger's crop production.

References:

Banaante CA 1986. Economic evaluation of alternative fertilizer technologies for tropical African agriculture. In: Mokwunye AU and PLG Vlek (eds.) Management of nitrogen and phosphorus fertilizers in sub-Saharan Africa. Martinus Nijhoff, Dordrecht, Netherlands: 223-256.

Bationo A, Chien SH, Henao J, Christianson CB and AU Mokunye 1990. Agronomic evaluation of two unacidulated and partially acidulated phosphate rocks indigenous to Niger. Soil Sci. Soc. Am. J. 54:1772-1777.

Bationo A, Ayuk E, and U Mokwunye 1995. Long-term evaluation of alternative phosphorus fertilizers for pearl millet production on the sandy Sahelian soils of West Africa semi-arid tropics. In: Gerner H and AU Mokwunye (eds.) Use of phosphate rock for sustainable agriculture in West Africa. IFDC, Miscellaneous Fert. Studies, 11:42-53.

Bationo A, Koala S and E Ayuk 1998. Fertilité des sols pour la production céréalière en zone sahelo-soudanienne et valorisation des phosphates naturels. Cahiers Agricultures, 7:365-371.

Dahoui KP 1995. Costs determinants of phosphate rock in some West African countries. In: Gerner H and AU Mokwunye (eds.) Use of phosphate rock for sustainable agriculture in West Africa. IFDC, Miscellaneous Fert. Studies 11:128-133.

Dumas MC 1971. Projet des phosphates de Tahoua - Niger, Rapport sur la phase I. Report of Watts, Griffis, and McOuat to the Canadian International Development Agency (CIDA), Toronto, Canada, 52pp.

Greigert J and R Pougnet 1967. Essai de description des formations géologiques de la République du Niger. Bur. Rech. Geol. Min. Memoir 48:178-179.

Gwosdz W 1996. Niger. In: Bosse H-R, Gwosdz W, Lorenz W, Markwich, Roth W and F Wolff 1996 (eds.) Limestone and dolomite resources of Africa. Geol. Jb., D, 102: 321-326.

Hambrey MJ and HM Kluyver 1981. Evidence of Devonian or Early Carboniferous glaciation in the Agades region of Niger. In: Hambrey MJ and WB Harland (eds.) Earth's pre-Pleistocene glacial record, Cambridge University Press, Cambridge, UK: 188-190.

Hammond LL, Chien SH, Roy AH and AU Mokwunye 1989. Solubility and agronomic effectiveness of partially acidulated phosphate rocks, as influenced by their iron and aluminum oxide content. Fert. Res. 19:93-98.

Hanon M 1990. Notice explicative sur la carte géologique de L'Ader Doutchi. Ministère des Mines et de l'Energie, Direction des Recherches Géologiques et Minières, Niamey, Niger, 36pp.

International Labour Organization 1999. Social and labour issues in small-scale mines. MSSM/1999, 99pp.

Johnson AKC 1995. Inventory and mining of local mineral resources in West Africa. In: Gerner H and AU Mokwunye (eds.) Use of phosphate rock for sustainable agriculture in West Africa. IFDC, Miscellaneous Fert. Studies 11:21-40.

Lamers J, Bruentrup M, Buerkert A and F Heidfus 1999. Profitability of innovative fertilizing practices for sustainable soil fertility management in Sudano-Sahelian West Africa. Report to German Technical Cooperation (GTZ), 67pp.

Lucas J, Ilyin AV and A Kuehn 1986. Proterozoic and Cambrian phosphorites - deposits: Volta Basin, West Africa. In: Cook PJ and JH Shergold (eds.) Phosphate deposits of the world, Vol. 1: Proterozoic and Cambrian phosphorites, Cambridge University Press, Cambridge, UK: 235-243.

Mahamane I, Bationo A, Seyni F and Z Hamidou 1997. Acquis recents des recherches sur les phosphates naturels du Niger. In: Renard G, Neef A, Becker K and M von Oppen (eds.) Soil fertility management in West African land use systems. Markgraf Verlag, Weikersheim, Germany. 73-78.

McClellan GH and AJG Notholt 1986. Phosphate deposits of sub-Saharan Africa. In: Mokwunye AU and PLG Vlek (eds.) Management of nitrogen and phosphorus fertilizers in sub-Saharan Africa. Martinus Nijhoff, Dordrecht, Netherlands:173-224.

McClellan GH and FN Saavedra 1986. Proterozoic and Cambrian phosphorites - specialist studies: chemical and mineral characteristics of some Precambrian phosphorites. In: Cook PJ and JH Shergold (eds.) Phosphate deposits of the world, Vol. 1. Proterozoic and Cambrian phosphorites. Cambridge University Press, Cambridge, UK: 244-267.

Mining Annual Review 1995. Niger. The Mining Journal Ltd. London, 153-154.

Mining Annual Review 2000. Niger. The Mining Journal Ltd. London.

Mokwunye AU 1995. Reactions in soils involving phosphate rocks. In: Gerner H and AU Mokwunye (eds.) Use of phosphate rock for sustainable agriculture in West Africa. IFDC, Miscellaneous Fert. Studies 11:84-92.

OECD/NEA 1980. World uranium - Geology and resource potential. Intern. Uranium Resource Evaluation Project, Miller Freeman Publ. Inc. San Francisco, USA: 524pp.

Pichot J, Truong B and A Traore 1982. Influence du chaulage du sol sur la solubilisation et l'éfficacité des phosphates naturels tricalciques d'Afriaque de l'Ouest: Etude en milieu controlé sur un sol ferralitique de Madagascar. Agron. Trop. 377:56-67.

Pons J, Barbey P, Dupuis D and JM Leger 1995. Mechanisms of pluton emplacement and structural evolution of a 2.1 GA juvenile continental crust: the Birimian of southwestern Niger. Precambrian Res. 70: 281-301.

Roesch M and J Pichot 1985. Utilisation du phosphate naturel de Tahoua en fumure de fond et en fumure d'entretien dans les sols sableaux du Niger. Agron. Trop. 40:89-97.

Trompette R 1986. Phosphorites of the northern Volta Basin (Burkina Faso, Niger and Benin). In: Notholt AJG, Sheldon RP and DF Davidson (eds.) Phosphate deposits of the world. Vol 2. Phosphate rock resources, Cambridge University Press, Cambridge, UK: 214-218

Truong B and C Fayard 1995. Small-scale fertilizer production units using raw and partially solubilized phosphate. In: Gerner H and AU Mokwunye (eds.) Use of phosphate rock for sustainable agriculture in West Africa. IFDC, Miscellaneous Fert. Studies, 11:181-197.

Truong B and D Montange 1998. The African experience with phosphate rock, including Djebel Onk, and case studies in Brazil and Vietnam. In: Johnston AE and JK Syers (eds.) Nutrient management for sustainable crop production in Asia. CAB International, Wallingford, UK: 133-148.

Van Kauwenbergh SJ, Johnson AKC, McClellan GH and HW Mueller 1991. Evaluation of the underdeveloped phosphate deposits of the Volta Basin and West Africa: Benin, Burkina Faso, Ghana, Mali, Mauritania, and Niger. International Fertilizer Development Center, Muscle Shoals, Alabama, USA, 237pp.

Wright JB, Hastings DA, Jones WB and HR Williams 1985. Geology and mineral resources of West Africa. Allen and Unwin, London, UK: 187pp.

Nigeria

Total population (July 2000 estimate): 123,338,000
Area: 923,768 km^2
Annual population growth rate (2000): 2.67%
Life expectancy at birth (1998): 50.1 years
People not expected to survive to age 40 (1998): 33.3% of total population
GDP per capita (1998): US $795

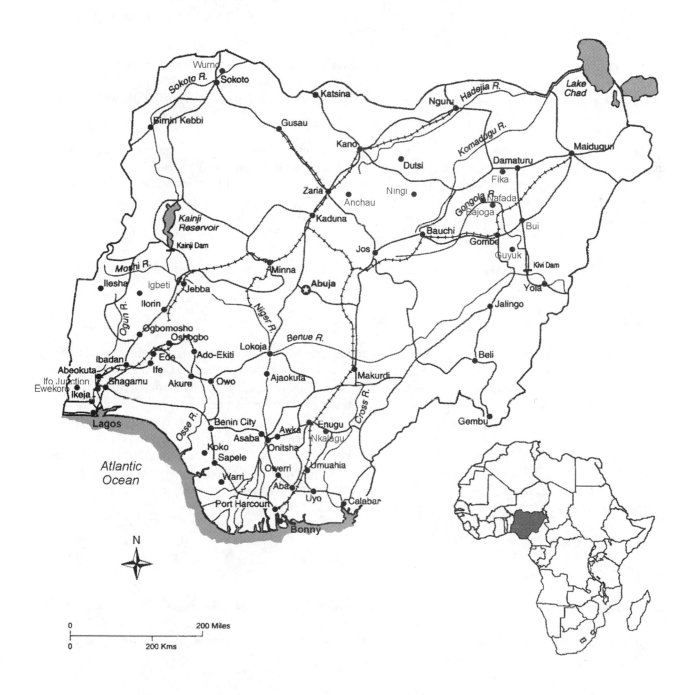

Nigeria is the most populated country in sub-Saharan Africa. Geographically, it can be divided into four main landscape units: the low-lying swampy areas in the south and southeast, the inland tropical forest, the open woodland and grass savanna beyond the tropical forest, and the open grassland in the north of the country.

Nigeria's economy is largely based on its oil resources. Although Nigeria is a country rich in natural resources, more than 40% of its population exists at the absolute poverty threshold of less than US $1 per day. The agricultural sector is expected to play an increasing role in the economy of the country. In 1999, agriculture accounted for 39% of the GDP and employed more than 50% of the population, mainly in subsistence farming and in estate farming. The main food crops are cassava, sorghum, maize, millet, rice and taro. Main export crops and agricultural products include palm oil, rubber, groundnuts and cocoa. One of the major soil related constraints of sustainable crop production on the acid soils of large parts of Nigeria is phosphorus deficiency (Adediran *et al.* 1998).

Nigeria is the largest oil producer in sub-Saharan Africa. In 1998, the oil reserves were estimated at 22.5 billion barrels. Also, the natural gas reserves are large with proven reserves of 124 trillion cubic feet (TCF). However, due to a lack of gas utilization infrastructure, Nigeria flares (burns off at the well) 75% of the gas it produces.

The sale of oil accounts for about 35% of Nigeria's GDP and more than 90% of its export revenues. Other potential mineral raw materials include gold, coal, aluminum, tantalum and tin. The Raw Materials Research and Development Council (RMRDC) advertises a list of non-metallic minerals with extensive reserves including asbestos, barite, bauxite, clay, kaolin, fireclay, diatomite, dolomite, feldspar, fluorspar, gypsum, ilmenite, kyanite, limestone, phosphate, salt, soda-ash and talc (Ministry of Solid Minerals Development 2000).

The RMRDC installed a 15,000 tonne per year pilot plant for the mining and processing of, among other things, phosphate rock at Katsina in the north of the country (Synge 1996).

Geological outline

Precambrian rocks of the 'Basement Complex,' including gneisses, amphibolites, marbles and the 'Older Granites' underlie large parts of Nigeria. Post-tectonic tin-tungsten-bearing 'Younger Granites' of late Paleozoic to Mesozoic age exhibit ring structures. The southwest-northeast striking Benue Trough is part of a down-faulted 'failed arm' of a triple junction that formed when Africa and South America separated in the Cretaceous. The Benue Trough is largely covered by Cretaceous continental and marine sediments (Figure 2.13). Transgressive marine Upper Cretaceous as well as Tertiary sediments are found in the northwestern Sokoto State near the Niger-Benin border as well as in the south of the country. Post-Eocene sediments cover large parts of northeast Nigeria, as well as the Niger Delta. Volcanic rocks including basaltic lava flows, trachytic plugs, central volcanoes and small basaltic cinder cones occur in the Jos Plateau and the Benue Trough, for instance in the Biu area.

AGROMINERALS

Phosphates

Lower Eocene sedimentary phosphates have been known from southern Nigeria since 1921 (Russ 1924, quoted in McClellan and Notholt 1986). Phosphatic sediments occur between the Ifo Junction and Ososum in southwestern Nigeria, approximately 43 km and 48 km north of Lagos (McClellan and Notholt 1986).

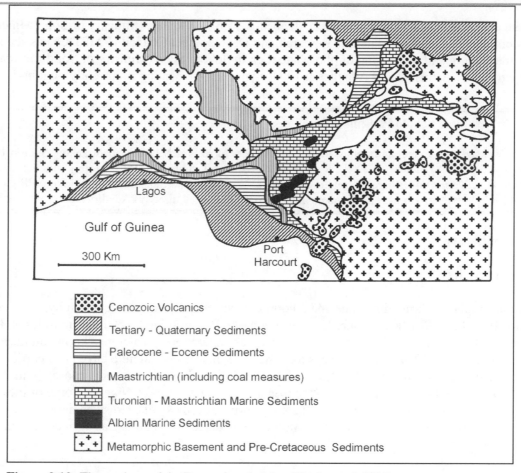

Figure 2.13: The geology of the Benue trough (after Wright *et al.* 1985).

In the southwestern part of the country, phosphate resources occur in the Eocene Ilaro Formation and are presently being mined at Ifo Junction in Orgun State. The resource estimate of this phosphate deposit is 40 million tonnes, but the reserve estimates need updating and confirmation (Ministry of Solid Minerals Development 2000). Other authors, for instance McClellan and Notholt (1986) estimate the PR reserves at this location as slightly over 1 million tonnes only. The Eocene sedimentary succession in the coastal zone of Nigeria is geologically similar to the succession with the economic Togo phosphates. Unfortunately, the phosphate-bearing sedimentary layer reaches only a thickness of 1.3 m and the overburden can reach up to 15 m (McClellan and Notholt 1986).

A phosphate deposit of greater significance is located in northwestern Nigeria in a Paleocene sedimentary sequence in Sokoto State. The Dange Formation (of Paleocene age) is mainly known for its wealth of vertebrate remains including crocodiles. The Dange sediments contain gypsiferous shales and phosphate nodules (Kogbe 1972, 1976). The overlying Paleocene Kalambaina and Gamba Formations are dominated by limestones and laminated ('paper') shales. A horizon with phosphatic pellets within the Gamba Formation (Kogbe 1976) is probably equivalent to the phosphate-containing marine sequence in neighbouring Niger and Mali (Wright *et al.* 1985; Hanon 1990). In southwestern Niger, in the striking continuation of the Sokoto phosphates, the phosphates occur mainly in the 'Formation de Garadaoua,' which is stratigraphically equivalent to Paleocene to Eocene sediments of northern Nigeria (Hanon 1900).

Mineralogical data of the Sokoto phosphate rock (Sokoto PR) indicate a francolitic composition with a unit-cell a-value of 9.353 Å and a molar PO_4/CO_3 ratio of 11.5 (Mokunywe 1995). The neutral ammonium citrate-soluble P_2O_5 is relatively high (3.1 to 3.7 % P_2O_5), as compared to 1.7 % for the Togo PR (Adediran *et al.* 1998).

The reserve estimate of the Sokoto phosphate deposit is 5 million tonnes (Ministry of Solid Minerals Development 2000). The Raw Materials Research and Development Council (RMRDC) has set up pilot plants for the mining and processing of phosphate rock in Sokoto State (Ministry of Solid Minerals Development 2000; Aribisala and Adegbesan 1994; Synge 1996). Mining is currently ongoing.

Agronomic Testing of Sokoto Phosphate Rock

Sokoto PR was used in several agronomic studies on a variety of soils in Nigeria (Adediran and Sobulo 1998; Adediran et al. 1998; Akande et al. 1998). Results indicate that this indigenous PR is largely suitable for direct application on acid soils under humid climatic conditions. Trials using partially acidulated Sokoto PR gave clearly higher relative agronomic effectiveness than Sokoto PR applied directly (Adediran and Sobulo 1998).

Other agrominerals

Limestone/dolomite

A substantial number of large limestone and dolomite occurrences have been reported by Bell (1963), Ola (1977) and Gwosdz (1996). The resources are grouped into Precambrian limestones, marbles and dolomites, Cretaceous and Tertiary limestones, as well as concretionary calcretes, known in northern Nigeria as 'jigilin' (Ola 1977). Most surveys for limestone, marble, or calcrete have been carried out for the purpose of finding raw material for the building industry, mainly for cement purposes (with low Mg content), for ornamental stone, or as flux in the iron and steel industries of Nigeria. Some of these resources have also been tested for road stabilization purposes (Ola 1977). No systematic surveys have been undertaken to study the limestone and/or dolomite resources for their use as agricultural liming material.

Precambrian marbles and dolomitic marbles occur predominantly in gneiss sequences. Dolomitic marbles of the area near Igbeti in western Nigeria have been regarded as suitable for agricultural purposes and a grinding plant was constructed in 1980 (Gwosdz 1996). However, no data on the agricultural performance of these dolomitic liming materials are available. Another Precambrian marble occurrence is reported from Ilorin. Extensive low Mg-marbles to the west of Lokoja were investigated for their suitability for the cement and steel industries. They are currently been worked for use as decorative stone. Additional dolomitic marbles with reserves exceeding 1 million tonnes are located southwest of Lokoja. Other Precambrian marbles, some of them dolomitic, occur southwest of Minna, and in the Anchau and Ningi areas (Gwosdz 1996).

Paleocene limestones in the coastal area close to Lagos include the deposit of Ewekoro with approximately 31 million tonnes, and Shagamu. Both deposits are mined for raw material in the cement industry.

Cretaceous limestones in the coastal basin and the Benue Trough include the limestone beds at:

- Nkalagu, east of Enugu (reserves 110 million tonnes),
- Yander, east of Makurdi (reserves in excess of 70 million tonnes),
- Mfamosin near Calabar,
- Gombe-Ashaka near Gombe.

Limestones are also extracted for cement manufacture in the northwest of the country, at Kalambaina near Sokoto.

Agricultural Lime Testing in Nigeria

Many agricultural experiments have been carried out in Nigeria with liming material. Among them are experiments carried out by Friesen *et al.* (1982) in very acid soils of southeastern Nigeria. In this area with high rainfall and underlain by Pleistocene coastal sediments, they evaluated the lime requirements and residual values of hydrated lime ($Ca(OH)_2$). The results showed that with very modest rates of lime application (0.5 tonnes per hectare), maize yield could be maintained at near maximum for 2 years. Sustained maize yield for 5 years of more were possible with a lime rate of 2 tonnes per hectare (Friesen *et al.* 1982).

Gypsum

Gypsiferous shales are reported from the upper Cretaceous Dukamaje Formation and the Paleocene Dange Formation in the Sokoto area. The 1.46-million tonne gypsum deposit at Wurno in Sokoto State is currently being mined by small-scale miners to supply the Sokoto cement plant. Other gypsum prospects are reported from Nafada/Bajoga in Gombe State, at Fika in Yobe State, and at Guyuk/Gwalura in Adamawa State (Ministry of Solid Minerals Development 2000).

Volcanic rocks/cinder cones

There are several cinder cones reported from the Jos Plateau and the Biu area.

Agromineral potential

There are two sedimentary phosphate deposits/occurrences in Nigeria, in the south and in the northwest of the country. The phosphate resource base seems to be small, and not economic for large-scale operations, but interesting for small-scale development. Initial results with Sokoto PR as a directly applied phosphorus resource and in modified forms, for example partially acidulated, are encouraging. More work on modification techniques and organic/inorganic interaction should be envisaged.

Equally, the dolomitic limestones in the Precambrian terrain seem to be interesting for small-scale dolomite/limestone production and utilization on acid soils. Low-level lime applications have proven to be effective in sustaining high yield responses of maize and cowpea in the southeastern part of Nigeria. Further systematic investigations using limestone and/or dolomitic limestone should be conducted to study the agronomic effectiveness of these resources on acid soils in various areas of Nigeria.

It is not known whether gypsum resources have been studied with the aim of using them in Nigeria's agriculture, for instance for the fertilization of groundnuts, or to supplement fertilizers with the much-needed sulphur nutrient component, or for remediation of alkaline saline soils.

The potential of using basaltic scoria and other light, consolidated, volcanic, gravel-size materials as a means of rock mulching, as successfully tested in Ethiopia, should be explored, especially in semi-arid areas of Nigeria, in close vicinity to volcanic scoria cones.

References:

Adediran JA, Oguntoyinbo FI, Omonode R and RA Sobulo 1998. Agronomic evaluation of phosphorus fertilizers developed from Sokoto rock phosphate in Nigeria. Comm. Soil Sci. and Plant Anal. 29:2659-2673.

Adediran JA and RA Sobulo 1998. Evaluation of phosphorus availability from three phosphorus sources in Nigerian soils. Comm. Soil Sci. and Plant Anal. 29:2415-2428.

Akande MO, Aduayi EA, Olayinka A and RA Sobulo 1998. Efficiency of Sokoto Rock Phosphate as a fertilizer source for maize production in southwestern Nigeria. J. Plant Nutr. 21:1339-1353.

Aribisala OA and BA Adegbesan 1994. Exploitation and export prospects of Nigerian industrial minerals. In: Mathers SJ and AJG Notholt (eds.) Industrial minerals in developing countries. AGID Report Series Geosciences in International Development 18:107-110.

Bell JP 1963. A summary of the principal limestone and marble deposits of Nigeria. Geol. Surv. Nigeria, Rep. 1192.

Friesen DK 1991. Fate and efficiency of sulfur fertilizer applied to food crops in West Africa. Fert. Res. 29:35-44.

Friesen DK, Juo ASR and MH Miller 1982. Residual value of lime and leaching of calcium in a kaolinitic Ultisol in the high rainfall tropics. Soil Sci. Soc. Am. J. 46:1184-1189.

Gwosdz 1996. Nigeria. In: Bosse H-R, Gwosdz W, Lorenz W, Markwich, Roth W and F Wolff 1996 (eds.) Limestone and dolomite resources of Africa. Geol. Jb., D, 102:326-333.

Hanon M 1990. Notice éxplicative sur la carte géologique de L'Ader Doutchi. Ministère des Mines et de l'Energie, Direction des Recherches Géologiques et Minières, Niamey, Niger, 36pp.

Kogbe CA 1972. Geology of the Upper Cretaceous and lower Tertiary sediments of the Nigerian sector of the Iullemmeden Basin (West Africa). Geol. Rdsch. 62:197-211.

Kogbe CA 1976. Outline of the geology of the Iullemmeden Basin in North-Western Nigeria. In: Kogbe CA (Ed.) Geology of Nigeria. Elizabethan Publ. Co. Sulurere (Lagos) Nigeria, 331-343.

McClellan GH and AJG Notholt 1986. Phosphate deposits of sub-Saharan Africa. In: Mokwunye AU and PLG Vlek (eds.) Management of nitrogen and phosphorus fertilizers in sub-Saharan Africa. Martinus Nijhoff, Dordrecht, Netherlands:173-224.

Ministry of Solid Minerals Development 2000. An inventory of solid mineral potentials of Nigeria. Prospectus for Investors, 15pp.

Mokwunye AU 1995. Reactions in soils involving phosphate rocks. In: Gerner H and AU Mokwunye (eds.) Use of phosphate rock for sustainable agriculture in West Africa. IFDC, Miscellaneous Fert. Studies 11: 84-92.

Ola SA 1977. Limestone deposits and small scale production of lime in Nigeria. Engineering Geol. 11:127-137.

Russ W 1924. The phosphate deposits of Abeokuta Province. Bull. Geol. Surv. Nigeria 7, 43pp.

Synge R 1996. Nigeria. Mining Annual Review 1996, Mining Journal Ltd. London, p.164.

Wright JB, Hastings DA, Jones WB and HR Williams 1985. Geology and mineral resources of West Africa. Allen and Unwin, London, UK, 187pp.

Rwanda

Total population (July 2000 estimate): 7,229,000
Area: 26,338 km^2
Annual population growth rate (2000): 1.14%
Life expectancy at birth (1998): 40.6 years
People not expected to survive to age 40 (1998): 45.9% of total population
GDP per capita (1998): US $660

Rwanda is a landlocked mountainous country in Central Africa. The landscape of this 'land of a thousand hills' is characterized by rolling highlands in the central and eastern part of the country and rift-related volcanic mountains and rift lakes in the west and northwest.

Rwanda is one of the most densely populated countries in sub-Saharan Africa (more than 270 persons per km^2), putting considerable pressure on the cultivated land. There is only one hectare of arable land per person in Rwanda. The economic base is mainly small-scale and subsistence agriculture with about 90% of the population involved in farming. The agricultural sector contributes approximately 46% of the GDP. Food crops of Rwanda include plantains, sweet potatoes, cassava, potatoes, sorghum, beans and maize. The main export crops are tea and coffee.

Soil erosion, soil nutrient depletion and soil acidity with associated Al toxicities are the main soil related constraints to agricultural development in Rwanda.

The mineral resource base of Rwanda is restricted to small deposits of cassiterite, wolframite, tantalite and gold, extracted mainly by small-scale methods. Large amounts of methane gas are found in Lake Kivu (Lac Kivu), along the border with the Congo Democratic Republic. The methane reserves at the bottom of Lake Kivu are estimated to be in the order of 2 trillion cubic feet (TCF). They are believed to have a regenerative capacity of more than 8 billion cubic feet per annum. Presently, the gas is used in the Rwanda Brewery and Lemonade Company on the shore of Lake Kivu.

Geological outline

The geology of Rwanda is similar to the geology of neighbouring Burundi and southern Uganda. The oldest rocks of Rwanda are migmatites, gneisses and mica schists of the Paleoproterozoic Ruzizian basement overlain by the Mesoproterozoic Kibaran Belt. The Kibaran, composed of folded and metamorphosed sediments, mainly schists and quartzites intruded by granites, covers most of Rwanda.

Cenozoic to Recent volcanic rocks occur in the northwest and west. Some of these volcanics are highly alkaline and are extensions from the Birunga volcanic area of southwestern Uganda. Tertiary and Quaternary sediments fill parts of the Western Rift in the western part of the country.

AGROMINERALS

Phosphates

No phosphate occurrence of economic significance has been reported from Rwanda.

Limestone/dolomite/travertine

Very hard, dolomitic limestones with MgO contents up to 17% have been found in Precambrian rocks as thin beds and lenses in the area around Kibuye (Grigoriev 1981). The origin of this deposit has been questioned, as some authors discuss the possibilities that the Kibuye carbonates are not sedimentary, but may be of igneous, carbonatitic origin (Verhaeghe 1964). Other dolomitic limestones and dolomites are reported from Mbabara Island, northwest of Kibuye, where reserves are reported to be on the order of several million tonnes. Verhaeghe (1964) reports other crystalline dolomitic limestones, for instance near Mushao, Kariba and Kamanyola, at the border to the Democratic Republic of Congo.

Most travertine deposits in Rwanda are small and are spatially related to the Rift Valley area in western Rwanda (Verhaeghe 1964). The most extensive travertine deposit is located near Mashyuza, southeast of Cyangugu. This deposit consists of travertine, 5 m thick with reserves of more than 6 million tonnes. Plans have been discussed to use this travertine as raw material for a local cement plant and for the production of calcium cyanamide fertilizer.

Grigoriev (1981) reported the total reserves of travertine deposits, excluding Mashyuza, as 2.45 million tonnes (of which 1.47 million tonnes are in the 'possible' category). Verhaeghe (1964) reported several more travertine occurrences in areas along the Western Rift. They require further exploration, quantification, and studies on their site-specific agronomic value.

Testing of Liming Materials in Rwanda

Several studies have been undertaken using liming materials to overcome soil pH related constraints. The soil pH in the Gikongoro and Byumba regions for instance is commonly below 5, and subsoil pH levels are as low as 4.0 (Vander Zaag et al. 1984; Yamoah et al. 1992). Several agronomic investigations have shown that the use of up to 5 tonnes $CaCO_3$ per hectare may be necessary to reduce soil acidity and the associated Al toxicity to significantly increase yield (Vander Zaag et al. 1984). In some areas of Rwanda, the use of 2-4 tonnes per hectare of local limestone or dolomite resources has proved to be agronomically effective, significantly enhancing the yield of wheat, beans and potatoes (Yamoah et al. 1992).

Peat

There are several deposits and occurrences of peat in Rwanda. The main peat deposits are located south and east of Cyangugu, and in northern Rwanda, east of Ruhengeri. However, the extraction of these peat deposits for horticultural production or for energy purposes is problematic and there are environmental concerns with this practice.

Peat has been envisaged as an acidulating medium for phosphate rock. Composting experiments using peat and organic residues in combination with relatively insoluble phosphate rocks have been successfully applied in Canada (Mathur et al. 1987).

Agromineral potential

The potential of developing liming materials in Rwanda is largely limited to the availability of agricultural limestone along the Western Rift. Raising and maintaining the soil pH above 5.5 to keep extractable Al concentrations low is a desirable soil management technique.

The use of the locally available limestone/dolomite/travertine resources will be an important low-cost sustainable management technique for providing food security to farmers in Rwanda.

References:

Grigoriev S 1981. Les Travertines du Rwanda.-Programme des Nations Unies pour le Developpement - Projet de Recherches Minières - RW 80/001, 46pp.

Mathur SP, Proulx JG, Leveque M and RB Sanderson 1987. Composting of an igneous rock phosphate. In: Wachira JK and AJG Notholt (eds.) Agrogeology in Africa. Commonwealth Sci. Council, Technical Publ. Series 226:129-145.

Vander Zaag P and C Kagenzi 1986. The phosphorus requirements of five consecutive potato crops on an Andept in Rwanda. Am. Potato J. 63:121-129.

Vander Zaag P, Yorst RS, Tangmar BB, Yayashi K and RL Fox 1984. An assessment of chemical properties for soils of Rwanda with the use of geostatistical techniques. Geoderma 34:239-314.

Verhaeghe M 1964. Inventaire des gisement calcaires, dolomies et travertins du Kivu, du Rwanda et du Burundi. Département Géologie et Mines du Burundi, 95pp.

Yamoah CF, Burleigh JR and VJ Eylands 1992. Correction of acid infertility in Rwandan Oxisols with lime from indigenous source for sustainable cropping. Exp. Agric. 28:417-424.

São Tomé and Príncipe

Total population (July 2001 estimate): 165,034
Area: 1001 km^2
Annual population growth rate (2000): 3.18%
Life expectancy at birth (1998): 64.0 years
People not expected to survive to age 40 (1998): data not available
GDP per capita (1998): US $1,469

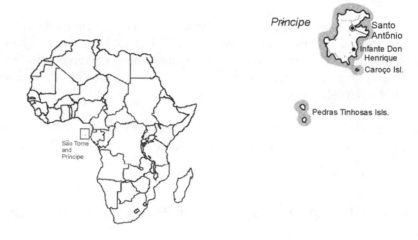

This island state of São Tomé and Príncipe consists of two major and a few very small islands in the Gulf of Guinea, some 275 km west of Gabon and southwest of Equatorial Guinea and Cameroon. The agricultural sector accounts for 23% of the GDP and employs some 27% of the working population. The main food crops are bananas, maize and coconuts. The largest export crop is cocoa, followed by coconut products and cinnamon.

The mineral industry of São Tomé and Príncipe is limited to the production of local building materials, small clay and stone open pit operations. Petroleum exploration in offshore areas has been intensified over the last few years.

Geological outline

All islands of this archipelago are made up of volcanic rocks. They occur as extensions of the 'Cameroon line' (Deruelle *et al.* 1991).

The volcano of São Tomé is a complex strato-volcano type with a total height of about 5,000 m, rising from the abyssal plain of the ocean floor to an elevation of 2,024 m above sea level. The volcano is principally made up of basaltic lavas resting on Cretaceous sandstones. Palagonitic tuffs and pillow lavas, representing submarine eruptions, are overlain by younger subaerial lavas. The oldest dated volcanic rocks are 15.7 million years old (Deruelle *et al.* 1991).

The island of Príncipe is also of volcanic origin, with basaltic, phonolitic and tephritic compositions. The island rests on the ocean floor at a depth of approximately 3,000 m, and reaches 948 m above sea level.

Agromineral potential

The potential of agromineral development on São Tomé and Príncipe is very limited due to the lack of suitable agrogeological resources.

References:

Deruelle B, Moreau C, Nkoumbou C, Kambou R, Lissom J, Njongfang E, Ghogomu RT and A Nono 1991. The Cameroon Line: a review. In: Kampunzu AB and RT Lubala (eds.) Magmatism in extensional structural settings. Springer Verlag, Berlin, Germany: 274-327.

Senegal

Total population (July 2000 estimate): 9,987,000
Area: 196,190 km^2
Annual population growth rate (2000): 2.94%
Life expectancy at birth (1998): 52.7 years
People not expected to survive to age 40 (1998): 28% of total population
GDP per capita (1998): US $1,307

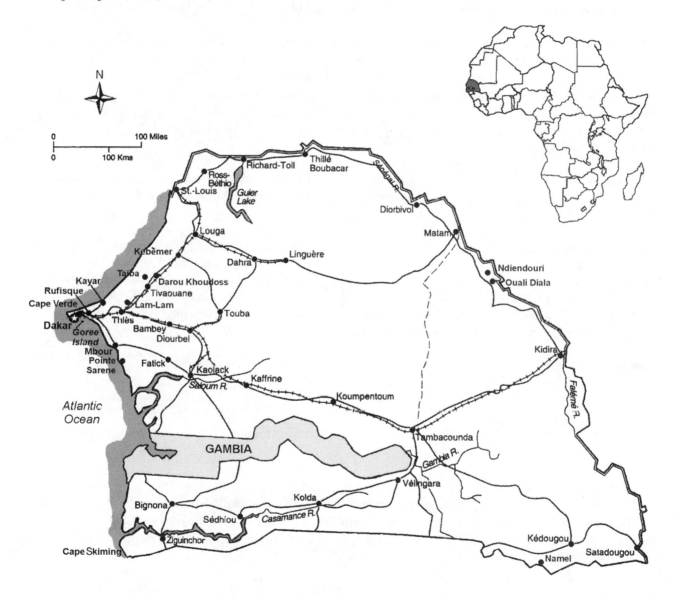

Senegal is located at the western-most part of Africa at the Atlantic Ocean. The Senegal, Gambia and Casamance Rivers drain from extensive inland plains with altitudes of less than 200 m. In the south-east of the country, plateaux with altitudes up to 600 m form the foothills of the north-south striking Bassaride mountain range. North of the Gambia River, much of the land is barren except for the floodplains of the Senegal River.

The agricultural sector, dominated by crop production and coastal fishing, as well as the tourist and mining sectors, forms an important part of the Senegalese economy. In 1999, agriculture accounted for 18% of the GDP, and employed more than 60% of the working population. The staple food of the Senegalese is rice, followed by millet and sorghum. The main export crops of Senegal are groundnuts and cotton. Extensive sugarcane production provides a large part of the total national sugar requirement.

The production and export of phosphate rock, and phosphate-based fertilizers dominate the mineral industry of Senegal and phosphate production has been relatively stable over the last few decades. Small occurrences of gold and industrial minerals are also reported from Senegal. Exploration for hydrocarbons has revealed limited offshore oil resources and substantial amounts of onshore natural gas (106 billion cubic feet).

Geological outline

Senegal is dominated by two major geological units: the folded Precambrian basement in the east of the country, and the shallow-dipping Upper Cretaceous to Quaternary sediments in most of the central and western parts of Senegal.

The Precambrian in the east and southeast of the country is subdivided into the Paleoproterozoic Birimian volcano-sedimentary sequence, the Neoproterozoic Madina-Kouta Basin Series, and the two folded Neoproterozoic/Cambrian Pan-African mountainous ranges, the Bassaride Branch and the Koulonton Branch. The Lower Cambrian is represented in the Faleme Basin with tillites, cherts and limestones. Between the two Neoproterozoic/Cambrian Pan-African sequences lies a basin filled with Cambro-Ordovician conglomerates, mudstones and sandstones.

AGROMINERALS

Phosphates

There are several phosphate occurrences and deposits in Senegal (Figure 2.14). The four main phosphate deposits are:

- the Neoproterozoic/Cambrian phosphates in the Namel area, southeast Senegal,
- the Eocene phosphate deposits along the Senegal River, including the 'Matam' deposits,
- the Eocene primary phosphate deposits in western Senegal, mined at Taiba and Lam Lam,
- the aluminous phosphates of Thies, weathering products of the Eocene phosphates, found also in western Senegal.

Senegal is one of the major phosphate producers in sub-Saharan Africa. In 1997, the total phosphate production from Senegal was 616,700 tonnes (British Geological Survey 1999), down from approximately 1 million tonnes of phosphate concentrate in 1993, which were exported to Canada, Australia, Mexico and China. A high proportion of the concentrate is used for the industrial processing and production of soluble P-fertilizers, for instance SSP, TSP, DAP and NPKs. Most of the processed P-fertilizers are exported.

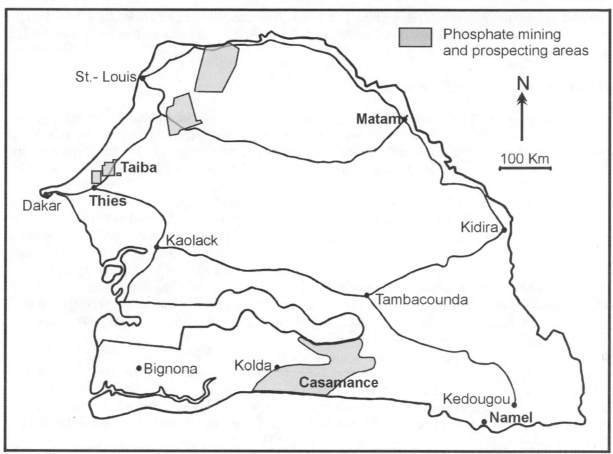

Figure 2.14: Location of phosphate occurrences and deposits in Senegal (after Pascal and Sustrac 1989).

The phosphates of Taiba.

The phosphate deposit of Taiba was discovered in 1948 and up to now has been the main phosphate mining area of Senegal. The deposit is mined by the Compagnie Sénégalaise des Phosphates de Taiba (CSPT).

The phosphate beds are part of a very extensive phosphate-bearing area northeast of Dakar. Phosphate mining takes place mainly in the Keur Mor Fall deposit area at Taiba, some 110 km by rail from Dakar. Here, the Middle Eocene (Lutetian) phosphatic sequence can be divided into three major beds. They are, from top to bottom:

- 2-3 m homogenous phosphates,
- heterogeneous phosphatic ore containing flint,
- thin indurated coprolitic phosphates (phosphate gravel), 3-4 m thick.

Below the 5-12 m (average 7 m) thick phosphatic beds are Middle Eocene finely laminated 'paper' clays, made up largely of palygorskite (attapulgite). Above the phosphates are up to 25 m thick Quaternary aeolian sands (Pascal and Sustrac 1989). The proven reserves of the Keur Mor Fall deposit are 100 million tonnes with ore grades ranging from 18-39% P_2O_5 (McClellan and Notholt 1986). The average grade is 24% P_2O_5.

The neutral ammonium citrate solubility of the Taiba phosphate concentrate (37.4% P_2O_5) is 3.1% P_2O_5 (McClellan and Notholt 1986). The Cd content of the Taiba phosphates are elevated, ranging from 60-115 mg/kg, and averaging 87 mg/kg.

The aluminous phosphates of Thies.

Aluminous phosphatic rocks, resulting from long periods of weathering of phosphatic sediments, cover large parts of the Thies Plateau of western Senegal. The city of Thies is located in the centre of this extensive, elevated area. Natural outcrops of the aluminous phosphates are sparse. The best exposures are seen in open pits between Lam Lam and Pallo, approximately 15 km northwest of Thies.

The aluminous phosphates of Thies are the result of lateritic weathering of the underlying Middle Eocene to Oligocene argillaceous phosphatic sediments. The weathering episode is estimated to have occurred from Middle Miocene to Lower Pliocene. For his doctorate thesis, Flicoteaux (1982) studied the genesis of this deposit in detail and found at least four stages of weathering: apatite leaching (stage 1), accumulation of kaolinite and Fe-millisite (stage 2), 'ochreous' aluminous phosphate development (stage 3), and leaching into 'white facies' phosphates in topographic depressions (stage 4). The main phosphatic weathering products are Ca-millisite, Sr-crandallite and wavellite. Mineralogical studies showed that the neutral ammonium citrate solubility of the typical Al-phosphate product of Pallo (32.0% P_2O_5) is high at 12.0% P_2O_5 (McClellan and Notholt 1986).

The Société Sénégalaise des Phosphates de Taiba (SSPT) mines these aluminous phosphates in open-pit operations near the village of Pallo, 10 km northwest of Thies. The mineable phosphate ore at Pallo is 10 m thick and has an overburden of 3 m. The aluminous phosphates are crushed, calcined to increase the grade to 34% P_2O_5 and also to increase citrate solubility, and marketed as 'Phosal' for use as a fertilizer or 'Polyphos' used in animal feed (Flicoteaux and Hameh 1989).

Proven aluminous phosphate reserves in the 32,000 hectare concession amount to 50 million tonnes with 29% P_2O_5 (Flicoteaux and Hameh 1989).

Between 1979 and 1983 the annual production of crude phosphate ore from the aluminous phosphate deposit of Pallo was 180,000-280,000 tonnes, and the corresponding calcined ore between 78,000 and 140,000 tonnes (Flicoteaux and Hameh 1989).

The Lam Lam phosphate deposit.

Unweathered Ca-phosphates are mined by the Société Sénégalaise des Phosphates de Taiba (SSPT) near the village of Lam Lam, northwest of Thies. These unweathered phosphates resemble the phosphates of Taiba and occur as 7 m thick layers under a thick iron crust. Proven reserves of this deposit are 4 million tonnes of marketable product with an average grade of 33% P_2O_5. Only 1.5 million tonnes of these reserves have an overburden of less than 24 m (McClellan and Notholt 1986).

The Matam (Ouali-Diala) phosphate deposits.

The Matam phosphate deposits, described in detail by Pascal and Cheikh Faye (1989), occur on the left bank of the Senegal River. The phosphate beds can be traced over a distance of at least 100 km (Figure 2.14). The phosphatic layers are 4-16 m thick. At places they lie at shallow depth along the slope of the Senegal River. In other places they occur more than 30 m below the flat and monotonous landscape. The first systematic prospecting took place between 1962 and 1966, and further work between 1980 and 1984 resulted in the delineation of this extensive phosphate deposit (Pascal and Cheikh Faye 1989).

Palaeontological studies on shark teeth assign the Matam phosphates to the Lower Eocene, but some reworked coarse-grained coprolitic phosphates also occur in the Quaternary. The main phosphate beds in the N'Diendouri and Ouali Diala area are slightly indurated, light grey, coarse grained 'arenites.' Here, the phosphatic sequence is exposed at or near to the surface. The main phosphatic unit is 6-10 m thick in a clay-rich matrix containing mainly palygorskite (attapulgite) and montmorillonite. The phosphate mineral has been identified as francolite. The neutral ammonium citrate solubility of the Matam phosphates (28.7% P_2O_5) is relatively high, 4.5% P_2O_5 (McClellan and Notholt 1986) indicating that the chemical and mineralogical composition of the phosphate rocks is favourable for direct application in agriculture (Pascal and Cheikh Faye 1989). The trace element content of this phosphate is low, with Cd concentrations of less than 5 mg/kg, and U concentrations of less than 40 mg/kg

Figure 2.15: Geological setting of phosphate mineralization along the Senegal River near Matam, Senegal (after Pascal and Cheikh Faye 1989).

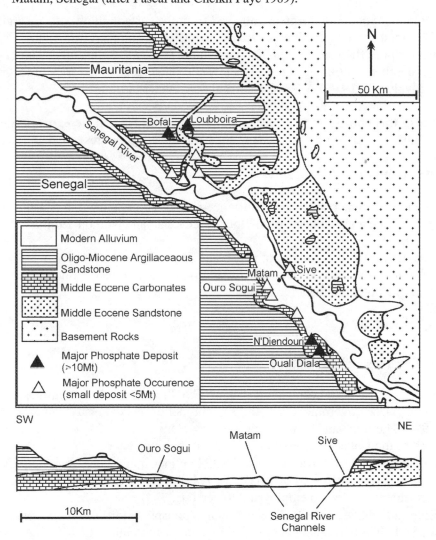

Pascal and Cheikh Faye (1989) reported seven major occurrences on the left bank of the Senegal River, two of them regarded as major deposits with reserves of more than 10 million tonnes. The overall reserves of the phosphates between N'Diendouri and Ouali Diala exceed 40 million tonnes at a grade averaging 28.7% P_2O_5. The deposit could be worked by open pit methods with a mean overburden-to-ore ratio of 4.5:1 (Pascal and Sustrac 1989). Industries Chimique du Sénégal (ICS) plans a new US $100 million phosphate mine in the Matam area (Leaky and Harrison 2000).

The Namel phosphate deposit.

The phosphate deposit near Namel in southeast Senegal was discovered during a systematic geochemical and geophysical exploration campaign in 1975. The Neoproterozoic to Lower Cambrian (approximately 650 million years of age) phosphates occur at the western edge of the Precambrian basement zone at the Kedougou inlier in eastern Senegal/northern Guinea (Pascal and Sustrac 1989). The rock sequence unconformably overlies the Paleoproterozoic (Birimian) basement. Below the phosphate sequence lies a 3 m thick tillite bed. It is overlain by 18 m of fine-grained siliceous rocks, 9 m of phosphatic pelites, 2 m of calcareous phosphates (15% P_2O_5) and 8 m coarse phosphates (22-32% P_2O_5). The phosphate layers with over 20% P_2O_5 contain abundant silica (Slansky 1986). The phosphate grains vary in size from 50 μm to several mm. The CaO/P_2O_5 ratios vary from 1.2 in the upper weathered zone to 1.8 at depth where carbonate gangue is present. Mudstones and dolomites overlie the phosphates.

Mineralogical studies of phosphate samples collected from the surface show deformed grains of re-crystallized fine-grained apatite in a siliceous matrix (McClellan and Saavedra 1986). Crystallographic data indicate a nearly pure fluor-apatite (unit-cell a-value = 0.9373 Å). Banded calcareous phosphorites samples from 8 m depth show that the apatite is a low carbonate-substituted francolite with a crystallo-graphic unit-cell a-value of 0.9360 Å (McClellan and Saavedra 1986).

The best exposure of this phosphate sequence is in the vicinity of Namel. Here, the phosphates are exposed over a length of 1 km on the east side of the Namel Valley. No reserve data are available.

Other phosphate resources

There are several more Eocene phosphate 'occurrences' reported in Senegal, for instance near Thies, Sebikotane, Pointe Sarene and southeast of M'Bour (McClellan and Notholt 1986).

Notholt (1994) reported 20 million tonnes of phosphate resources from 'wastes' in the western part of Senegal. Material that is finer than 40 μm is currently discarded as 'waste' although it contains 26% P_2O_5. No more details on this potential resource are given.

Current mining operations

There are several phosphate companies operating in Senegal.

- Compagnie Sénégalaise des Phosphates de Taiba (CSPT) mines and concentrates the Ca-phosphates at Taiba. The Senegalese government is a 50% shareholder of this company, which employed 1,400 persons in 1994. The mine and concentration-drying plant is located at Taiba. The concentrate is shipped by rail to the Dakar stockyard from where it is shipped abroad.
- Société Sénégalaise des Phosphates de Thies (SSPT) mines mainly palygorskite (attapulgite) and minor amounts of Al-phosphate from Thies. In 1994, the government and the French company Rhone Poulence were shareholders and employed 230 persons.
- Industries Chimique du Sénégal (ICS) manufactures phosphate fertilizers from phosphate concentrates supplied by CSPT. ICS is located next to the CSPT mine site. Sulphuric acid and phosphoric acid plants are located at Darou Khoudoss and the fertilizer unit is located at Mbao. Shipping of the various fertilizers, including NPK, DAP, TSP and SSP, is from the free port of Dakar. ICS plans a major extension of its mine capacity and chemical facilities (Leaky and Harrison 2000)

Limestones

Small occurrences of dolomitic limestones and marbles are known from the Paleoproterozoic in the Kedougou inlier in southeast Senegal, close to the border with Guinea. This greyish marble, 25 km west of Kedougou, has been exploited for the production of lime in the past (Roth 1996). Upper Cretaceous to Paleocene marly limestones occur east of Dakar in the Popenguine-Thies area. The Paleocene limestones are massive and coarse-grained and are up to 40 m thick. Eocene limestones occur in several locations in Senegal, east of Dakar in the area of Rufisque, and along the banks of the Senegal River (Roth 1996).

Other agrominerals

Peat resources, estimated at 52 million m^3 occur along the coast of Senegal. A surveying permit was granted to Cie des Tourbières du Sénégal (Mining Annual Review 1994).

Phospho-gypsum

Large amounts of phospho-gypsum are produced annually by Industries Chimique du Senegal (ICS). Parts of these 'waste' products are currently being applied on Senegalese soils within the framework of the national program aiming at increasing agricultural production in Senegal. Long-term experiments with phospho-gypsum were started in 1997 and are ongoing (Sene *et al.* unpublished). In 1999, the utilization of phospho-gypsum in Senegal was 62,153 tonnes (Diop, pers. comm. Oct. 2001).

Agromineral potential

The agromineral potential of the locally available phosphate resources is high not only for export but also for domestic use. Many small sedimentary phosphate beds occur in western Senegal, mostly, however, under considerable overburden. Extensive phosphatic sequences occur along the Senegal River and in the southeast of the country. Of considerable interest are the layered, near-horizontal Eocene phosphate beds close to the surface along the Senegal River. It is recommended that these layers, often covered by slope detritus, should not only be investigated for their large-scale extraction but also with the aim of small-scale excavations and local use in the agricultural area along the Senegal River.

The layered Precambrian Namel phosphates exposed over a length of 1 km on the western slopes of the Namel Valley should be evaluated as to their suitability for small-scale phosphate extraction and use.

The usefulness of these phosphates depends largely on ease of extraction, and proximity to suitable soils in agricultural areas with P-deficiencies. The mineralogy indicates that most of these phosphates are suitable for direct application and/or low-cost modification techniques. As part of ongoing projects of the Rodale Institute, Taiba PR is currently applied directly, or in combination with manure (Diop 1999).

The 'wastes' of the phosphate industry in western Senegal, mainly phosphate fines and phospho-gypsum, need further field testing as potential low-cost P-fertilizers, as soil amendment for alkaline soils and for groundnut production. Alternative further processing of phospho-gypsum 'wastes,' for instance by the Merseburg process (Burnett *et al.* 1996) should be envisaged. Liming materials are common in some areas of Senegal. The usefulness of these materials depends largely on their chemical characteristics and proximity to acid soils.

References:

British Geological Survey 1999. World Mineral Statistics 1993-1997 - Production, exports, imports. Keyworth, Nottingham, UK:286p.

Burnett WC, Schultz MK and DH Carter 1996. Radionuclide flow during the conversion of phosphogypsum to ammonium sulfate. J. Environm. Radioactivity 32:1-2, 33-51.

Diop AK 1999. Sustainable agriculture: New paradigms and old practices? Increased production with management of organic inputs in Senegal. Env. Developm. Sustainability 1:285-296.

Flicoteaux R 1982. Genèse des phosphates alumineux du Sénégal occidental. Etapes et guides de l'altération. (Th. Sci. Univ. Marseille St-Jerome 1980). Mem. Sci. Geol. Univ. Strasbourg 67, 229p.

Flicoteaux R and PM Hameh 1989. The aluminous phosphate deposits of Thies, western Senegal. In: Notholt AJG, Sheldon RP and DF Davidson (eds.) Phosphate deposits of the world. Vol 2. Phosphate rock resources, Cambridge University Press, Cambridge, UK:273-276.

Leaky K and A Harrison 2000. Senegal. Mining Annual Review 2000. The Mining Journal Ltd. London.

Ledru P, Pons P, Milesi JP, Feybesse JL and V Johan 1991. Transcurrent tectonics and polycyclic evolution in the Lower Proterozoic of Senegal-Mali. Precambr. Res. 50:337-354.

McClellan GH and AJG Notholt 1986. Phosphate deposits of sub-Saharan Africa. In: Mokwunye AU and PLG Vlek (eds.) Management of nitrogen and phosphorus fertilizers in sub-Saharan Africa. Martinus Nijhoff, Dordrecht, Netherlands:173-224.

McClellan GH and FN Saavedra 1986. Proterozoic and Cambrian phosphorites - specialist studies: chemical and mineral characteristics of some Precambrian phosphorites. In Cook PJ and JH Shergold (eds.) Phosphate deposits of the world. Vol. 1. Proterozoic and Cambrian phosphorites. Cambridge University Press, Cambridge, UK:244-267.

Ministry of Energy, Mines and Industry of Senegal 1996. Senegal. In: Mining Annual Review 1996, p.165.

Notholt AJG 1994. Phosphate rock in developing countries. In: Mathers SJ and AJG Notholt (eds.) Industrial minerals in developing countries. AGID Rep. Series Geosciences in International Development 18:193-222.

Pascal M and M Cheikh Faye 1989. The Matam phosphate deposits. In: Notholt AJG, Sheldon RP and DF Davidson (eds.) Phosphate deposits of the world. Vol 2. Phosphate rock resources, Cambridge University Press, Cambridge, UK:295-300.

Pascal M and G Sustrac 1989. Phosphorite deposits of Senegal. In: Notholt AJG, Sheldon RP and DF Davidson (eds.) Phosphate deposits of the world. Vol 2. Phosphate rock resources, Cambridge University Press, Cambridge, UK:233-246.

Roth W 1996. Senegal. In: Bosse H-R, Gwosdz W, Lorenz W, Markwich, Roth W and F Wolff (eds.) Limestone and dolomite resources of Africa. Geol. Jb., D, 339-344.

Sene M, Diack M and A Badiane (1998). Phosphogypsum efficiency to correct soil P deficiency and/or soil acidity. Unpublished report, 5p.

Slansky M 1986. Proterozoic and Cambrian phosphorites - regional overview: West Africa. In: Cook PJ and JH Shergold (eds.) Phosphate deposits of the world, Vol. 1: Proterozoic and Cambrian phosphorites, Cambridge University Press, Cambridge, UK:108-115.

Sustrac G 1986. BRGM phosphate prospecting methods and results in West Africa. Trans. Instn. Min. Metall. (Sect. A: Min. Industry) 95:A134-A143.

Seychelles

Total population (July 2000 estimate): 79,330
Area: 455 km^2
Annual population growth rate (2000): 0.49%
Life expectancy at birth (1998): 71.0 years
People not expected to survive to age 40 (1998): data not available
GDP per capita (1998): US $10,600

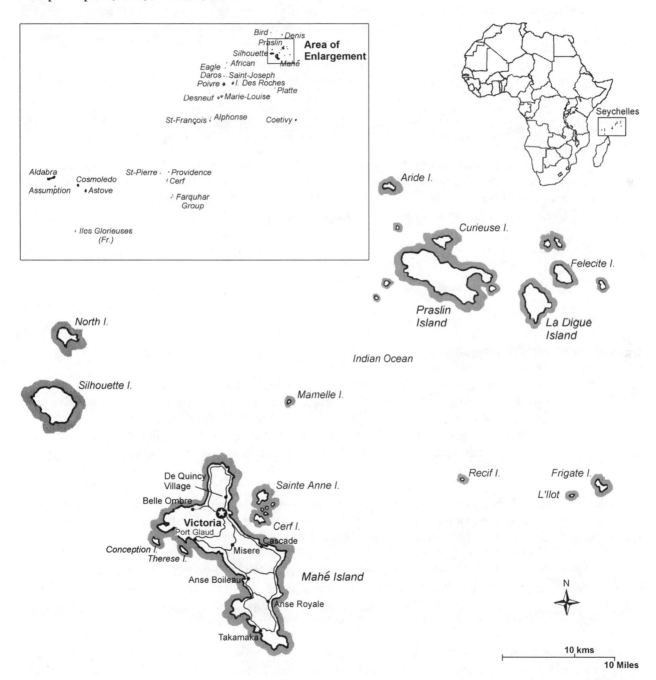

The Seychelles is an island state in the western Indian Ocean, approximately 1,600 km east of Kenya and Tanzania. The Seychelles consists of more than 90 widely scattered islands, most of which are uninhabited. The main island is Mahe with mountains reaching up to 1,000 m. The other main islands are Praslin and La Digue.

The economy is largely based on tourism (25% of GDP) and processing of coconut and vanilla, as well as fishing.

The agricultural sector (4% of GDP, 6% of labour) of the Seychelles is dominated by coconut, vanilla and cinnamon plantations. Vegetables are grown on brown soils for local consumption. The soil productivity of the Seychelles shows a strong relationship with the underlying geology. In general, the soils developed on calcareous rocks are more productive than the soils overlying granitic rocks.

The mineral sector is very small. Apart from occasional production of guano there is some extraction of granitic dimension stone. Polymetallic nodules are known to occur on the deep ocean floor near the Admirante Islands.

Geological outline

The principal islands of the Seychelles, the Mahe and Praslin-La Digue islands, are made up mainly of Neoproterozoic (Pan-African) granites and hornblende granites, intruded by dolerites and olivine dolerites. The continental crust of the Seychelles is widely regarded as a continental fragment left behind when the continent of Gondwana broke up and the Indian Ocean widened.

Most of the smaller islands in the Seychelles are made up of coral atolls or calcareous sands built on reefs.

AGROMINERALS

Phosphates

Guano/guano-derived phosphates

The main agromineral resources of the Seychelles are guano deposits and phosphatic sandstones. Most of these deposits are found on coral atolls and reefs, where sooty tern (*Sterna fuscata*) and boobies (*Sula dactylarta melanops*) live. Hutchinson (1950) reports that in 1931, some 5 million pairs of terns populated the island of Desneufs and the excrement left behind by these seabird colonies formed guano deposits. Leaching of the guano converted the underlying sands to phosphatic sandstones and phosphatized reef rock.

According to Baker (1963), most of the guano is composed of hydroxy-apatite with minor ammonium phosphates and organic compounds derived from the fish diet of the birds. The P_2O_5 content of the guano ranges from 15-35% and the N content varies from 0.2-1.6%.

Most of the easily extractable guano has been exported over the last 90 years, mainly to Mauritius as fertilizer for the sugar estates, with smaller amounts being shipped to Reunion and New Zealand. Guano exports started in 1895. Until 1960 a total of approximately 700,000 tonnes of guano were exported, with approximately 200,000 tonnes remaining, mainly on the island of Assumption (Baker 1963).

Braithwaite (1980) describes oolitic phosphorites, mainly of hydroxy-fluor-apatite composition, resting on solution-eroded limestone surfaces on the island of Esprit, which is part of Aldabra Island. The formation of the oolitic phosphates is related to relocation of phosphates and deposition in caves between 170,000 and 230,000 years ago (Braithwaite 1980).

Officially, output of guano from the Seychelles ceased in the mid-1980s. However, a 5,000 tonne per year production capacity remains and guano is mined unofficially on an occasional basis.

Other agrominerals

Coral limestones, calcareous sands and conglomerates are currently being used for building purposes. They are not used at present for agricultural or horticultural applications.

Agromineral potential

The guano and guano-derived phosphate deposits of the Seychelles have little potential as an export commodity due to their limited reserves. Yet, the potential for using small, locally available guano resources for small-scale agricultural, horticultural and vegetable production on the soils of the Seychelles, specifically on granitic soils, should be considered. It is important, however, to address environmental concerns related to mining of the guano.

References:

Baker BH. 1963. Geology and mineral resources of the Seychelles Archipelago. Geol. Surv. Kenya, Mem.3, 140pp.

Braithwaite CJR 1980. The petrology of oolitic phosphorites from Esprit (Aldabra), western Indian Ocean. Philos. Trans. R. Soc. London, Ser. B, 288:511-540.

Hutchinson GE 1950. Survey of existing knowledge of biogeochemistry - The geochemistry of vertebrae excretion. Bull. Am. Mus. Nat. History, 96, 554 pp.

Sierra Leone

Total population (July 2000 estimate): 5,233,000
Area: 71,740 km^2
Annual population growth rate (2000): 3.67%
Life expectancy at birth (1998): 37.9 years
People not expected to survive to age 40 (1998): 50%
GDP per capita (1998): US $458

Sierra Leone is a relatively small West African country located between Guinea and Liberia. Almost half of the country consists of coastal lowlands with extensive mangrove swamps. To the east of the coastal plains are rolling wooded hills, leading into mountainous plateau areas. The climate is hot and humid with annual precipitation reaching more than 3,000 mm.

Sierra Leone is one of the poorest nations in sub-Saharan Africa and, since 1992, has been ravaged by a civil war, which has had catastrophic impacts on human lives and on the economy.

Sierra Leone is endowed with a large natural resource base, including minerals, agriculture, and marine fishing. In times of peace, the agricultural sector generated more than 52% of the GDP and employed more than 60% of the working population. The main food crop is rice, followed by cassava, maize and yams. Before the war, the principal export crops were coffee and cocoa.

Prior to 1992, the mineral industry generated between 15 and 18% of the GDP, with rutile, bauxite, diamonds and gold being the main export mineral commodities (Mobbs 1995). During the civil war, the mineral production of diamonds and gold continued by artisanal mining. The International Labour Organization (1999) estimates the number of persons involved in small-scale mining at 30,000-40,000.

Geological outline

Most of Sierra Leone is underlain by Archean rocks of the Man Domain, which is divided into the Liberian granite-greenstone terrain and the metamorphic Kasila Group Mobile Belt (Williams 1978, 1988). Other Precambrian lithologies include the Marampa supracrustal sequence of possible Archean age, which was affected by the Paleoproterozoic Eburnian metamorphism (Morel 1979; Wright *et al.* 1985). The Marampa supracrustal sequence is made up of metavolcanics, pelites and banded ironstones. Another geological unit in Sierra Leone is the 30 km wide and 225 km long Neoproterozoic Rokelide Belt, with basal tilloids underlying mainly clastic sediments with small lava and pyroclastic intercalations. Late Mesozoic gabbros and dolerites are exposed close to the capital of Freetown. A narrow belt of mainly clastic Tertiary and Quaternary coastal sediments flank the Precambrian hinterland of Sierra Leone. Fossil fishes of Eocene age have been described from boreholes (Morel 1979).

AGROMINERALS

To date, no agrominerals have been reported in Sierra Leone and the chances of finding agrominerals in the Archean shield area and in the Neoproterozoic Rokelide belt are very limited. The Eocene coastal sediments require further investigation to assess their potential for phosphate mineralization.

References:

International Labour Organization 1999. Social and labour issues in small-scale mines. TMSSM/1999, 99pp.

Mobbs PM 1995. The mineral industry of Sierra Leone. Minerals Yearbook, Vol. III, US Geol. Surv. 91-92.

Morel SW 1979. The geology and mineral resources of Sierra Leone. Econ. Geol. 74:1563-1576.

Williams HR 1978. The Archean geology of Sierra Leone. Precambr. Res. 6:251-268.

Williams HR 1988. The Archean Kasila Group of western Sierra Leone: Geology and relations with adjacent granite-greenstone terrain. Precambr. Res. 38:201-238.

Wright JB, Hastings DA, Jones WB and HR Williams 1985. Geology and mineral resources of West Africa. Allen and Unwin, London, UK, 187pp.

Somalia

Total population (July 2000 estimate): 7,253,000
Area: 637,657 km^2
Annual population growth rate (1998): 2.9%
Life expectancy at birth (2000): 46.23 years
GDP per capita (1999 estimate): US $600

Somalia forms the Horn of Africa at the Indian Ocean and southern entrance to the Red Sea. The coastline of this semi-arid country is longer than 3,000 km. Somalia consists of a mountainous area in the north and an extensive flat area in the southern part. The Juba River traverses the country in the southern part and the Wabi Shebeli River crosses the centre. Only 2% of the land is arable, mainly along the rivers.

Some 60% of the Somali population is involved in livestock rearing, cattle, camels, sheep and goats. Only small areas are cultivated, mainly for subsistence farming but also as estate farms for sugar cane, and bananas for export.

The mineral sector of Somalia used to be very small, the main export being sepiolite ('meerschaum').

Political instability and the absence of a central government since 1991-1992 has resulted in a continued lack of security.

Geological outline

Mesozoic to Recent sediments make up most of the exposed rocks of Somalia. Two isolated uplifted Neoproterozoic and early Cambrian complexes occur to the west of Mogadishu in the Bur region (Bur Massif), and in northern Somalia paralleling the Gulf of Aden. The Bur Massif in central Somalia (Fig. 2.16) consists of gneisses, amphibolites, quartzites and marbles, intruded by granites. It is part of the Neoproterozoic Mozambique Belt. The northern area with outcropping crystalline rocks, including the Darkainle alkaline complex, is part of an early Paleozoic fold belt.

Clastic and marine Jurassic sediments overlie the Precambrian and early Paleozoic. Cretaceous to Tertiary sediments with clastic sequences, evaporites and marine successions cover large parts of Somalia. Small areas with young basaltic to liparitic volcanics are exposed close to Djibouti and in the Gulf of Aden area, as well as in an area close to the Ethiopia/Kenya/Somalia border junction.

AGROMINERALS

Phosphates

Metamorphosed phosphorites containing 24% P_2O_5 have been described in the Bur Massif, at Modu-Mode, some 25 km from Buurhakaba on the road to Baidoa (Figure 2.16). The metamorphosed phosphorites are associated with Neoproterozoic marble beds of the Mozambique Belt (UNDP 1970; Greenwood 1982; Frizzo 1993). The extent of the phosphate deposit is not known.

The 33 km long and up to 3 km wide Darkainle alkaline complex with nepheline-syenites and small carbonatite intrusives northeast of Borama has been summarized in Heinrich (1980) and Frizzo (1993). Apatites have been reported as accessory minerals.

Bird guano deposits have been worked on Mait Island, also called Bur-da Rebschi, in the Gulf of Aden, east of the port of Berbera (Hutchinson 1950). They were mainly exported to Saudi Arabia. Enormous numbers of birds including the Red Sea noddy (*Anous stolidus plumbeigularis*) were reported by previous observers, and 400,000-600,000 pounds of guano were collected annually from this island in 'recent years' (Hutchinson 1950).

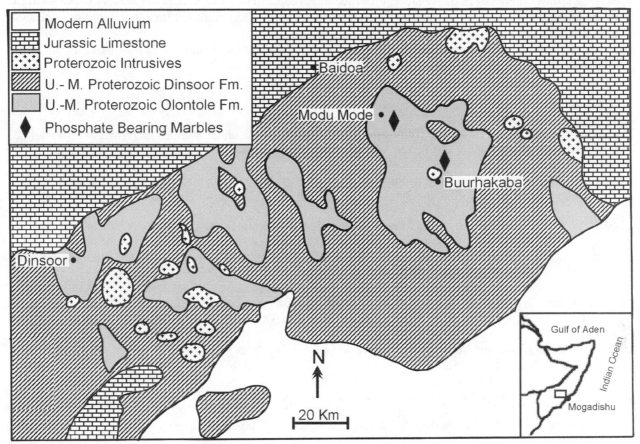

Figure 2.16: Geology and phosphate deposits of the Bur region, Somalia (after Frizzo, 1993). Insert shows the location of the Bur Region.

Other agrominerals

Limestone/dolomite

Limestone, gypsum and scpiolite ('mccrschaum') were mined commercially before the recent political instability and civil war. The limestone and dolomite resources of Somalia are very large. Apart from local unmetamorphosed stromatolitic limestones located in the southern part of Somalia (Merla *et al.* 1979) there are extensive limestone resources in Jurassic-Cretaceous and Tertiary sediments. A cement plant with an annual capacity of 300,000 tonnes has operated since 1987 in Berbera, in the north of the country (Roth 1996).

Gypsum

Thick Lower Cretaceous evaporite sequences with substantial gypsum resources have been recorded in the central coastal part of Somalia. Some 1,620 tonnes of gypsum per year were utilized from this source as cement additive (Yohannes 1994).

Agromineral potential

The potential of finding sedimentary phosphates in Somali is good, especially in the Upper Cretaceous Faf Formation and the Eocene Auradu Formation. Both sequences have been singled out in the Ogaden region of eastern Ethiopia as having a high potential for phosphate accumulations, and some phosphorites have been detected in boreholes in the Ogaden Province of Ethiopia. These sequences are widely exposed in Somalia and should be explored in the post-civil war era for possible phosphorite accumulations.

The potential for utilizing limestones or dolomites as soil amendments is very limited because of adverse climatic and soil conditions in most areas of Somalia.

References:

Frizzo P 1993. Ore geology of the crystalline basement of Somalia. In: Geology and mineral resources of Somalia and surrounding regions. 1st Agron. Oltremare, Firenze, Italia, Relaz. e Monogr. 113:517-540.

Greenwood WR 1982. A preliminary evaluation of the non-fuel mineral potential of Somalia. US Geol. Surv. Open file report 82-788, 42pp.

Heinrich W 1980.The geology of carbonatites. Krieger Publ. Co, Huntington, New York, USA, 585pp.

Hutchinson GE 1950. Survey of existing knowledge of biogeochemistry - The geochemistry of vertebrae excretion. Bull. Am. Mus. Nat. History, 96, 54pp.

Merla G, Abbate E, Azzaroli A, Bruni P, Catuni P, Fazzuoli M, Sagri M and P Tacconi 1979. A geological map of Ethiopia and Somalia (1973), 1:2,000,000 and comments. Conrigli nazionale delle richerche Italia, 95pp.

Roth W 1996. Somalia. In: Bosse H-R, Gwosdz W, Lorenz W, Markwich, Roth W and F Wolff 1996 (eds.) Limestone and dolomite resources of Africa. Geol. Jb., D, 102:348-353.

UNDP 1970. Mineral and ground water survey - Somalia: United Nations report. 133pp.

Yohannes 1994. Somalia, In: Mining Annual Review 1994, Mining Journal Ltd. London, p.144.

South Africa

Total population (2001 estimate): 43,586,097
Area: 1,219,912 km^2
Annual population growth rate (2001 est.): 0.26%
Life expectancy at birth (2001): 48.09 years
People not expected to survive to age 40 (1998): 25.9% of the total population
GDP per capita (2000 est.):US $8,500

The landscape of South Africa is characterized by an extensive central inland plateau, mountainous areas in the east and northeast of the country, and gentle and 'table mountain' landscapes in the Cape Province. The climatic conditions differ in the various parts of the country. While in the eastern parts of the country, specifically along the coast, humid, subtropical conditions prevail, the west of the country is dry with semi-arid to arid conditions.

The wealth of South Africa is largely based on its natural resources sector, specifically mining and farming, and its developed industrial sector. South Africa is a relatively developed country in terms of modern mining and farming practices. Over many decades, however, the country has been divided by unequal distribution and access to land, mineral and other resources. In both the mining and farming sector there are gradual changes taking place that have the goal of a non-discriminatory, equitable and profitable sharing of resources.

The mining industry of South Africa, one of the best developed in the world, forms a crucial part of South Africa's economy. Sales of minerals and mineral products contribute about 16% of the GDP. The mining sector directly employs approximately 550,000 people. Indirectly, the mining sector involves many more people. It is estimated that approximately 10 million people, a third of South Africa's population, rely on the mining sector. Mineral production is dominated by gold, diamonds, platinum-group metals, chromium, manganese, vanadium and other metals as well as coal and industrial minerals. Mineral exports made up about 37% of all exports from South Africa. Most of these resources are developed by large national and trans-national companies. Only in recent years has the government encouraged small-scale mining.

The agricultural sector, including the government, farmers, agribusiness and national and international organizations expressed the common commitment to a more equitable partnership for a united globally competitive profitable and sustainable agricultural sector. Although the primary agricultural sector accounts for only 4.5% of the GDP, the larger agri-food sector accounts for another 9%. The farming sector consists of about 50,000 large commercial farms with a labour force of about 1 million workers. The small-scale farming sector provides livelihoods to more than 1 million persons, and occasional employment for another half-million persons. Another 3 million farmers live in 'communal areas,' primarily producing food for their own families. Unused productive soils are rare in South Africa and expansion is limited. Therefore the agricultural sector has to increase output per unit of land. Soil degradation is a major concern to the farming community.

The agriculture of South Africa is largely based on the production of maize, but is also diversified in many producing and value-added agro-based industries. Other crops include wheat, oats, sugar cane and sunflower. South Africa is well known for its deciduous fruits and grapes.

Only about 13% of the surface area of South Africa can be used for crop production but large areas of the country are used for grazing. The soils of much of South Africa are nutrient deficient.

Geological outline

Large parts of South Africa are underlain by Precambrian rocks, including:
- the Archean granite/greenstone terrain, including the Barberton and Murchison belts
- the Archean Limpopo mobile belt,
- the Archean Witwatersrand Supergroup with its extensive gold deposits,
- the Paleoproterozoic Transvaal Supergroup,
- the Bushveld Complex with platinum, chromium and vanadium deposits,
- the Vredefort Dome, one of the earth's largest meteorite impact structures,
- the Paleoproterozoic (Mokolian) Waterberg Supergroup,
- the Mesoproterozoic Namaqualand Metamorphic Province.

The lower Paleozoic is characterized by sediments and granites that were folded into the Cape Fold Belt in the southwestern part of the country. Approximately two-thirds of South Africa's surface is covered by rocks of the Paleozoic to Mesozoic Karoo Supergroup, comprising several thousand meters of mainly clastic sediments and volcanics. The rocks of the Karoo Supergroup (300-140 million years in age) include glacial sediments of the Dwyka Group, coal-bearing strata of the Ecca Group, thick sandstone formations (Beaufort Group) and extensive, up to 1,400 m thick, sequences of basaltic lavas. Cenozoic terrestrial and fresh-water sediments, mainly sands, of the Kalahari Group cover large parts of northwest South Africa along the borders with Botswana and Namibia.

Several alkaline complexes, carbonatites and kimberlites (some of them diamond bearing) have intruded the Precambrian and the Karoo.

AGROMINERALS

Phosphates

South Africa has a highly-developed domestic and export oriented phosphate industry. There are several types of phosphate rocks in South Africa, the main source being of igneous origin (currently mined at Phalaborwa), as well as sedimentary and biogenic resources. The latter two types are however not mined at present. Large resources of phosphate-rich sediments are located offshore.

Igneous phosphates

Phalaborwa

The largest igneous phosphate deposit in Africa is that of Phalaborwa (old name Palabora) in the low veld of the Northern Province of South Africa, adjacent to the Kruger National Park. The Phalaborwa Complex, about 2,050 million years old, is an igneous intrusion composed of three vertical pipes that continue, according to gravity data, to depths of more than 5 km. The central feeder pipe is composed of copper-bearing carbonatite and serpentinized olivine-apatite-magnetite rock, (named foskorite after the company Foskor) set in a large body of pyroxenites and syenites. The total complex occupies an area of about 20 km^2. Pyroxenites occupy about 95% of the surface area (excluding the syenites), 3% are coarse-grained foskorites, 2% are carbonatite rocks. Apatite is not distributed equally. It is almost absent in the central part of the northern pyroxenite, but is enriched in foskorite and apatite-rich pyroxenite and glimmerite, a rock type with apatite and more than 75% phlogopite. Typical grades are: carbonatite 1-8.5% P_2O_5, massive pyroxenite 6% P_2O_5, glimmerite 9% P_2O_5 and foskorite 10% P_2O_5.

Palabora Mining Company (PMC) Ltd., a subsidiary of Rio Tinto, shares the mining area of the Phalaborwa Complex with Foskor Ltd., a wholly owned subsidiary of the state owned Industrial Development Corporation (IDC). While PMC focuses on the production of copper from the central carbonatite of the Phalaborwa Complex, Foskor Ltd. is primarily a phosphate mining company. However, until recently Foskor also produced the zirconium mineral baddeleyite.

Foskor Ltd. receives phosphate ore from 3 different sources of Phalaborwa mining operations:
- Foskor's own pyroxenite ore from the open pit (20%),
- Foskorite ore mined by PMC on Foskor claims (40%),
- High grade phosphate tailings from PMC's copper operation (40%).

The average feed grades from foskorite are 8% P_2O_5, from PMC tailings 9% P_2O_5, and from the pyroxenite 7.5 % P_2O_5 (de Jager 1989). They are then concentrated by various methods into high grade phosphate concentrates (36-40% P_2O_5). These three sources of PR supply Foskor Ltd. with about 2.9

million tonnes of phosphate concentrate per year. The apatite concentrate is traded under the name Palfos (Palfos 80 = 36.5% P_2O_5, and Palfos 86 = 39.5% P_2O_5). Some 900,000 tonnes are exported directly, 1,000,000 are sold for domestic fertilizer consumption, and the remaining 1 million tonnes are converted by local phosphoric acid producers and exported (Sims 1999). As a result of the changes at PMC, which produced 80,000 tonnes per day of copper ore and will change in 2002 into a 30,000 tonnes per day underground mining operation, Foskor plans to expand its direct mining operation and generate a total of 3,650,000 tonnes of phosphate concentrate per year (Sims 1999). A large amount of PR from Foskor is converted to phosphoric acid and fertilizer products by Indian Ocean Fertilizers (IOF), a wholly owned subsidiary of Foskor Ltd., at its Richards Bay facility and exported, largely to Asian markets.

Drill-proven and stockpiled phosphate ore reserves exceed 300 million tonnes at an average grade of 7.45% P_2O_5 (Wilson 1998). The total *in-situ* resources of PR at Phalaborwa, to a depth of 600 m, are estimated at 13,000 million tonnes with an average grade of 6.8% P_2O_5 (de Jager 1989).

Agronomically, the phosphate rock from Phalaborwa is not suitable for direct application because the main phosphate mineral is a fluor-apatite with very low reactivity.

Glenover

Phosphate mineralization at the Glenover Carbonatite Complex, located in the Northern Province, is associated with a breccia zone along the carbonatite-pyroxenite contact. The whole ovoid-shaped complex is 4.7 km long and 3.5 km wide The iron- and apatite-rich breccia body occurs near the centre of the Glenover complex. Between 1962 and 1983 the high grade (> 30% P_2O_5) central portion of the 10-million tonne ore body was mined by Goldfields of South Africa (GFSA) producing some 1,445,000 tonnes of 36% P_2O_5 concentrate. The ore consisted of 75-95% apatite, the rest being hematite, martite, limonite and clay (Wilson 1998). Considerable ore resources grading 20-25% P_2O_5 remain *in situ* below the open cast floor in the northwestern section of the mine. Approximately 2.5 million tonnes of residues finer than 12 mm (from crushing and screening) were left on dumps. Plans are underway by the company Fer-Min-Ore Ltd. to leach these fines (P_2O_5 20-37%) to produce phosphoric acid for animal feed products.

Schiel

The Schiel Complex, also located in the Northern Province is a large syenitic complex with subordinate carbonatite, foskorite, and syeno-gabbro. With an age of 2,095 ± 36 million years, it is almost the same age as Phalaborwa (Wilson 1998). The deposit of apatite, associated with magnetite and vermiculite was discovered in 1953. Subsequent exploration revealed ore reserves of 36 million tonnes at 5.1% P_2O_5 in the weathered zone to a depth of 39.6 m (Verwoord 1986).

Spitskop

The Spitskop Complex in the Northern Province, emplaced 1,341 ± 41 million years ago, consists of a ring complex with pyroxenite, ijolite, nepheline-syenite and carbonatite. The whole complex is about 14 km across. Three concentric apatite-rich zones occur in the complex as ring zones 27-37 m wide and 400 m in diameter. The average grade is 7.5% P_2O_5 (Wilson 1998). The apatite is finely intergrown with iron-oxides, and attempts to produce a phosphate concentrate with more than 20% P_2O_5 proved difficult (Wilson 1998).

Other small igneous phosphate occurrences

Small apatite enrichments of igneous origin are those of Kruidfontein, 40 km east of Pilansberg in the Rustenburg District, and the Bandolier Kop in the Northern Province. While the apatite mineralization in the Kruidfontein area occurs in a carbonatite, the apatite of Bandolier Kop occurs in veins and lenses in pegmatites. The occurrences are of no economic value.

Sedimentary phosphates

Several types of sedimentary phosphates are described from offshore and onshore South Africa. The largest sedimentary phosphate resources are the replacement deposits offshore west and south of South Africa. On the western margin of South Africa, phosphorite pellets are found not only offshore, but are also abundant on the adjacent coastal terraces on land. Small occurrences are associated with Upper Tertiary sediments in the coastal area of KwaZulu and Upper Dwyka Shales and Upper Ecca Shales of the Karoo Supergroup.

Offshore sedimentary phosphate resources

Extremely large diagenetic replacement phosphate resources occur as near-continuous 'pavements' or cappings of limestones offshore between Cape Agulhas and Cape Recife on the continental shelf. The Agulhas Bank deposits consist of boulders and cobbles of phosphatized limestone, in a matrix of glauconite, microfossils and quartz sand. Goethite-rich apatite cement and replacement of limestone by phosphate indicate diagenetic formation. The age of these phosphates is considered Neogene (between Miocene and 0.61 million years ago) (Birch 1990). Samples from the Agulhas Bank range from 10-25% P_2O_5. With an area of 35,000 million m^2, an average thickness of 0.5 m, and an average grade of 16% P_2O_5 the Agulhas Bank offshore phosphate deposits would contain about 5,000 million t P_2O_5 (Birch 1990). However, on technical and economic grounds they are not considered for mining at present.

The authigenic pelletal phosphorites along the western coast of South Africa, south of the Orange River are extensions of the rich marine offshore deposits of Namibia. These offshore resources contain approximately 3,500 million tonnes of P_2O_5 (Birch 1990).

Onshore sedimentary phosphate resources

Part of the major sedimentary phosphate province that stretches along the western coast of South Africa into Namibia is the onshore phosphorite deposits of the Saldanha embayment in the Langebaan area in the Sandveld region of the Western Cape Province. Here, several types of phosphates occur, from guano-derived Al-rich phosphates to unconsolidated pelletal and consolidated crust type (phoscrete) deposits. The phosphatic sediments are of Miocene to Pliocene age (Hendey and Dingle 1989). It is thought that the phosphorites in the Saldanha area were formed in an estuary adjacent to a region with upwelling and high biological productivity (Birch 1990).

Some of the phosphorites have been mined in the past, others are, for various reasons, not developed. Among the Ca-phosphate occurrences and deposits in the Saldanha area is the Varswater deposit, the mined out phosphorites from the Baards Quarry and Old Varswater Quarry, as well as Sandheuvel, Paternoster and Duyker Eiland. The main phosphates at Varswater consist of pelletal sands of francolitic composition with 'collophane' cement (Hendey and Dingle 1989). The average thickness of the mineable layer is 10 m at 10% P_2O_5. The Varswater deposit at Langeberg near Langebaanweg has 49 million tonnes of reserves at 10% P_2O_5. Mining started in 1965. By 1970 production of phosphate concentrate was at 163,300 tonnes annually.

The deposit at Sandheuvel (23.6 million tonnes at 6% P_2O_5) is unexploited. Also the Paternoster ore body is unexploited. It contains unconsolidated low-grade ore, at Pelgrimsrust 10 million tonnes at 5% P_2O_5 and at Noodhulp 2.7 million tonnes at 4% P_2O_5. The Varswater deposit on the farm Langeberg 188 near Langebaanweg produced about 24 million tonnes before it closed in 1992. Some 25 million tonnes of ore at a grade of 8.5% P_2O_5 remain as proven reserves. The ore was concentrated to 29-30% P_2O_5 and sold as 'Langfos' fertilizer. The apatite from Langebaan was chemically and mineralogically analyzed and proved a carbonate-substituted apatite with a unit-cell a-value of 9.364 Å. This a-cell value is considered 'intermediate' with marginal value for direct application on agricultural soils (Thibaud *et al.* 1992). Agronomic evaluation by Thibaud *et al.* (1992) showed that Langebaan PR (Langfos) was not an effective substitute for superphosphate. In a further study they showed that the relative agronomic effectiveness of a superphosphate-Langfos blend increased in close association with an increase in the proportion of the superphosphate (Thibaud *et al.* 1993).

Uloa

Frankel (1966) described a small bed of nodular phosphate in Miocene beds in the Uloa area along the lower reaches of the Umfolosi River in coastal northern KwaZulu-Natal. The nodular bed with francolitic composition (refractive index 1.622) varies from 30-100 cm in thickness but is of importance as it is one of only a few Tertiary sedimentary phosphate occurrences along the eastern coast of Africa. In the northerly extension from Uloa, in southern Mozambique, the extensive glauconite-bearing Eocene Cheringoma Formation with fossil fish and teeth beds is seen as an excellent potential source rock for phosphorites.

Karoo phosphates

Small phosphate occurrences are described from shales of the Upper Dwyka Group in the Western Cape Province (east of Matjiesfontein). Concretions, up to 6 m long and 0.3 m thick occur in shales directly overlying tillites (Wilson 1998). The resources are very small and of no economic value. Very thin phosphorite beds have also been found in Dwyka Group sediments overlying the Dwyka diamictite near Stanger, north-east of Durban in coastal northern KwaZulu-Natal (Buehmann and Buehmann 1987).

Phosphatic nodules in the Ecca Group have been known for a long time from the Weenen area, north-northwest of Pietermaritzburg in KwaZulu-Natal Province. The flattened nodules, up to 1.2 m long and 0.5 m thick, are confined to small localized areas in the Upper Ecca Group shale horizons. Local low-grade lenticular phosphate 'reefs' have also been encountered, but have no economic potential.

Guano deposits

Several small island guano deposits were mined at the beginning of the 20th century off the coast of South Africa, north of Cape Town (Hutchinson 1950). For example, some 771 tonnes were produced in 1919 from Dassen Island (Hutchinson 1950). The islands are part of a chain that is inhabited by seabirds feeding on the fish in the nutrient-rich upwelling zone of the Benguela Current.

A small aluminum phosphate deposit with a grade of 15% P_2O_5 was mined in the early 1900s on the farm Klipfontein in the Hoedjes Bay area on the Atlantic coast, near Saldanha Bay. The Hoedjes Bay deposit (also referred to as Kreeftebaai and Klipvlei) was formed from the reaction of sea-bird excretions and granite (Atkinson and Hale 1993). The small operation ceased shortly after World War I. Another guano-derived Al-phosphate mineralization that has been mined is that of Constable Hill, with an average grade of 22.48% P_2O_5. The ore was processed to yield aluminum sulphate and feed-grade calcium-phosphate Wilson 1998).

K-silicates

There are no known evaporite-related potash deposits reported in South Africa. The only K sources of significance are K-silicates, specifically feldspar, phlogopite from the Phalaborwa igneous complex and, in small amounts, glauconite. The feldspar resources from pegmatites are considerable, but are of little use for agricultural purposes. Most researchers found that the solubility of feldspar is too low to warrant direct application of this K source. A better source from the point of K-release is that of phlogopite and glauconite. While glauconite resources are very small (glauconitic sandstone pebbles reported by Frankel 1966) phlogopite resources are extensive, forming large portions of the pyroxenite complex of Phalaborwa.

Phlogopite is also found in foskorite (or phoscorite) and in the carbonatite of Phalaborwa. Large parts of this complex are rich in phlogopite: the phlogopite pyroxenite contains 25-50% phlogopite, the pyroxenitic glimmerite 50-75% phlogopite and the glimmerite more than 75% phlogopite (de Jager 1989). The chemical composition of glimmerites averages about 8.2% K_2O and 7-24% MgO and various amounts of CaO and SiO_2 (Fourie and de Jager 1986). Electron microprobe analyses of phlogopite show a narrow range of K_2O from 9.3% to 10.4%, and MgO from 23.1 to 26.5% (Erickson 1989). In the weathering zone the phlogopite is altered into vermiculite. The total phlogopite resources in the Phalaborwa complex exceed 1,500 million tonnes. Up to 1,5 million tonnes of phlogopite are discarded every year. In the late 1990s this 'waste resource' was studied by the Industrial Development Corporation (IDC) of South Africa and Foskor on their viability as a source of alumina, magnesia and potassium sulphates. However, similar efforts using inorganic acidulation techniques on an industrial scale were unsuccessful in Finland (at the Siilinjaervi carbonatite complex). On a smaller scale, acidulated phlogopite showed some promising agronomic results in Sri Lanka (Weerasuriya *et al.* 1993). Whether there have been attempts to extract K and Mg from phlogopite, for example, through biological means (bioprocessing or through plants like rye grass), is unknown.

Liming material

Limestone and dolomite resources occur in several different forms in South Africa. A large proportion of the 178 sedimentary, igneous, calcrete and travertine limestone and dolomite occurrences and deposits reported by Gwosdz (1996) are of Precambrian age, including more than 14 of Archean age and 61 of Proterozoic age. Many of the Archean limestone/dolomite resources occur in the form of marble. The Proterozoic limestone and dolomite resources occur largely as compact, fine-grained dolomitic limestones. Many of these resources are used for dimension stone purposes, for metallurgical uses and in agricultural applications. Due to their relatively high Mg content, they are generally not used in the cement industry. In contrast to the hard sedimentary carbonates, the Cretaceous to Recent carbonates that occur intermittently along the coast from Saldanha Bay to East London are called 'soft' carbonates (Martini and Wilson 1998). Much of these soft carbonates are suitable for agricultural purposes. Some soft limestones containing oyster shells have been mined for use as poultry grit and as additive in animal feed.

In addition, Gwosdz (1996) described the calcitic and dolomitic resources in 7 carbonatite complexes, Phalaborwa, Spitskop, Glenover, Goudin, and the carbonatites near Kruidfontein, Tweerivier-Bulhoek, Nooitgedacht, Kruidfontein. Ca-carbonatites (soevites) containing 1.7% P_2O_5 have been mined for agricultural purposes by a local development corporation from the Spitskop alkaline complex, between Pietersburg and Middelburg.

Calcrete deposits are numerous in South Africa. Calcretes occur in nodular form and as caprocks with variable thicknesses, from nodules a few centimetres across to 30 m thick beds. They are often used as local sources for building material, for road construction and for agriculture. Gwosdz (1996) described the location and composition of the main 48 calcrete occurrences, several of which are mined for agricultural purposes. Extensive deposits of this kind are exposed and mined as agricultural liming materials in the Zeerust-Dwaalboom area near the border with Botswana (Martini and Wilson 1998). The 18 occurences of travertine in South Africa reported by Gwosdz (1996) are mostly small and are high-Ca and low-Mg limestones. Exceptions are the travertine deposits along the 250 km long escarpment north of Kimberley, and the 20-30 m thick travertine layer at Ulco, some 70 km northeast of Kimberley (Martini and Wilson 1998).

Agricultural applications made up about 5.9% of the total limestone sold in South Africa in 1987 (Griffiths 1989). The major producers of agricultural limestone are Aglime Ltd. at Riversdale, Bontebok Limeworks Ltd., Coetzee Limeworks Ltd., and Leo Dolomite Quarry at Potgietersrus, Bryttenmyn Ltd. at Bloemhof, Buhrmannsdrifmyn Ltd. at Groot Marico, Marine Lime Ltd. at Vredenburg near Saldanha, and Spitskalk Ltd. at Nebo (Griffiths 1989).

Limestone fines from 'wastes' include limestone fines from slimes dams in Groot Marico excavated by Maricomyn. The fines from the AMCOR slime ponds at Droogegrond, Lyttelton, south of Pretoria planned to be marketed as dolomitic agricultural limestone (Gwosdz 1996).

Hiqualime Ltd. produces agricultural lime from 'waste' material at Highveld Steel (Griffiths 1989). The dolomitic residue from a fluorspar mine south of Zeerust was pumped to slimes dumps and is currently reworked and sold as magnesium-rich agricultural lime (Martini and Wilson 1998).

In 1994 the sales statistics of unburnt limestone in South Africa included 726,406 tonnes of agricultural lime, out of a total of 15,006,064 tonnes (Skillen 1995).

Sulphur, pyrite and gypsum

There are no commercial natural resources of elemental sulphur in South Africa. Sulphur is solely won as by-product from the oil refineries (35,000-40,000 tonnes), and 140,000 tonnes sulphur are extracted from coal during the synthetic-fuel process (Boelema and Ehlers 1998).

Pyrite is a common by-product from the gold mining and the coal industry. While large resources of pyrite are extracted by flotation and converted into sulphuric acid from the gold mines in the Witwatersrand Basin, the pyrites from gold deposits in various Archean greenstone belts are unsuitable for sulphuric acid production because of their relatively high arsenic concentrations.

Sulphuric acid is also extracted as by-product from smelter gases, for example from processing of copper ores from Phalaborwa. Sulphuric acid is used for many purposes including the production of superphosphate fertilizers. Once lower SO_2 emission standards are enforced, substantial more quantities of sulphuric acid will become available.

Most of South Africa's natural gypsum deposits formed in surficial terrestrial arid to semi-arid environments. Extensive surface to near surface deposits are located in the Northern Cape Province and the northern part of the Western Cape Province. Smaller deposits and occurrences are found in the Eastern Cape Province and in the KwaZulu-Natal Province (Oosterhuis 1998). Gypsum formed in the upper portion of the weathering profile in shales of the Ecca Group of the Karoo Supergroup and in salt pans. These types of deposits form in areas where evaporation rates are high and precipitation rates are low. Gypsum precipitates largely in clay layers.

The richest gypsum field in South Africa are located in the so-called Bushmanland, west of Van Wyksvlei in the Northern Cape Province. The gypsum deposits consist of several different types, from high-grade powdery gypsum (90% gypsum) to gypsum mixed with clay (65-85% gypsum). The deposit is approximately 3 m thick. Total reserves are in excess of 30 million tonnes (Oosterhuis 1998). The deposits at Vanrhynsdorp, West Coast and Steytlerville-Jansenville are all comparatively small in size.

By-product gypsum resources form strong competition to natural gypsum deposits. High-grade gypsum by-product is generated during the salt recovery from seawater near Port Elizabeth. Other sources of inexpensive by-product gypsum are phospho-gypsum, a by-product from phosphate fertilizer and phosphoric acid manufacture (Griffiths 1989).

The agricultural sector consumed some 41,000 tonnes of gypsum in 1987, which is 12% of the total gypsum consumption in South Africa (Griffiths 1989).

Vermiculite

Palabora Mining Company (PMC) Ltd. is the world's largest producer of vermiculite. With an annual capacity of 230,000 tonnes per year, PMC is more than double the size of any other vermiculite producer in the world. In 1998, PMC accounted for 43% of the world's vermiculite production and 87% of the export market (Ellicott 2000). The vermiculite deposit at the Phalaborwa complex has been mined since 1940 and is currently operated by the Vermiculite Operations Department (VOD) of the Palabora Mining Company Ltd.

From the start of vermiculite mining until 1993 the VOD has produced more than 4.9 million tonnes of 90% pure vermiculite concentrate (Wilson 1998). The Vermiculite Operations Department extracts vermiculite from three separate sources: the VOD open pit in the north of the Phalaborwa complex, the so-called PP&V (Palabora Phosphate and Vermiculite Company) pit in the southern part of the complex, and various rock and tailings dumps. At present the PP&V deposit is being mined together with the reclamation of tailings dumps created from earlier mining of the VOD deposit.

The vermiculite deposit at Phalaborwa was formed by surface weathering of phlogopite. Commonly the deposit is confined to the upper 50 m from the surface, although in some areas the vermiculitization of phlogopite goes deeper than 50 m. The VOD extracts about 8,500 tonnes of ore per day at a head grade of 22% and a cut-off grade of 15%. The flake size is extremely variable, resulting in 6 commercial grades after winnowing: Premium, large, medium, fine, superfine and micron. All materials are sold in the unexfoliated form. About 75% of the materials pass through the harbour of Richards Bay as bulk, the remainder is shipped in containers via Durban.

The quality of the Phalaborwa vermiculite is very good, it has one of the highest expansion coefficients of any vermiculite in the world, 26 times its original volume compared to 10-18 times for US material.

Other vermiculite occurrences are found in the eastern section of the Schiel alkaline complex, at the Glenover complex and a few other places with small amounts and various grades.

Zeolites

Zeolite occurrences have been reported from two principal areas of South Africa, the Heidelberg-Riversdale area in the Western Cape Province (approximately 250 km east of Cape Town, and the Nxwala Estate near the Mkuze Game Reserve of the Lebombo Mountains in northern KwaZulu-Natal (Wipplinger and Horn 1998).

The up to 75% pure zeolite beds (clinoptilolite-heulandite and mordenite) of the Heidelberg-Riversdale area occur in altered tuff beds overlying bentonite-rich horizons of the Upper Mesozoic Uitenhage Group. The zeolite beds are several metres thick and can be followed intermittently over a distance of 30 km.

They are located in an agricultural area and should be investigated for their potential application as animal feed, odour control, ammonium capture from manures, and as soil amendments.

The zeolite occurrences in the Lebombo Mountains of northern KwaZulu-Natal occur in association with perlite in chill zones of rhyolitic ashflows and other volcanic and volcaniclastic rock suites of the Lebombo Group (Karoo Supergroup). Mineable ore reserves are 1 million tonnes (Griffiths 1989). The zeolite deposits, consisting of 85-90% clinoptilolite and mordenite, have been extracted at the rate of 7,000 tonnes per year by Pratley Perlite Mining Co Ltd. Potential applications of the zeolites from Natal include removal of ammonium from mine waters of gold mines, and the use of ammonium-charged zeolites for mine tailings reclamation (Griffiths 1989). A portion of the zeolite product is also sold as animal feed under the trade name 'Clinomix' (Skillen 1995).

Perlites

Small amounts of perlites are mined from the deposits in an area close to the Mkuze Game Reserve of KwaZulu-Natal (Strydom 1998). The perlite deposits occur as lenses of irregular shape associated with rhyolitic lavas of the Lebombo Group (Karoo Supergroup). Perlite is extracted by selective mining techniques by Pratley Perlite Mining Co Ltd. and then crushed and expanded at their Krugersdorp plant for use in horticultural and construction industries. Annual production from this resource is approximately 1,200 tonnes (Skillen 1995) from a resource base of 3 million tonnes. The other company in South Africa that produces expanded perlite is Chemserve Perlite Ltd., which imported 10,000 tonnes of crude perlite in 1997 (Strydom 1998).

Rock and mineral wastes

There are large resources of 'wastes' from diamond, vermiculite, phosphate and various industrial mineral operations stored in tailings. Examples are the tailings at Phalaborwa (containing among other things, phlogopite, apatite fines and carbonates), the phosphate fines at Glenover and the magnesium-rich reprocessed kimberlite fines. In addition, there are large amounts of 'by-products,' that can be used for agricultural application, for example, flue gas desulphurization (gypsum) products, fly ash, slags from the steel industry, as well as 'wastes' from building and cement industries. Organic wastes could be used together with mineral wastes, or as a medium to increase nutrient release from minerals. Organic wastes that need to be investigated include those from sugar cane, pineapple and fruit processing industries.

Agromineral potential

The potential for development of agromineral resources in South Africa is good. The indigenous fertilizer industry is well developed to provide processed P-fertilizers for modern farming practices. However, the potential to develop alternative, low-cost fertilizers for smallholder farmers and subsistence farmers in high-population density, low-income areas has not been investigated. As a first step, areas have to be identified where low-cost mineral amendments are available, where nutrient and crop needs are defined, and where poverty is widespread. Soils in these areas have to be investigated for their deficiencies, and nutrient replenishing strategies have to be tailored for the different soils and crops.

In addition, a systematic survey of nutrient containing 'waste' materials, both inorganic-mineral and organic for use on nutrient deficient soils in high-density population areas needs to be undertaken.

The major phosphate mine in the country, Phalaborwa, produces inexpensive PR concentrates. The closed Glenover phosphate mine has substantial 'fines' as potential P resources. These concentrates should be tested on their potential for development of low-cost, agronomically effective phosphate blends for communal and small-scale farmers. Experiences from Kenya and Zimbabwe indicate that PR concentrate and phosphate fines currently discarded as 'wastes,' can be pelletized or compacted with acidifying superphosphates or with other nutrients and nutrient-containing 'waste products' to form low-cost alternative fertilizers and soil amendments.

Alternative uses of mineral wastes should also focus on crops with high K and Mg requirements and trees. For example, the K-Mg silicate phlogopite in combination with various locally available N- and P-supplying materials should be agronomically tested on local soils in rural areas close to Phalaborwa. Biological processing techniques using organic 'wastes' should be tested on locally available silicate and phosphate rocks. Strong collaboration with scientists of the Agricultural Research Council or universities is recommended.

References:

Atkinson H and M Hale 1993. Phosphate production in central and southern Africa, 1900-1992. Minerals Industry International September 1993:22-30.

Birch G 1990. Phosphorite deposits on the South African continental margin and coastal terrace. In: Burnett WC and SR Riggs (eds.) Phosphate deposits of the world, Vol. 3, Neogene to modern phosphorites. Cambridge University Press, Cambridge, UK:153-158.

Boelema R and DL Ehlers 1998. Sulphur and pyrite. In: Wilson MGC and CR Anhaeusser (eds.) The mineral resources of South Africa: Handbook 16:597-598.

Buehmann D and C Buehmann 1987. Phosphorites from glaciogenic Dwyka sediments in Natal, South Africa. Abstract, 14th Colloq. Afric. Geol. Techn. Univ. Berlin, p.113.

De Jager DH 1989. Phosphate resources in the Palabora Igneous Complex, Transvaal, South Africa. In: Notholt AJG, Sheldon RP and DF Davidson (eds.) Phosphate deposits of the world. Vol 2. Phosphate rock resources, Cambridge University Press, Cambridge, UK:267-272.

Ellicott G 2000. Crude vermiculite, producers and refined markets. Industrial Minerals April 2000: 21-27

Eriksson SC 1989. Phalaborwa: A saga of magmatism, metasomatism and miscibility. In: K Bell (editor) Carbonatites, genesis and evolution. Unwin Hyman, London, pp. 221-254.

Fourie PJ and DH de Jager 1986. Phosphate in the Phalaborwa complex. In: Anhaeusser CR and S Maske (eds.) Mineral deposits of South Africa. Geol. Soc. S. Afric. Johannesburg, pp. 2239-2253.

Frankel JJ 1966. The basal rocks of the Tertiary at Uloa, Zululand, South Africa. Geol. Mag. 103:215-230.

Griffiths J 1989. South Africa's minerals, diversity in adversity. Industrial Minerals August 1989:18-53.

Gwosdz W 1996. South Africa. In: Bosse H-R, Gwosdz W, Lorenz W, Markwich, Roth W and F Wolff (eds.) Limestone and dolomite resources of Africa. Geol. Jb., D, 102:354-408.

Hendey QB and RV Dingle 1989. Onshore sedimentary phosphate deposits in southwestern Africa. In: Notholt AJG, Sheldon RP and DF Davidson (eds.) Phosphate deposits of the world. Vol 2. Phosphate rock resources, Cambridge University Press, Cambridge, UK:200-206.

Hutchinson GE 1950. Survey of existing knowledge of biogeochemistry - The geochemistry of vertebrae excretion. Bull. Am. Mus. Nat. History, 96, 554 pp.

Martini JEJ and MGC Wilson 1998. Limestone and dolomite. In: Wilson MGC and CR Anhaeusser (eds.) The mineral resources of South Africa: Handbook 16:433-440.

Oosterhuis WR 1998. Gypsum. In: Wilson MGC and CR Anhaeusser (eds.) The mineral resources of South Africa: Handbook 16:394-399.

Sims C 1999. IM profiles: Foskor. Industrial Minerals May 1999:36-38.

Skillen A 1995. Welcome to the new South Africa. Industrial Minerals June 1995:25-53.

Strydom JH 1998. Perlite. In: Wilson MGC and CR Anhaeusser (eds.) The mineral resources of South Africa: Handbook 16:522-524.

Thibaud GR, Farina MPW, Hughes JC and MA Johnston 1992. The effectiveness of Langebaan rock phosphate and superphosphate in two acid, phosphate deficient soils. S. Afr. J. Plant Soil 1992, 9:19-28.

Thibaud GR, Farina MPW, Hughes JC and MA Johnston 1993. Maize response to Langebaan rock phosphate-superphosphate mixtures under glasshouse conditions. S. Afr. J. Plant Soil 1993, 10:110-118.

Verwoord WJ 1986. Mineral deposits associated with carbonatites and alkaline rocks. In: Anhaeusser CR and S Maske (eds.) Mineral deposits of South Africa. Geol. Soc. S. Afric. Johannesburg, pp. 2173-2191.

Weerasuiya TJ, Pushpakumara S and PI Cooray 1993. Acidulated pegmatitic mica: a promising multi-nutrient fertilizer. Nutr. Cycl. Agroecosyst. 56:67-77.

Wilson MGC 1998. Phosphate. In: Wilson MGC and CR Anhaeusser (eds.) The mineral resources of South Africa: Handbook 16:525-531.

Wipplinger PE and GFJ Horn 1998. Zeolite minerals. In: Wilson MGC and CR Anhausser (eds.) The mineral resources of South Africa: Handbook 16:671-675.

Sudan

Total population (July 2000 estimate): 35,080,000
Area: 2,505,810 km^2
Annual population growth rate (2000): 2.84%
Life expectancy at birth (1998): 55.4 years
People not expected to survive to age 40 (1998): 26.6% of the total population
GDP per capita (1998): US $1,394

Sudan is the largest country in sub-Saharan Africa. The landscape of Sudan can be divided into several major physiographic zones: the northern desert, the mountainous Red Sea Hill area with altitudes reaching over 2,000 m, the western desert areas and volcanic mountains, and the clay plains and swampy areas in central and southern Sudan. The centre of the country is flat, with plains at altitudes between 300 and 800 m and mountainous areas such as the Nuba Mountains. The country is crossed by the two main arms of the River Nile, the White Nile that drains through the swampy areas of southern Sudan, and the Blue Nile, which flows from the Ethiopian Highlands.

Agriculture is the mainstay of Sudan's economy, contributing approximately 40% to the GDP and employing more than 70% of the working population. The main food crops of the subsistence farmers are sorghum, cassava and millet. The main agricultural export crop is cotton. Other main crops are sugar cane, groundnuts, sesame, wheat and gum arabicum.

Until very recently, the mineral industry of Africa's largest country has been very small. Apart from export minerals like chromite, gold and salt, Sudan produced only a few minerals, such as limestone and gypsum, for the domestic cement industry. Recent oil and gas discoveries have changed the energy sector and the economy of Sudan. The oil finds resulted in increased activities and the building of a pipeline to the Red Sea through which oil started to flow in August 1999. In the first and second quarter of 2000, Sudan produced 200,000 barrels of crude oil per day. The reserves of crude oil are estimated at 262.1 million barrels.

The long-lasting war in the southern part of the country with the associated large human costs and conflicts with neighbouring countries continues to be a hindrance to economic development, including the development of mineral and agricultural resources. Some 2.3 million people in Sudan are currently in need of emergency food assistance due to the long-running civil war.

Geological outline

Largely undifferentiated crystalline igneous and metamorphic rocks form the Proterozoic 'basement complex' that underlies large parts of Sudan. Pre-Neoproterozoic rocks include gneisses of Paleoproterozoic age and are part of the 'Saharan Metacraton' (Abdelsalam 2001). Parts of the Precambrian crust have been remobilized by the Pan-African thermo-tectonic rejuvenation episode between 900 and 550 million years ago. These basement rock formations outcrop in 5 uplifted Precambrian blocks separated by deep depressions which are filled with Phanerozoic sedimentary sequences (Khalil 2001).

Extensive areas of northern Sudan are covered by continental clastic sequences of the predominantly Mesozoic Nubian Series, and southern areas are covered by Tertiary-Quaternary unconsolidated surficial sediments. Some Tertiary and younger basalts occur in areas along the border with Ethiopia and northern Kenya. Approximately 100 anorogenic alkaline ring complexes have been delineated in Sudan (Vail 1985). In addition, small occurrences of carbonatite plugs and dikes are reported from the nepheline-syenite in the Nuba Mountains at Jebel Dummbeir (Mageed 1998).

Sudan is crossed by major fault systems and shear zones. Some of these shear zones have been repeatedly reactivated, including the Neoproterozoic to Cretaceous and Tertiary Central African Fault Zones. These fault zones can be traced across the African continent from Cameroon through the Central African Republic and across western and central Sudan into the Red Sea Hills.

Several large rift systems have been identified in central Sudan, the major ones being the Southern Sudan Rift, the White Nile Rift, the Blue Nile Rift and the Atbara Rift (Mageed 1998). The rift zones are generally northwest- to southeast-striking and exhibit half-graben symmetries. The basins are filled with sediments and igneous rocks, at some places more than 3.5 km thick. These extensive rift-related basins are the target for oil and gas exploration.

AGROMINERALS

Phosphates

Several types of phosphate occurrences and deposits have been reported from Sudan: phosphates in pegmatites, phosphates in sediments, and phosphates in uraniferous breccias.

Interesting for potential agricultural applications are the phosphate occurrence of Hailab and the two uraniferous phosphate occurrences at Kurun and Uro.

Hailab phosphate rocks

Information on the sedimentary phosphate rocks from Halaib District, 300 km north-northwest of Port Sudan, is sparse. Here, Upper Cretaceous to Tertiary phosphorites occur in association with clastic sediments and thick evaporites (Whiteman 1971). No data on volume and grade or geological details are currently available.

Uro and Kurun phosphate rocks

Two occurrences of phosphate breccias (Uro and Kurum) were discovered in the northeastern Nuba Mountains in 1983 during exploration work by geologists of the German Geological Group (Mageed 1998).

The phosphate mineralization of Uro (11°40'N; 31°23'E) is associated with a uranium anomaly on the northeastern border of the Nuba Mountains, some 250 km southeast of El Obeid (Al-Ubayyid). Secondary Al-rich phosphates occur in a north-south striking breccia zone within graphite schists. Chemical analyses from 12 trench samples, from the middle portion of the Uro anomaly contain 6.44% P_2O_5. In addition, small amounts of phosphates with mean P_2O_5 concentrations of 5.77% were detected in samples from small (30 x 5 m) lens-shaped quartzite breccia bodies in the northern part of this anomaly (unpublished reports by BGR, quoted by Mageed 1998).

The uranium concentrations in these rocks ranged from 61-602 mg U kg^{-1}, with a mean of 397 mg U kg^{-1} (Mageed, quoting unpublished reports of Brinkmann 1985). Sam *et al.* (1999) calculated the mean uranium activity concentrations from 17 samples of Uro at 336 mg U kg^{-1} (range 100-1117 mg U kg^{-1}). Green and yellow wavellite and crandallite minerals were found as crusts in the surficial environment. Relatively high concentrations of As, Mo and Hg indicate a hydrothermal origin of this occurrence, although the identified mineralization is found in the secondary weathering environment. Obviously, it is important to explore deeper levels of this mineralization and establish grade and volume.

Another uranium anomaly associated with phosphate mineralization was discovered 1 km south of Kurun (11°35' N; 31°25'E), about 15 km northeast of the village of Abu Gubeiha and approximately 25 km south of the Uro anomaly. The phosphate mineralization at this west-southwest- to east-northeast-striking elongated hill (length 500 m, width 100 m in the west, 200 m in the east, height 25 m above the surrounding plain) is concentrated in a brecciated zone in graphite schist. The breccia fragments consist of graphite schist, chert, quartzite and apatite. Secondary Al-phosphates (crandallite, woodhousite and wavellite), as well as variscite and Cu-bearing phosphates (turquoise), are weathering products of the underlying phosphate-rich breccias (Mageeed 1998).

Chemical analyses of 52 surface samples taken on a grid showed P_2O_5 concentrations between 0.27 and 36.48%, with a mean of 20.06%. The mean Fe_2O_3 concentration in these surface samples was 11.75% (Brinkmann 1985, quoted by Mageed 1998) and the mean U concentration was 139.6 mg kg^{-1} (range 20-504 mg kg^{-1}). The highly elevated copper and mercury concentrations (mean 2,187 mg Cu kg^{-1}, 334.13 μg Hg kg^{-1}) are indicative of a hydrothermal origin of these anomalies. The reserve estimate for the Kurun mineralization is based on the chemical analyses of supergene secondary phosphates that rest on a zone of apatite-rich breccia.

A preliminary resource estimate at Kurun indicates 1.68 million tonnes of phosphate ore grading 20% P_2O_5, which amounts to about 336,000 tonnes of P_2O_5. The depth is calculated to the base of the hills (12 m in the west and 20 m in the east), but the true depth of the phosphate mineralization is not known.

The Finish geologist Kiukkola carried out a preliminary assessment of the agricultural suitability of the Kurun phosphates in 1988-1989 (Mageed 1998). Surface samples, analysed by Kemira Oy of Finland, contain 26.2% P_2O_5, 28% CaO, 14% SiO_2, 12% Al_2O_3, 4% Fe_2O_3, 1.4% F and small amounts of Zn, Mn, Cu, and Ni. The main minerals of these samples were apatite, silica, crandallite and phlogopite (Mageed 1998). Calcination tests indicate that the citric acid-soluble P_2O_5 only slightly increases from 4.5% P_2O_5 to 6.5% P_2O_5 for uncalcined phosphates, making this modification technique unattractive. Fine grinding (80% finer than 66 microns - 230 mesh), however, increased the citric acid phosphate solubility from 4.5% to 9.6% P_2O_5 (or 37% of the total P_2O_5). The energy requirement for grinding these phosphatic rocks was 25 kWh per short ton (Mageed 1998).

Sam and Holm (1995) and Sam et al. (1999) carried out radiological assessments of the Uro and Kurun phosphates. They concluded that the application of 300 kg phosphate rock containing 336 mg kg^{-1} eU (equivalent mass concentration of uranium) for Uro phosphates and 31.9 mg kg^{-1} eU for the Kurun phosphates per hectare would not contribute to the mean terrestrial radiation exposure of the farming population. The radionuclide contribution of the Kurun phosphate rocks to the natural radionuclide content of arable land is considered 'comparatively insignificant' (Sam et al. 1999).

Other phosphates

Another potential prospect for further phosphate exploration is the area at Jebel Dumbeir near Er Rahad (12°31' N; 30°45'E) where small carbonatite plugs and dykes close to a nepheline-syenite are reported by Mageed (1998). The area is strongly affected by potassic metasomatism and is fractured. Anomalous values of F, U, Ba, Sr are reported, but no phosphates have been described so far.

The occurrences of apatite in pegmatites in the Baiyuda Desert, 130 km north-northwest of Atbarah, are of no practical and economic importance.

Other agrominerals

Limestone/dolomite/travertine

There are considerable limestone and dolomite resources in Sudan. The Red Sea coastal area is endowed with extensive Mesozoic and younger sedimentary limestone resources. In addition, extensive coral reef deposits of Pleistocene age rise up to 16 m above the sea level of the Red Sea. Many of these limestone deposits have been characterized by geologists for their suitability as raw material for the cement industry.

Precambrian marble and dolomitic marble beds are numerous in Sudan. In the compilation by Gwosdz (1996), 36 limestone and dolomite resources, mainly Precambrian, are described. Mageed (1998) provides a detailed inventory including reserves, chemical composition and utilization of many more marble and dolomitic marble deposits of Sudan. The marble deposits of Wadi Kurmut, west of Atbarah, and the El Jebelien marble deposits, form the raw material base for the cement factories of Atbarah and Rabak (near Kosti) respectively. Only limited use is made of these extensive resources for decoration purposes, for lime burning or whitewash.

Gypsum

Gypsum is produced as a by-product from salt-production and from the major Bir Eit gypsum deposit approximately 77 km north of Port Sudan, some 8 km from the Red Sea coast.

The well studied Bir Eit gypsum beds, of Miocene age, are 2.5 km in length, 300-700 m in width and have a drill-proven depth of more than 120 m. The reserves of this deposit, to a depth of 50 m, are 190 million tonnes (Mageed 1998). Other gypsum deposits close to Bir Eit include the Tabonam deposit and the Jebel Saghum gypsum deposit. The estimated reserves of the Jebel Saghum deposit, some 19 km north of Bir Eit, are about 34 million tonnes. However, if the reserves of this deposit are extrapolated to a depth of 50 m, about 124 million tonnes are available (Mageed 1998).

Approximately 20,000 tonnes of gypsum are sold annually to the domestic cement works at Atbarah and Rabak on the River Nile. A limited amount of gypsum is produced for the chalk industry in Port Sudan.

Agromineral potential

The potential of developing agrominerals in Sudan is difficult to assess due to the relative scarcity of published industrial mineral resource information and soils data.

The phosphates of the Hailab area need more detailed geological investigations and the small but important phosphate mineralization at Kurun needs additional exploration to establish the depth extent and provide a more accurate estimate of the resource base. Further agronomic testing is needed, including direct application of Kurun phosphate rock to acid soils, as well as testing various phosphate modification techniques to make the phosphates more plant available and to reduce the potentially detrimental metal and radionuclide contents.

The potential use of liming materials using existing limestone/marble and dolomitic limestone resources for agricultural needs should be assessed in view of potential needs for liming materials on acid soils.

Unfortunately, the large gypsum resources along the Red Sea coast are far from potential areas of application, for instance to ameliorate saline-alkaline soils and as a nutritional source for groundnuts.

References:

Gwosdz W 1996. Sudan. In: Bosse H-R, Gwosdz W, Lorenz W, Markwich, Roth W and F Wolff (eds.) Limestone and dolomite resources of Africa. Geol. Jb., D, 409-419.

Khalil B 2001. Uranium mineralization of the Nuba Mountains - Central Sudan: a natural radioactive hazard. Presentation. Regional Conference Geological Society of Uganda/Geological Society of Africa, Kampala, Uganda September 10-12, 2001.

Mageed AA 1998. Sudan industrial minerals and rocks. Centre for Strategic Studies, Khartoum, Sudan, 553pp.

McClellan GH and AJG Notholt 1986. Phosphate deposits of sub-Saharan Africa. In: Mokwunye AU and PLG Vlek (eds.) Management of nitrogen and phosphorus fertilizers in sub-Saharan Africa. Martinus Nijhoff, Dordrecht, Netherlands:173-224

Sam AK and E Holm 1995. The natural radioactivity in phosphate deposits from Sudan. Sci. Total Environment 162:173-178.

Sam AK, Ahamed MMO, El Khangi FA, El Nigumi YO and E Holm 1999. Radiological and chemical assessment of Uro and Kurun phosphates. J. Env. Radioactivity 42:65-75.

Vail JR 1985. Alkaline ring complexes in Sudan. J. Afr. Earth Sci. 3:51-59.

Whiteman AJ 1971. The geology of the Sudan Republic. Clarendon Press, Oxford, UK, 290pp.

Swaziland

Total population (July 2000 estimate): 1,083,000
Area: 17,363 km^2
Annual population growth rate (2000): 2.02%
Life expectancy at birth (1998): 60.7 years
People not expected to survive to age 40 (1998): 20.2% of total population
GDP per capita (1998): US $3,816

Swaziland is a small landlocked mountainous country in southern Africa, surrounded by the Republic of South Africa and Mozambique. Swaziland consists of well-defined north-south striking landscape regions, (the rugged and mountainous 'high-veld' at altitudes between 1,200-1,800 m in the west, the plateaux of the 'middle-veld' at altitudes between 600 and 1,000 m, and the 'low-veld' at approximately 300-600 m). The Lebombo Mountain range at 'middle-veld' altitudes forms the border with Mozambique. Most farming activities are concentrated in the 'middle-veld' area.

The economic bases of Swaziland are manufacturing, tourism, agriculture and the pulp and paper industries. The agricultural sector accounts for 10% of the GDP and employs approximately 18% of the people. Most farmers cultivate only 2-3 acres for maize, sorghum and vegetables on a subsistence basis and some crops (e.g. cotton) for sale. Swaziland has one of the highest cattle-to-land ratios in Africa, which results in serious erosion problems. Swaziland is the second-largest sugar exporter in Africa but other export crops and products include canned pineapple, cotton lint and cotton seed.

The mining sector accounts for only 2% of the GDP. It is in transition after the exhaustion of high-grade iron deposits and the decline of the asbestos industry. Swaziland holds a substantial resource base of coal.

Geological outline

Geologically, Swaziland can be divided into two distinct units, Archean in the western part of the country and the Permo-Triassic and younger Karoo sediments and volcanics in the eastern part of the country. The Precambrian is made up of Archean gneisses (Ngwane and Mahamba gneisses) and granite greenstone terrain (Swaziland and Pongola Supergroups), and is intruded by various plutons, including the extensive Usushwana gabbro/pyroxenite complex (Government of Swaziland 1982). Karoo sediments and volcanics (basaltic and rhyolitic/rhyodacitic in composition) form the north-south striking Lebombo Mountains.

AGROMINERALS

No phosphates have been found in Swaziland so far.

Small occurrences of siliceous limestone have been reported from Karoo sediments and small calcrete deposits occur in the low-veld, overlying Ca-rich Karoo sediments. The calcrete is restricted in thickness and extent, but can be of local importance.

Calcium-magnesium-rich alumino-silicate talc-carbonate rocks are found at the base of the Swaziland Supergroup in large amounts. The CaO analysis of one sample from near Forbes Reef contains 9.25% CaO, 15.41% MgO, but also 10.39% Al_2O_3 (Lorenz 1996). Obsidians and siliceous fine-grained tuffs but no natural zeolite deposits have been reported in the volcanic sequences of Swaziland. An occurrence of vermiculite is known from north of Manzini (Government of Swaziland 1982).

Agromineral potential

The potential for substantial amounts of agrominerals in Swaziland is low. The potential of applying talc/carbonate rocks on highly depleted and Mg deficient soils should be investigated. The potential for finding natural zeolites in the felsic volcanics of the Lebombo Mountains is good.

References:

Government of Swaziland 1982. 1:250,000 Geological Map of Swaziland.

Lorenz W 1996. Swaziland. In: Bosse H-R, Gwosdz W, Lorenz W, Markwich, Roth W and F Wolff (eds.) Limestone and dolomite resources of Africa. Geol. Jb., D, 420-423.

Tanzania

Total population (July 2000 estimate): 35,306,000
Area: 945,087 km^2
Annual population growth rate (2000): 2.57%
Life expectancy at birth (1998): 47.9 years
People not expected to survive to age 40 (1998): 35.4% of total population
GDP per capita (1998): US $480

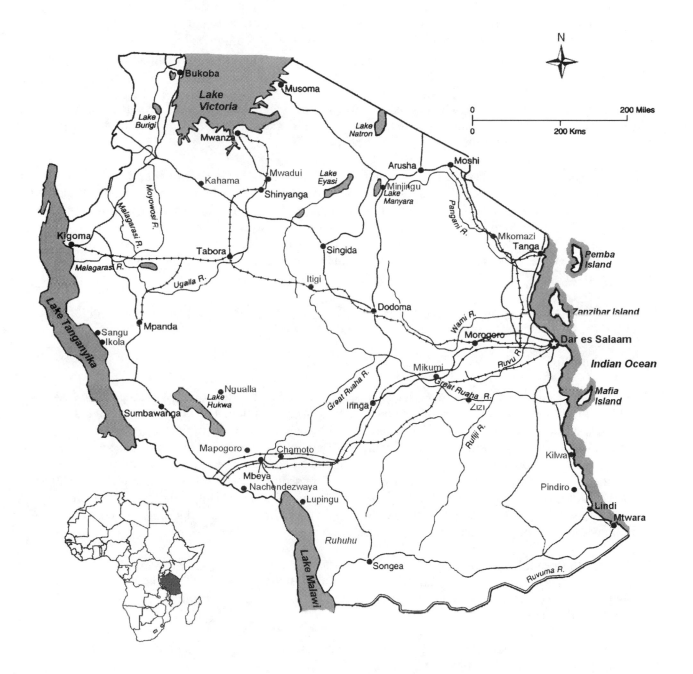

The United Republic of Tanzania (referred to here as Tanzania) is made up of the islands of Zanzibar and Pemba, and the mainland of Tanzania.

Tanzania's landscapes and climates can be grouped into several zones:

- the hot and humid coastal zone near the Indian Ocean,
- the hot dry central plateau zone, with altitudes around 1,000-1,200 m,
- the semi-temperate mountainous areas around Mt. Kilimanjaro, and the Southern Highlands in the south-central and south-western part of the country.

Agriculture is the mainstay of Tanzania's economy. In 1999, the agricultural sector accounted for 45% of the GDP. More than 80% of the employed population work in agriculture, mainly at a subsistence level. Ninety-three percent of farmers work small-holdings with an average cultivated area of less than 2 hectares. Over 50% of persons living in rural areas of Tanzania are poor, many of them under the 'one dollar a day' level commonly used to define poverty.

The main food crops are cassava, maize, bananas, rice, sorghum and sweet potatoes. Export crops are coffee and tea, cloves (from Zanzibar), cotton, sisal, pyrethrum, cashew nuts, flowers and seeds. Other crops include sugar cane, coconut, mangoes and pineapple.

The mineral sector of Tanzania is becoming a more significant part of the economy with the opening of several new gold mines. Large-scale diamond and gold mining as well as small-scale mining operations play a major role in Tanzania's mineral development. Gold production from the small-scale mining sector alone provided some 76% of Tanzania's total mineral export in 1992, when small-scale miners sold 4.5 tonnes of gold worth US $40.4 million to the Bank of Tanzania. The International Labour Organization (1999) estimated the number of people employed in small-scale and artisanal mining in Tanzania at 450,000-600,000.

Tanzania is in the planning stage of developing the 880 billion cubic feet natural gas resources of the Songo Songo Island deposit, southeast of Dar es Salaam.

Geological outline

Precambrian rocks underlie most of central and western Tanzania. Archean granite and greenstone rock assemblages form the central nucleus of the country, the Tanzania Craton. The craton is surrounded by Proterozoic belts: the Paleoproterozoic Usagaran-Ubendian belt, and the Mesoproterozoic Kibaran (Karagwe-Akolean). The Neoproterozoic Mozambique Belt occurs in the eastern part of the country. Parts of the Usagaran-Ubendian belt were rejuvenated during the Neoproterozoic to early Cambrian Pan-African thermo-tectonic event (Gabert 1984). Shallow water sediments of the Neoproterozoic (900-800 million years) Malaragazi Supergroup underlie parts of western Tanzania (Halligan 1962). The Karoo basin crosses southern Tanzania in a northeasterly direction. Mesozoic and younger marine sediments occur along the coast of Tanzania.

The Tertiary to Recent Eastern Rift Valley reaches into Tanzania from Kenya in the north. Lake Tanganyika and Lake Nyassa (Lake Malawi) form part of the Western Rift of Tanzania. Volcanics and carbonatites are associated with both the Eastern and the Western Rift. Lacustrine sediments fill large parts of the rift valleys.

There are several distinct kimberlite fields in the Archean craton of Tanzania, including the Mwadui kimberlite pipe in central Tanzania.

AGROMINERALS

Phosphates

Tanzania hosts different types of phosphate deposits and occurrences (Harris 1981; Mtuy 1986; Chesworth et al.1989; Mchihiyo 1991; Mwambete 1991; Van Kauwenbergh 1991; van Straaten 1995).

The four main types of phosphates in Tanzania are:

- igneous phosphates, associated with carbonatites,
- lacustrine phosphates in rift valley sediments,
- metamorphic phosphates,
- guano deposits.

Igneous phosphates

All known igneous phosphates in Tanzania are associated with Precambrian and Mesozoic carbonatites (Figure 2.17). These carbonatites are related to the two rift systems that cross Tanzania, the Eastern Rift and the Western Rift.

The phosphorus content in carbonatites of the Eastern Rift is generally low. The carbonatites in the southern extension of the Eastern Rift, near Morogoro, contain generally high concentrations of Light Rare Earth Elements (LREE) but only low concentrations of phosphorus.

The carbonatites with the highest phosphorus concentrations occur along the tectonically active Western Rift. They include the carbonatites of:

- Sangu-Ikola at Lake Tanganyika,
- Ngualla,
- the carbonatites in the vicinity of Mbeya and Mbozi, specifically the carbonatites of Mbalizi, Songwe Scarp, Nachendezwaya, Sengeri Hill, and Panda Hill.

In west and southwest Tanzania, several carbonatites are known to have intruded along re-activated north-northwest striking shear and fault zone (van Straaten 1989). Their ages vary from Proterozoic (Sangu-Ikola, Ngualla, and Nachendezwaya) to Mesozoic (Panda Hill, Sengeri Hill, Mbalizi, Songwe Scarp).

The Sangu-Ikola carbonatite

The Sangu-Ikola carbonatite at Lake Tanganyika is the most extensive carbonatite in Tanzania. The carbonatite is composed of three elongated bodies, the largest of which is 14 km long and 1.5 km wide. The total length of this elongated carbonatite complex is more than 30 km. Coetzee (1959) reported 'the presence of ubiquitous and fairly abundant apatite in the carbonate rocks, locally as much as 50% by volume.' Initial phosphate exploration work delineated residual phosphate-rich soils on parts of the Sangu-Ikola Carbonatite Complex. At places the P_2O_5 concentration reached up to 10% and 15% P_2O_5 (van Straaten 1983). The primary soevitic (Ca-carbonate) carbonatite contained up to 7% P_2O_5. So far, no detailed phosphate surveys in the primary and residual environments have been undertaken.

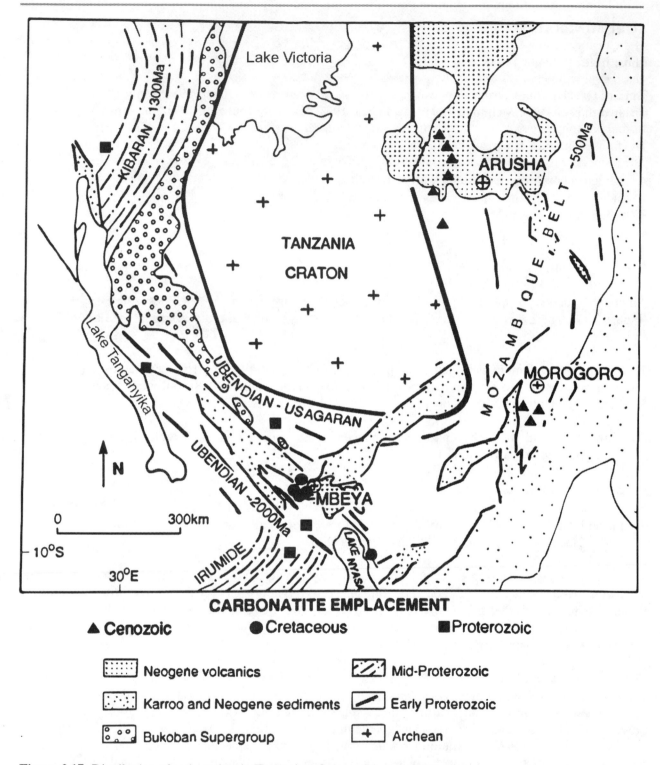

Figure 2.17: Distribution of carbonatites in Tanzania (after van Straaten 1989)

The Ngualla carbonatite

The Proterozoic Ngualla carbonatite (±1,000 million years old), is located in a remote area, approximately 200 km north of Mbeya in southwest Tanzania (7° 42'S; 32° 50'E). This plug-like intrusive carbonatite with a diameter of about 3 km is made up of various successive carbonatite phases. Phosphorus concentrations of the primary carbonatite decrease from 3 to 6% P_2O_5 in the Ca-rich phase of the carbonatite, to 3% P_2O_5 in the Mg-carbonatite phase, to 0.4% P_2O_5 in the Fe-rich carbonatite phase (van Straaten 1995). A late-phase magnetite-apatite vein, 15-20 m wide and several hundred metres long, was discovered during the work of the Tanzania-Canada agrogeology project (Chesworth *et al.* 1988). Several exploration pits in residual red soils revealed phosphate concentrations of 12-20% P_2O_5 to a depth of 5 m and more. No formal phosphate resource evaluation has been undertaken as yet at this remote site.

The more accessible Cretaceous carbonatites of Mbalizi (8° 55' S; 33° 21'30" E), Songwe Scarp 8° 45-54'S; 33° 12-30'E), and Sengeri Hill (8° 57'30"S; 33° 11'30"E) contain only small igneous phosphate resources.

Panda Hill

Presently, the only phosphate resource in the Mbeya area of economic and agronomic interest is located at Panda Hill (8° 59'30"S; 33° 14'E), some 25 km west-southwest of Mbeya along the Tanzania-Zambia railway. The Yugoslav Mining Association RUDIS (1980) calculated the primary carbonatite resources suitable for Nb and P recovery to be 480 million tonnes with an average grade of 0.33% Nb_2O_5 and 3.5% P_2O_5. The Tanzania-Canada agrogeology team delineated approximately 1 million tonnes of residual phosphates with an average grade of 10.31% P_2O_5 in the Kunja-Mtoni zone of Panda Hill (van Straaten *et al.* 1992; van Straaten 1995). Niobium concentrations in the 1 million tonnes residual soils have a mean concentration of 0.77% Nb_2O_5.

Detailed investigations of the chemistry and mineralogy of apatites from Panda Hill show a unit-cell a-value of 9.387 to 9.397 Å (Mchihiyo 1990) indicating a fluor-apatite with very low rate of substitution and hence low solubility.

Modification Techniques of Panda Phosphate Rock

Several agronomic studies using Panda phosphate rock (PR) concentrates from the Panda residual phosphate occurrence have been conducted. Most of the studies confirmed the low solubility of this igneous phosphate rock and hence low yield response (van Straaten *et al.* 1992; Mnkeni *et al.* 1994; Weil 2000).

In order to increase the reactivity of Panda PR several modification techniques were tested, including partial acidulation (Lombe, unpubl. report) and reaction with a natural zeolite as a cation exchanger (Mkeni *et al.* 1994). Initial tests using blending techniques with the soluble P fertilizer triple superphosphate (TSP) blended and pelletized with Panda PR at a 50/50 ratio showed significantly increased yield and P uptake responses for maize (van Straaten *et al.* 1992). More pronounced results have been achieved using canola (rapeseed) as the test crop (Mnkeni *et al.* 2000). These results show that the roots of rapeseed can extract P from blended unreactive PRs. Weil (2000) tested Panda PR and Minjingu PR on their suitability as direct application rock P fertilizers and showed that a cabbage variety was able to effectively extract P from the unreactive Panda PR.

Metamorphic apatite-limestones

Stockley (1946) described apatite-bearing limestones from the remote Zizi area in the Morogoro District, and van Straaten *et al.* (1992) observed apatite-bearing folded limestones near Lupingu along Lake Nyassa (Lake Malawi). The Zizi apatite-limestone in the northern Selous Game Reserve, in a remote location south of Morogoro, was discovered by Stockley in 1931 (Stockley 1946). He described them as apatite-limestones. The reserves of this 20 m wide, 1,150 m long lens in high grade metamorphic rocks were reported as 2 million short tons to a depth of 100 feet (average grade of 6.9% P_2O_5). RUDIS (1980) reinterpreted the Zizi apatite-carbonate 'dyke' as a carbonatite with estimated reserves of 1 million tonnes to a depth of 20 m. The average grade of the primary apatite-carbonate rock was calculated as 4.4% P_2O_5. The phosphate content of grab samples taken by the Tanzania-Canada agrogeology team vary widely, ranging from 0.5-7% P_2O_5 (Chesworth *et al.* 1988). The REE and Nb values are low, and seem to confirm that this body is probably not of igneous origin, but rather a metamorphosed phosphatic limestone, as suggested by Stockley (1946).

Lacustrine phosphates

Minjingu

The lacustrine-biogenic Minjingu phosphate deposit in Northern Tanzania is unique. Situated about 110 km southwest of Arusha, the phosphate deposit was discovered in 1956 during a search for uranium. The deposit has been mined since 1983. The layered phosphates of Minjingu are located in the Eastern Rift Valley, in a paleo-rift valley lake environment. The phosphate beds are intercalated with greenish claystones, chert beds and cm-thin analcime bearing volcanic tuff beds. Extensive drilling proved that the phosphate beds are confined to the close vicinity of the small Minjingu Hill, which in Upper Pliocene or Pleistocene times (Schlueter 1997) was a small island on which large colonies of cormorants roosted. Detailed geological, geophysical (radiometric) and palaeontological studies by Schlueter and van Straaten in 1985 (unpublished manuscript) and Schlueter and Kohring (1992) revealed that the coarse-clastic laminated phosphate beds consist mainly of detrital cormorant *Phalacrocorax khueneanus* bones (Schlueter 1991) and vertebrae, fins, spines, etc. of cichlid fishes. The beds also contain clastic silicate fragments, derived from the metamorphic rocks that form the centre (paleo-island) of Minjingu Hill.

Two types of phosphate ores have been identified at Minjingu, the 'soft' ore and the 'hard' ore. The soft ore is composed of several up to 2-3 m thick, whitish-grey, coarse-clastic phosphate bone beds. The grade of most of these beds is 22-25% P_2O_5. The hard phosphate ore surrounds Minjingu Hill, overlying and rapidly grading into the soft phosphates below. The hard phosphate ore is several metres thick and consists of indurated, massive, siliceous phosphorites. The grade of the hard ore averages about 24% P_2O_5.

Early reserve calculations of the deposit were 10 million tonnes. More recent reserve figures, cited by the mine geologist (Mwambete, pers. comm. July 1997), are 3.3 million tonnes soft ore and 4.8 million tonnes hard ore.

Detailed chemical and mineralogical investigations of the soft ore, carried out by the International Fertilizer Development Centre, USA (Van Kauwenbergh 1985, 1991) and by the author, show high fluorine (F) contents in the bones (up to 4% F), as well as lower P_2O_5 content than expected of a typical fluor-apatite. Van Kauwenbergh (1985) noted that bones originally composed of slightly soluble carbonate-hydroxy-apatite may have been altered into francolites or fluor-apatites. The high F content in the bones could indicate a francolitic composition.

Agronomically, the Minjingu soft phosphates are well suited for direct application because of the relatively high solubility of the phosphates. The neutral ammonium citrate solubility ranges from 5.6% P_2O_5 in the raw phosphate product to 12.9% P_2O_5 in bird bone concentrate (Van Kauwenbergh 1985). These values are very high and compare well with the most soluble phosphate rocks in the world (Van Kauwenbergh 1991). Of particular interest is the relatively high concentration of barium (1,100 to 2,100 mg/kg), strontium (2,500 to 9,900 mg/kg), and uranium (410 to 1,100 mg/kg) in the Minjingu PR. For comparison, uranium concentrations from marine PR in northern Florida are in the range of 60-100 mg/kg, in Morocco 80 mg/kg, and in North Carolina 50 mg/kg.

Makweba and Holm (1993) and Banzi *et al.* (2000) published data on the radioactivity of Minjingu phosphate rocks. They conclude that workers at the mine could possibly become affected by direct external radiation from the phosphates and through inhalation of dust from the mine. This confirms the unpublished data of Mustonen and Annanmaeki (1988) from the Finnish Centre for Radiation and Nuclear Safety who carried out studies on radiation exposure of workers at the Minjingu phosphate mine, at the processing plant, at the store, the loading station (in Arusha) and at the fertilizer factory in Tanga. The results of their findings showed that the major part of the total radiation exposure is through inhalation of long-life natural radionuclides associated with the phosphate dust. They concluded that these risks could largely be reduced by wearing masks at both the mine and the processing site.

The external radiation for farmers who use Minjingu PR and Minjingu PR-based fertilizers is considered insignificant compared to that of normal background terrestrial sources (Makweba and Holm 1993). But results of Banzi *et al.* (2000) show that the radiation dose of ambient air over five years time at the mine site is 12 times the allowed average dose limit for public exposure. The findings suggest a potential health risk when the phosphates are ingested. Samples taken from the phosphate ores, phosphate wastes, water at the site and wild and edible leaf vegetables at Minjingu, as well as chicken feed using Minjingu PR as a component, show elevated concentrations of ^{226}Ra and ^{228}Ra (Banzi *et al.* 2000). A full risk assessment of radiation exposure for people living in Minjingu and those who handle and use Minjingu PR was recommended (Banzi *et al.* 2000).

Agronomic Testing of Minjingu Phosphate Rock

Results of agronomic experiments using Minjingu PR as direct application P-fertilizer on Tanzanian soils are reported by Anderson (1970), Mnkeni *et al.* (1991), Ikerra *et al.* (1994), and on Kenyan soils by Okalebo and Woomer (1994), Sanchez *et al.* (1997), Buresh *et al.* (1999), ICRAF (1999), Mutuo *et al.* (1999), and Ngoze (2001). Extensive studies by scientists from the Kenya Agricultural Research Institute (KARI) and the International Centre for Research in Agroforestry (ICRAF) in western Kenya showed a generally high yield increase upon directly applied ground Minjingu PR. The relative agronomic effectiveness (RAE) of Minjingu PR on maize in the first season averaged 74% at application rates of 50 kg P ha^{-1} and 80% at 250 kg P ha^{-1}. In general, the RAE of Minjingu PR in comparison to imported soluble P-fertilizers ranged from 65-85% (Sanchez *et al.* 1997). On the same soils, Mutuo *et al.* (1999) calculated the RAE of Minjingu PR in the range of 84-98% in the short rainy season. The results of pot and field trials by Ngoze (2001) confirm these results. The RAE of Minjingu PR was 75% and 91% for the long and short rains period respectively.

Other experiments with Minjingu PR on P-deficient ultisols of Ethiopia with the forage crop *stylosanthes guianensis* showed excellent responses. Minjingu PR applied directly to these soils was as effective as triple superphosphate (TSP). The partially acidulated form was found to be similarly effective (Haque *et al.* 1999). It seems evident that acidulation or partial acidulation of Minjingu is not necessary to make this highly reactive PR an agronomically effective P fertilizer in acid P-deficient soils.

Farmers using the product for direct application complained about the product's dustiness. Tests at IFDC showed that fine soft Minjingu ore mixed with urea and granulated or compacted gave a product that handles well and that contains not only P but also N.

The Minjingu Phosphate Company (a subsidiary of the State Mining Corporation) started production of Minjingu phosphate concentrate in 1983 and shipped the concentrate to the fertilizer plant in Tanga for processing into single superphosphate (SSP). However the Tanga fertilizer plant closed in 1991 and subsequently no further phosphate concentrates were shipped there. In 1996, the Minjingu Phosphate Company sold only small quantities (1,000 tonnes) of Minjingu PR for direct application, of which some 300 tonnes were sold to Kenya. Small amounts of Minjingu PR were sold to tea and sisal estates, for bean production and for pasture experiments (Mwambete, pers. comm. 1997).

Other lacustrine phosphates:

Additional lacustrine phosphatic sediments of similar origin are reported from 'The Pyramides,' a group of hills 12 km south of Minjingu. The amount and grade of the phosphates have not been established as yet.

Another much smaller phosphate occurrence, of possibly similar origin, is reported from the Chali Hills in the central Dodoma Region. A thin phosphatic layer covers bare quartzite rocks and fills joints in the isolated Chali Hill that stands out at the southern end of the Bahi depression, a paleo-lake in a rift structure.

Another small lacustrine phosphate occurrence in Pleistocene in rift valley sediments is known from Chamoto in the Usangu Flats in southwest Tanzania. Slightly radioactive nodules of 'cherts' were found by Williams in the early 1960s (Williams, unpubl.). Field work by Guest (1956), McKie (1958) and geologists of the Tanzania-Canada agrogeology project (Chesworth *et al.* 1988) delineated a 10-60 cm irregular bed of cherty phosphorite in lacustrine sediments and volcaniclastic beds.

The occurrences of Chali Hills and Chamoto are of importance as they confirm the presence of other lacustrine phosphate deposits in the rift valley and demonstrate the potential for finding other phosphate rock occurrences in rift valley sediments.

Other sedimentary phosphates

Kreuser *et al.* (1990) describe phosphate pebbles and 'phosphate-enriched horizons in the bone-bearing nodular K6 Formation' of the Karoo sediments in the Mikumi area of eastern Tanzania. However, the economic value of these occurrences is regarded as insignificant.

Kent *et al.* (1971) described phosphatized ammonites in the lower Cretaceous (Albian) in the Mandawa area of southern Tanzania. The extent of this mineralization is unknown.

Other agrominerals

Limestone/dolomite

A comprehensive account of limestone, dolomite, calcrete and travertine resources in Tanzania is presented by Bosse (1996). The calcitic and dolomitic rocks in Tanzania include young calcrete, travertine, lacustrine limestones, coral reef limestones, massive limestones and dolomites of Jurassic to Tertiary age, as well as Precambrian crystalline limestones, dolomites, and carbonatites.

Precambrian marbles and dolomitic marbles are mainly found in the Neoproterozoic Mozambique Belt, to the east of the central Tanzania Craton, in the Paleoproterozoic Usagaran and, to a lesser extent, in the Paleoproterozoic Ubendian System in western Tanzania. The limestone and dolomite resources in southwest Tanzania have been compiled by the Tanzania-Canada agrogeology team (van Straaten *et al.* 1992). No limestone deposits are exposed in the Mesoproterozoic Kibaran (Karagwe-Ankolean) in northwest Tanzania.

Compact, fine-grained limestones and dolomitic stromatolitic limestones, in places silicified, occur in the Neoproterozoic platform sediments of the Malaragazi Supergroup. They are found mainly in the sparsely populated area northeast and east of Kigoma and used at several places used for the production of lime.

Several smaller limestone occurrences are reported from the Karoo basins of the Lake Rukwa and Ruhuhu areas (Bosse 1996). Mesozoic to Tertiary limestones occur in abundance in the coastal area of Tanzania. Jurassic limestones near Tanga are utilized for the local cement industry. Tertiary to Recent coral limestones occur in numerous locations along the Indian Ocean and are mined for several purposes. At Wazo Hill, a few km north of Dar es Salaam, a 15 m thick coral limestone bed is quarried for use in the cement industry.

Bosse (1996) describes 64 calcretes of varying quantity and quality from many parts of Tanzania. Calcrete deposits are usually thin indurated carbonate rocks mixed with sand and clay. These calcareous duricrusts, surface crusts or secondary limestones are developed largely under semi-arid conditions on crystalline rocks rich in calcium and magnesium silicates. They are often found in seasonal wetlands in morphological depressions (locally called 'mbugas'). Calcretes are the only carbonate rocks found in the area of the central Tanzania Craton. In some areas in the northeastern part of the country and in the Shinyanga region, the resources are very extensive and lend themselves to extraction. Commonly the calcretes are calcium-rich but poor in magnesium. Many of these resources are developed for local lime production, mainly for use as whitewash.

Travertine deposits are located in several rift-related areas of Tanzania. The most voluminous travertine (about 50 million tonnes) is located along the Songwe River area, near Mbeya in southwest Tanzania. The travertine is used for the Mbeya cement industry and local lime producers.

There are several carbonatites exposed in Tanzania. Most of them have extensive volumes of either soevitic (Ca-carbonatite) and/or dolomitic carbonatites. Some of the carbonatites (for instance Ngualla and Sangu-Ikola) occur in remote areas and their usefulness is inevitably much reduced. But carbonatites located in farming areas with acid soils should be further investigated and agronomically tested, for instance, the Nachendezwaya carbonatite in southwestern Tanzania along the border with Zambia.

Guano

Bat guano deposits are known from Sukumavera in southwest Tanzania near Mbeya, from the Amboni caves, 10 km from Tanga, and from the Haitajwa and Manapwani caves on Zanzibar Island. The bat guano deposits of Sukumavera in the Mbeya area are located in caverns in horizontal travertine formations. From 1934 to 1957 some 3,223 tonnes were excavated from these caves (Spurr 1954). A re-investigation of the guano deposit at Sukumavera revealed only small easily accessible resources (a few hundred tonnes) with grades between 26 and 37% P_2O_5. Small amounts of bat guano have also been extracted from the Amboni caves near Tanga (Harris 1981) and the caves on Zanzibar (Hutchinson 1950).

A small bird guano deposit is located on the Lantham Island, a coral island some 65 km east-southeast of Dar es Salaam (Hutchinson 1950; Harris 1981). The coral limestone of this island, 1,000 x 500 feet in extent, is covered with a thin veneer of bird guano. The limestone has been phosphatized by solutions from the overlying guano. The grade of the phosphatized limestone is low at 8.5% P_2O_5 and reserves are estimated at 190,000 tonnes (Harris 1981). No guano or phosphatized limestones have been excavated at this location, partially because of environmental concerns.

Sulphur/sulphides/sulphates

Only a small amount (approximately 2,500 tonnes) of elemental sulphur has been reported from Tanzania, and this is located in a remote location, the inner crater of Kilimanjaro, at an altitude of almost 6,000 m(!).

No major, easily extractable pyrite deposits have been identified and although sulphides are 'waste products' of the gold mining industry their grades are low and their heavy metal content is high.

A major rock gypsum and anhydrite resource is located in a remote area, at Pindiro and Mandawa in southeastern Tanzania, about 100 km north of Lindi (Harris 1981). The deposit is part of a salt dome structure. Proven reserves of a section of this deposit, as determined by the State Mining Corporation (STAMICO), are 5 million tonnes containing 85% gypsum. The gypsum rock has not been extracted as yet.

Low-grade and low-volume gypsum resources are found in seasonal swamp environments (mbugas) at Msagali and Itigi in central Tanzania and at Mkomazi in the Lushoto District of eastern Tanzania (Harris 1981). As so-called 'gypsite' the gypsum occurs in crystal form in nodules and as finely distributed crystals in a sandy, silty and clay-rich groundmass. Small-scale mining of gypsum from the low-grade gypsite deposit of Mkomazi in northeast Tanzania started in 1952. The ore is hand-sorted to produce a concentrate of 60-80% gypsum. Since 1953, annual production has been in the range of 4,000-9,000 tonnes with a maximum annual production in the late 1970s of 22,000 tonnes (Richardson 1982).

Natural zeolites

The Tanzania-Canada agrogeology team discovered several small zeolite occurrences in southwest Tanzania (Chesworth *et al.* 1988), including the phillipsite occurrence at Mapogoro in the Rukwa Rift Valley (more than 84,000 tonnes) and chabazite tuff beds of Shingo (more than 80,000 to 100,000 tonnes). Other natural zeolites (erionite) are reported from the Lake Natron area in the Eastern Rift.

Natural Zeolites to Induce Apatite Breakdown

Phillipsite from Mapogoro in combination with phosphates from Tanzania (Panda Hill PR and Minjingu PR) was tested by Mnkeni *et al.* (1994) as a means of inducing apatite breakdown. The results clearly showed that the addition of large amounts of Mapogoro phillipsite had no effect on the dissolution of the unreactive Panda PR, but that the breakdown of Minjingu PR could be enhanced. However, Mnkeni *et al.* (1994) noted that the amount of zeolite necessary to enhance the breakdown of Minjingu PR (ratio = 100 phillipsite: 1 Minjingu PR) is large. Other methods should be devised which require lower quantities of zeolites, for example the method of using NH_4^+-exchanged zeolites (Lai and Eberl 1986).

Rock wastes

Large-scale diamond mining from primary kimberlite pipes started in 1940 at Mwadui near Shinyanga in central Tanzania. Tailings and waste rock from the kimberlite pipe and overlying tuffs and crater sediments have been stockpiled for more than 50 years. Chemical analyses of the Mwadui tailings indicate calcium contents of more than 10% CaO, more than 11% MgO and 2% K_2O. The tailings are located within the perimeter of the Mwadui mine site and are currently not accessible. Several million tonnes of waste rock and tailings from the abandoned Nyamwele kimberlite diamond field, some 40 km north of Kahama, are stored adjacent to farmers fields near Lake Nyamwele.

Agromineral potential

The potential for developing agromineral resources in Tanzania is good. There are several phosphate rock resources in Tanzania. The mineralogical and chemical characteristics of phosphates from Minjingu in northern Tanzania are excellent. Agronomic tests with directly applied Minjingu PR have shown good agronomic response on acid P-deficient soils. Blending and granulation techniques should be tested to make this phosphate product less dusty and more attractive to the farmers and a good marketing effort needs to be launched to bring this valuable resource to market.

A potential drawback is the relatively high content of radio-nuclides in the phosphate rock. Geochemical dispersion and plant uptake studies must be undertaken to study element transport in soils and to determine to what extent the radio-nuclides are taken up by crops.

The easily accessible and easily extractable residual and igneous phosphate resources at Panda Hill contain approximately 1 million tonnes of PR grading 10% P_2O_5. To utilize these resources, small-scale mining techniques could be applied for extraction. Phosphate solubility problems have to be overcome as the apatites are unreactive. Locally adapted modification techniques, or the application of Panda phosphates as blended P-fertilizer (Panda PR + TSP for example) should be tested on crops like cabbage, a phosphorus-responsive crop (Weil 2000).

Other phosphate resources for future considerations are the residual and primary phosphate resources at Ngualla and Sangu-Ikola. However, both occurrences are located in remote areas.

Upper Cretaceous and Tertiary sediments along the coast should be investigated for their phosphorite potential. Paleogeographic and facies analyses should focus on Cretaceous and Tertiary sediments, similar to those in other parts of Africa that have yielded major phosphate accumulations. As a first step, samples from oil and gas exploration campaigns should be checked for elevated radioactivity in drill cores using a gamma-ray spectrometer.

In areas where soil acidity and associated aluminum and manganese toxicities are the limiting factors for crop production. For example, in southern Tanzania, the use of locally available liming materials should be initiated. There are extensive dolomitic limestone occurrences in southern and eastern Tanzania and their agricultural effectiveness should be tested. In order to serve a greater number of small farmers over large areas, a study of the suitability of locally manufactured crushing and grinding units is suggested. Small crushing plants could be utilized for several purposes, for gravel and concrete aggregate production as well as for agricultural limestone and/or dolomite production.

The natural zeolites found in Tanzania should be studied for their potential usefulness in agricultural, horticultural and environmental applications.

Calcareous 'waste materials' from the existing cement industries should be investigated for their potential use in agriculture in the immediate surroundings. The diamond tailings at Nyamwele, north of Kahama should be analyzed for their calcium and magnesium contents and agronomically tested on the nearby infertile sandy soils on granitic parent material.

References:

Anderson GD 1970. Fertility studies on sandy loam in semi-arid Tanzania. II. Effects of phosphorus, potassium and lime on yields of groundnuts. Exp. Agric. 6:213-222.

Banzi FP, Kifanga LD and FM Bundala 2000. Natural radioactivity and radiation exposure at the Minjingu phosphate mine in Tanzania. J. Radiol. Prot. 20:41-51.

Bosse H-R 1996. Tanzania. In: Bosse H-R, Gwosdz W, Lorenz W, Markwich, Roth W and F Wolff (eds.) Limestone and dolomite resources of Africa. Geol. Jb., D, 102:424-459.

Buresh RJ, van Straaten P, Place FM and BA Jama 1999. Agronomic and economic evaluation of phosphate rocks as phosphorus source in Kenya. Abstract, Ann. Meeting Am. Soc. Agron., Salt Lake City, Utah, USA, p.43.

Chesworth W, Semoka JMR, van Straaten P, Mnkeni PNS, Kamasho JAM and EP Mchihiyo 1988. Tanzania-Canada Agrogeology Project. Report on completion of the first phase. Univ. of Guelph, Ont., Canada, 93pp.

Chesworth W, van Straaten P and JMR Semoka 1989. Agrogeology in East Africa: The Tanzania-Canada project. J. Afr. Earth Sci. 9:935-939.

Coetzee GL 1959. Unpublished report, Western Rift Exploration Company, Chunya, Tanganyika.

Gabert G 1984. Structural-lithological units of Proterozoic rocks in East Africa, their base, cover and mineralisation. In: Klerkx J and J Michot (eds.) Geologie Africaine - African Geology, Musee Royale de l'Afrique Centrale, Tervuren, Belgium:11-22.

Guest NJ 1956. Radioactivity north of Igurusi, Mbeya District. Geol. Surv. Tanganyika, Rec.IV, 1954:43-44.

Halligan R 1962. The Proterozoic rocks of Western Tanzania. Bull. Geol. Surv. of Tanganyika, 34, 34pp.

Haque I, Lupwayi NZ and H Ssali 1999. Agronomic effectiveness of unacidulated and partially acidulated Minjingu rock phosphates on Stylosanthes guianensis. Trop. Grasslands 33:159-164.

Harris JF 1981. Summary of the geology of Tanganyika, Part IV: Economic geology. Geol. Surv. Mem. 1, 143pp.

Hutchinson GE 1950. Survey of existing knowledge of biogeochemistry - The geochemistry of vertebrae excretion. Bull. Am. Mus. Nat. History, 96, 554pp.

ICRAF 1999. International Centre for Research in Agroforestry. Report to the Rockefeller Foundation on preparation of Ugandan phosphates (September 1998 to August 1999). Nairobi, Kenya, 25pp.

Ikerra TWD, Mnkeni PNS and BR Singh 1994. Effects of added compost and farmyard manure on P release from Minjingu phosphate rock and its uptake by maize. Norw. J. Agr. Sci. 8:13-23.

International Labour Organization 1999. Social and labour issues in small-scale mines. TMSSM/1999, 99pp.

Kent PE, Hunt JA and DW Johnstone 1971. The geology and geophysics of coastal Tanzania. Inst. Geol. Sci., Geophys. Paper 6, 101pp.

Kreuser T, Wopfner H, Kaaya CZ, Markwort S, Semkiwa PM and P Aslandidis 1990. Depositional evolution of Permo-Triassic Karoo basins in Tanzania with reference to their economic potential. J. Afr. Earth Sci. 10:151-167.

Lai TM and DD Eberl 1986. Controlled and renewable release of phosphorus in soils from mixtures of phosphate rock and NH_4-exchanged clinoptilolite. Zeolites 6:129-132.

Makweba MM and E Holm 1993. The natural radioactivity of the rock phosphates, phosphatic products and their environmental implications. Sci. Tot. Environm. 133:99-110.

Mchihiyo EP 1990. Geochemical and mineralogical aspects associated with weathering of apatite from Panda Hill carbonatite SW Tanzania. M.Sc. Thesis Univ. of Guelph, Canada, 147pp.

Mchihiyo EP 1991. Phosphate potential in Tanzania. Fert. Res. 30:177-180.

McKie D 1958. A radioactive phosphorite at Chamoto, north of Igurusi, Mbeya District. Geol. Surv. Tanganyika Rec., Vol. VI 1956:85-86.

Mnkeni PNS, Semoka JMR and JBBS Buganga 1991. Agronomic effectiveness of Minjingu phosphate rock as a source of phosphorus for maize in four soils of Morogoro District, Tanzania. Zimbabwe J. Agric. Res. 30:27-37.

Mnkeni PNS, Semoka JMR and EG Kaitaba 1994. Effects of Mapogoro phillipsite on availability of phosphorus in phosphate rocks. Trop. Agric. (Trinidad) 71:249-253.

Mnkeni PNS, Chien SH and G Carmona 2000. Effectiveness of Panda Hill phosphate rock compacted with triple superphosphate as source of phosphorus for rape, wheat, maize, and soybean. Commun. Soil Sci. Plant Anal. 31:3163-3175.

Mtuy FT 1986. The agrogeological resources of Tanzania. In: Wachira JK and AJG Notholt (eds.) Agrogeology in Africa. Commonwealth Sci. Council, Technical Publ. Series 226:84-89.

Mustonene R and M Annanmaeki 1988. Studies on the radiation exposure of workers in connection with processing of the Minjingu phosphate in Tanzania. Suppl. Report to the Finnish Center for Radiation and Nuclear Safety, 666/622/87, 18pp.

Mutuo PK, Smithson PC, Buresh RJ and RJ Okalebo 1999. Comparison of phosphate rock and triple superphosphate of a phosphorus deficient Kenyan soil. Comm. Soil Sci. Plant Anal. 30:1091-1103.

Mwambete I 1991. Tanzania fertilizer mineral deposits. Fert. Res. 30:181-185.

Ngoze SO 2001. Agronomic evaluation of Tanzanian and Ugandan phosphate rocks in western Kenya. Unpubl. Master's thesis, Moi University, Eldoret, Kenya, 114pp.

Ngunangwa FE 1982. Potential of small scale mining in Tanzania. In: JM Neilson (editor) Strategies for small-scale mining and mineral industries, AGID report 8:55-61.

Okalebo JR and PL Woomer 1994. Use of rock and fertilizer phosphate in Eastern and Southern Africa: A data summary. Presentation 14th conference Soil Sci. Soc. East Africa, Mbarara, Uganda.

Richardson DS 1982. Small scale mining of gypsum at Mkomazi, Tanzania. In: JM Neilson (editor) Strategies for small-scale mining and mineral industries, AGID report 8:112-120.

RUDIS (1980). Prefeasibility study. Fertilizer raw materials. Report, Lubljana, Yugoslavia.

Sanchez PA, Shepherd KD, Soule MJ, Place FM, Buresh RJ, Izac AMN, Mokwunye AU, Kwesiga FR, Ndiritu CG and PL Woomer 1997. Soil fertility replenishment in Africa: An investment in natural resource capital. In: Buresh RJ, Sanchez PA and F Calhoun (eds.) Replenishing soil fertility in Africa. Soil Sci. Soc. Amer. Special Publ. 51:1-46.

Schlueter T 1991. Systematik, Palaeo-oekologie and Biostratonomie von *Phalacrocorax kuehneanus* nov. spec., einem fossilen Kormoran (Aves: Phalacrocoracidae) aus mutmasslich oberpliozaenen Phosphoriten N-Tansanias. Berl. Geowiss. Abh. A 134:279-309.

Schlueter T 1997. Geology of East Africa. Gebrueder Borntraeger, Berlin-Stuttgart, 484pp.

Schlueter T and R Kohring 1992. Trace fossils from a saline-alkaline lake paleoenvironment in northern Tanzania. Berl. Geowiss. Abh. E3:295-303.

Spurr AMM 1954. The Songwe guano caves, Mbeya District. Geol. Surv. Tanganyika Records 1,1951:35-37.

Stockley GM 1946. Phosphate deposits in Tanganyika Territory, south of Kisaki. Min. Res. Pamphl. Geol. Surv. Tanganyika 45, 12pp.

van Straaten P 1983. Interim report on results from the Sangu-Ikola carbonatite. Eastern and Southern African Mineral Resource Centre, Rep. ESAMRDC/83/TECH/26, 26pp.

van Straaten P 1989. Nature and structural relationships of carbonatites from southwest and west Tanzania. In: K Bell (ed.) Carbonatites - Genesis and Evolution, Unwin Hyman, London, UK:177-199.

van Straaten P 1995. Mineral exploration for carbonatite related phosphates in SW Tanzania. In: Blenkinsop TG and PL Tromp (eds.) Sub-Saharan Economic Geology, Geol. Soc. Zimbabwe Spec. Publ., Balkema, Rotterdam, Netherlands:87-102.

van Straaten P, Semoka JMR, Kamasho JAM, Mnkeni PNS and W Chesworth 1992. Report on the Tanzania-Canada agrogeology project, Phase II (1988-1991). Univ. of Guelph, Ont., Canada, 127pp.

Van Kauwenbergh SJ 1985. Cursory characterization of a phosphate ore and concentrate sample from Minjingu, Tanzania. Unpubl. Rep. International Fertilizer Development Center (IFDC), 10pp.

Van Kauwenbergh SJ 1991. Overview of phosphate deposits in East and Southeast Africa. Fert. Res. 30:127-150.

Weil RR 2000. Soil and plant influences on crop responses to two African phosphate rocks. Agr. J. 92:1167-1175.

Togo

Total population (July 2000 estimate): 5,019,000
Area: 56,785 km^2
Annual population growth rate (2000): 2.7 %
Life expectancy at birth (1998): 49.0 years
People not expected to survive to age 40 (1998): 34.2 % of total population
GDP per capita (1998): US $1,372

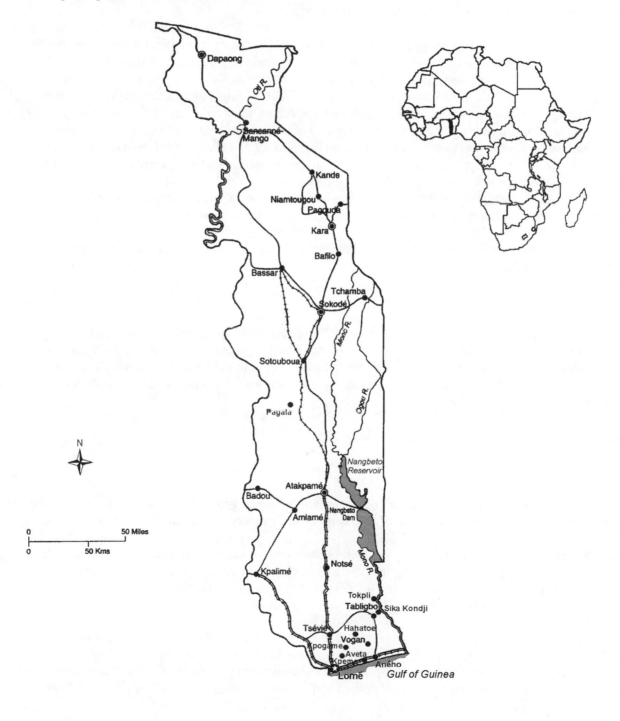

Togo is a small country north of the Gulf of Guinea. It extends in a north-south direction over a length of 550 km. The narrowest part of Togo is at the coastline (55 km) and the widest is in the centre (about 225 km). The coastal area consists of flat sandy beach areas and a series of lagoons and lakes. The centre of the country is mountainous and forested with deciduous trees. The northern area is gently undulating savanna country. The average annual precipitation in the north of Togo reaches 1,000 mm, in the south it is approximately 1,800 mm.

Togo's economy is based on farming and phosphate mining. The agricultural sector provides 41% of the GDP and more than 65% of the working population are involved in commercial and subsistence farming. The main food crops are yams, cassava, maize, sorghum, bananas and rice. The export of cocoa, coffee and cotton together generate about 30% of the export earnings.

Togo's mineral industry is dominated by the government-owned phosphate producer, Office Togolaise des Phosphates (OTP). Phosphate rock mining began in 1961 and exports of phosphates remain Togo's principle source of foreign earnings. Export of phosphate concentrate accounts for 20-30% of export earnings, 10-13% of government revenues and 6-10% of the GDP (Mobbs 1995). Currently Togo is the largest sedimentary phosphate rock producer in sub-Saharan Africa. Production in 1997 was 2,686,600 tonnes (British Geological Survey 1999), although the sale of phosphates to western countries has slowed down considerably, partially due to technical problems (Palut 2000), but also as a result of environmental concerns related to the relatively high cadmium content in the phosphate rock concentrate. A transfer of 40% of OTP into the private sector is planned. Also, the increase of production and the development of downstream chemical processing facilities are envisaged (Palut 2000). Apart from the export of phosphates, the mining industry is small with a local cement and construction industry.

Togo has experienced several environmental problems including coastal water pollution, deforestation and associated soil erosion problems.

Geological outline

Precambrian to early Cambrian rocks underlie most of Togo. The north-south striking Togo Belt (Dahomeyan Belt) forms a strongly deformed series of supracrustal rocks and volcanics of Neoproterozoic to early Cambrian age. The Togo Belt has been thrusted westward onto the Volta Basin, which is exposed in the northeast of the country. Cretaceous to Tertiary gently southward-dipping basin sediments occur only in the most southern part of the country.

AGROMINERALS

Phosphates

There are two types of phosphate deposits in Togo: strongly deformed Proterozoic phosphates near Bassar in northern Togo, and unmetamorphosed flat-lying Tertiary sedimentary phosphates in the south.

From an economic point of view, the most important phosphates are the phosphate-bearing Eocene beds of southern Togo. They form part of the shallow basin stretching from the southeast corner of Ghana eastward through Togo and Benin into Nigeria. In Togo, the basin sequence strikes in a northeasterly direction and dips at very shallow angles ($< 2°$) towards the southeast.

Detailed mapping and mineral exploration of the phosphorites has identified the stratigraphic sequence and the facies distribution of the Upper Cretaceous, Paleocene and Eocene beds (Figure 2.18). Paleo-geographic reconstruction shows that the phosphates are concentrated at the margin of the basin where the thickness of the whole Eocene sequence is condensed and at a minimum (Slansky 1986, 1989; Johnson *et al.* 2000). A limestone barrier effectively cut off a lagoon in which the phosphates accumulated in a sedimentary trap (Figure 2.19). Postdepositional leaching (decarbonation) has caused enrichment of the Bed 1 ore zone (Van Kauwenbergh and McClellan 1990, Johnson *et al.* 2000). The phosphatic sediments are of lower - middle Eocene age (upper Ypresian - lower Lutetian) and are overlain by a continental sequence of clastic sediments ('Terminal continental'). The whole sequence is covered by ferruginous lateritic soils. A typical lithological sequence in this area (Van Kauwenbergh and McClellan 1990), from top to bottom, is as follows:

- Top soil,
- partially indurated gravel, sand and clay of the Terminal continental (up to 22 m thick),
- Bed 0 - Eocene; wheathered phosphorite, kaolinitic, Al- and Fe- phosphates (0-2 m thick),
- Bed 1 - Eocene, pelletal phosphorite ore (francolite), currently mined (0-6 m thick),
- Bed CSC - phosphatic bedded limestone and marl. This bed is probably the lateral equivalent of bed 1,
- bicoloured clay - marker bed (0-2 m thick),
- Bed 2/3 - Eocene, marl with calcitic sand, clay beds, limestone, thin high-grade phosphorite beds (total sequence 2-8 m thick),
- Palygorskite (attapulgite) clay bed.

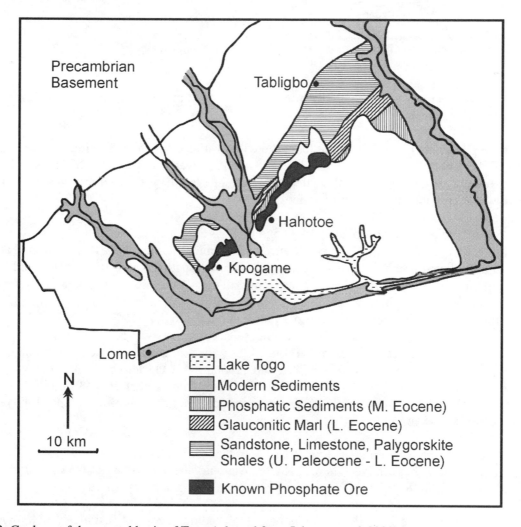

Figure 2.18: Geology of the coastal basin of Togo (adapted from Johnson *et al.* 2000).

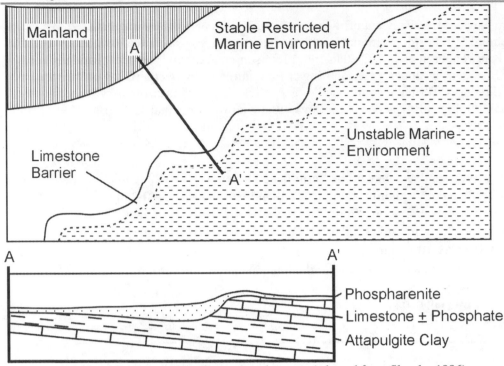

Figure 2.19: Depositional trap of the Togo phosphate ore (adapted from Slansky 1986).

The phosphate rock deposit that is currently mined is confined to the zone between the 'calcareous barrier' and the margin of the basin.

The size of the phosphate deposit is 30 km long; the width varies from a few hundred metres to 2 km. The unconsolidated ore body varies in thickness from 2-6 m and is overlain by 7-30 m of sands and clays. When the extraction of the Togo phosphate deposit began in 1961 the identified reserves of marketable concentrate were estimated at 130 million tonnes.

A typical concentrate of Togo phosphate rock (Togo PR) has a P_2O_5 concentration of 36 to 37% and is low in Al_2O_3 (1%) and Fe_2O_3 (1.5%). Mineralogical and chemical studies show that the mined and concentrated phosphate mineral is a low-substituted unreactive apatite. Van Kauwenbergh and McClellan (1990) carried out detailed mineralogical studies from drill cores from the mining area. They report variations in the crystallographic and chemical properties of the francolites. The crystallographic unit-cell a-values of the Togo francolites vary from bed 1 (9.348 Å) to 9.326 Å and 9.324 Å in Bed 2/3 of the deposit. The average unit-cell a-value of the concentrate, according to Van Kauwenbergh and McClellan (1990), is 9.349 Å. The refractive index of the francolites varies from 1.618 in Bed 1 to 1.608 in Bed 2/3. Mokwunye (1995) reports an a-value of 9.354 Å, and a molar PO_4/CO_3 ratio of 12.3 of the concentrate. These mineralogical data together with solubility data from Kpomblekou *et al.* (1991) (citrate solubility = 1.7% P_2O_5) and Abekoe and Tiessen (1998) (neutral ammonium citrate solubility = 1.3% P_2O_5) illustrate the low reactivity of the Togo PR.

The specific surface area of Togo PR is low: 7.1 m^2/g in the 0.5 mm fraction and 9.9 m^2/g in the 0.1 mm fraction. In comparison, the reactive Tilemsi PR from Mali has a surface area of 26.4 m^2/g in the 0.5 mm fraction and 34.2 m^2/g in the 0.1 mm fraction respectively (Truong and Fayard 1995).

A chemical drawback of the Togo PR is its relatively high cadmium content (Cd mean = 58 mg/kg, range 48-67 mg/kg). The Cd concentrations are greater than that permitted for use in Western Europe, and this has some obvious influence on sales. Currently, the ore is excavated by large bucket/wheel excavators in quarries, one progressing south-westward from Kpogame, the other northeastward from Hahotoe. A railway transports the ore to Kpeme, approximately 30 km from the mines. Here, the ore is scrubbed, screened, and hydrocylconed to remove clays. The product is a concentrate with P_2O_5 contents of 36-37%. The plant capacity is 3.5 million tonnes per year.

There is no facility for downstream processing of Togo PR into phosphate fertilizer. In the 1990s most of the concentrate was exported to Canada, the Far East and South Africa. In recent years, an agreement was negotiated with Indian Ocean Fertilizers to establish downstream processing (Bowyer 1996).

In 1997, the Office Togolaise des Phosphates (OTP) produced 2,686,600 tonnes of Togo PR (concentrate) for export, the corresponding export figures for 1996 and 1995 are 2,685,500 and 2,652,100 tonnes respectively (British Geological Survey 1999). In recent years exports of Togo phosphates have declined, especially after the cancellation of a large export contract to Canada. Large tonnages of Togo PR concentrate are currently shipped to South Africa where they are blended with phosphates from Phalaborwa and processed before being shipped to India.

The physical processing (beneficiation) of the Togo phosphate ore in Togo results in the recovery of 1 metric tonne of phosphate concentrate per 2 tonnes of raw ore. Up to 500,000 tonnes of phosphate fines are discarded annually into the Gulf of Guinea (Gulf of Benin), which, environmentally speaking, is a cause for concern.

Gnandi and Tobschall (1998) analyzed the concentration and distribution of major and trace elements in coastal sediments near the dumping site of the phosphate fines. They showed high concentrations of Cd, Cr, Pb, Zn, Cu and Ni in the coastal sediments near the dumping site. The highest Cd enrichment factor of 100 was measured in relatively coarse sediments, close to the dumping site and along the shore, transported by longshore currents. Gnandi and Tobschall (1998) also point out that Cd is easily mobilized in seawater and thus pollutes much larger areas of the Gulf of Guinea (Gulf of Benin).

Agronomic Testing of Togo Phosphate Rock

Many agronomic tests have been carried out with Togo PR. Studies by Nnadi and Haque (1988), Uyovbisere and Lombim (1991), Kato et al. (1995), and Abekoe and Tiessen (1998) confirm that the unmodified, mineralogically 'unreactive' Togo PR is largely ineffective on tropical P-deficient soils. Only one study, on acid soils of southeastern Nigeria (Maduakor 1994), showed slightly more promising results for directly applied Togo PR, especially in the second year of cropping.

It seems evident that Togo PR with its low solubility requires modification to become more agronomically effective. Agronomic experiments with partially acidulated and compacted Togo PR show encouraging potentials (Bationo et al.1986; Kato et al. 1995). Togo PR was applied in the unacidulated and partially acidulated form on alfisols in northern Nigeria and Togo, as well as on ultisols in Sierra Leone (Bationo et al. 1986). The agronomic data show that the unacidulated directly applied Togo PR was ineffective on all sites due to its low reactivity. However, as partially acidualted PR (PAPR - 50% H_2SO_4) it proved 72% as effective as SSP in Nigeria, 82% in northern Togo and 103% in Sierra Leone (Bationo et al. 1986).

The evaluation of the effectiveness of natural and partially acidulated acidulated PR using P-32 isoptopic dilution techniques (Kato et al.1995) showed that Togo PR in a blended (50% Togo PR, 50% TSP) and compacted form as well as partially acidulated (PAPR) had a relative agronomic effectiveness in comparison to SSP of over 72% and 84% respectively for dry matter yield of maize.

Other phosphates

Apart from the flat-lying relatively unconsolidated Eocene sedimentary phosphates in the south of the country there are compact and folded Neopropterozoic phosphorites reported from north-central Togo (Castaing 1989). The Neoproterozoic phosphates in the Bassar area are of comparable age to the phosphates in Benin, Burkina Faso and Niger (Castaing 1989). The phosphate beds, up to 1 m thick, have been explored by means of geological mapping and drilling. North of Bassar these folded beds are more than 7 km long. East of Bassar they can be traced over a distance of 6 km, and south of Bassar over a distance of 7 km. No specific details on grade, volume and mineralogical and chemical composition of the phosphate beds are available.

Limestone/dolomite

There are large deposits of dolomitic marbles, dolomitic limestones and limestones in Togo. Dolomite marbles are economically exploited by Société Togolaise de Marbrerie et Matériaux (SOTOMA) at Gnaoulou, 30 km south-southwest of Atakpame. Reserves are estimated at 20 million tonnes. The deposit is used for the production of ornamental marble, and to a lesser degree, calcined lime. Whether any of the fines or the dolomitic lime are used for agricultural purposes is not known. Another 19 occurrences of dolomitic marbles, many of them of smaller extent, have been reported by Lorenz (1996).

Dolomitic marbles and limestones are known from the Voltaian. The dolomitic marbles at Pagala in central Togo have been worked by SOTOMA since 1984 for building and ornamental purposes. Lorenz (1996) noted that lime could be produced from the wastes produced during the extraction of the blocks. The dolomitic 'wastes' account for approximately 30% of the production of the blocks. This material has a favourable composition (CaO = 29%, MgO = 20%) for use as agricultural dolomitic limestone.

Very extensive limestone resources also occur in the coastal basin of Togo. Extensive Paleocene limestones occur between Sika Kondji, Tokpli and Tabligbo. The deposit at Tabligbo (Fig. 2.18) provides the cement industry of Togo with limestone raw material. Annual production capacity of this plant is 1.2 million tonnes.

It is noteworthy that the 100 million tonnes of limestones at Aveta (18 km northeast of Lome) cannot be used as raw material for the cement industry because of elevated phosphorus concentrations (Lorenz 1996).

Glauconite

Glauconitic sands are commonly associated with the Togo phosphate beds. However, no details of grade and volume are available.

Rock wastes

As described earlier, a total of 500,000 tonnes of phosphate fines resulting from phosphate beneficiation are currently discarded into the Gulf of Benin each year, creating serious environmental problems along the coast.

Other mine 'wastes' include the dolomite fines produced during the production of ornamental stone and marble.

Agromineral potential

Togo's potential to provide agrominerals for agricultural production is high. Most of the existing phosphate resources of Togo are currently exported in the form of phosphate concentrate (Togo PR). Local modification techniques of Togo PR concentrate and phosphate fines, for instance phospho-composting, partial acidulation, blending with N-fertilizers and compacting or pelletizing with other nutrient compounds, should be explored.

Efforts should be made to substantially reduce the disposal of phosphatic material into the ocean, and develop low-cost phosphatic soil amendments from these 'waste' materials.

In addition, there are many dolomite and dolomitic limestone occurrences in the country, which could be used on a small-scale if soil conditions require liming materials and/or Mg additions.

'Wastes' from the marble and ornamental stone industry may be suitable for the use as agricultural limestone.

References:

Abekoe MK and H Tiessen 1998. Fertilizer P transformation and P availability in hillslope soils of northern Ghana. Nutr. Cycl. in Agroecosystems 52:45-54.

Bationo A, Mughogho SK and AU Mokwunye 1986 Agronomic Evaluation of Phosphate Fertilizers in Tropical Africa. In: Mokwunye AU and PLG Vlek (eds.) Management of Nitrogen and Phosphorus Fertilizers in Sub-Saharan Africa. Martinus Nijhoff Publishers, Dordrecht, Netherlands: 283-318.

Bowyer G 1996. Togo. Mining Annual Review 1996, Mining Journal Ltd. London, p.158.

British Geological Survey 1999. World Mineral Statistics 1993-97. Keyworth, Nottingham, UK, 286pp.

Castaing C 1989. Influence de la tectonique panafricaine sur le mode de gisement des phosphates proterozoiques de Bassar (Togo). Chron. Rech. Min. 494:59-68.

Gnandi K and HJ Tobschall 1998. The pollution of marine sediments by trace elements in the coastal region of Togo caused by dumping of cadmium-rich phosphorite tailing into the sea. Envir. Geol. 38:13-24.

Johnson AK, Rat P and J Lang 2000. Le bassin sedimentaire à phosphate du Togo (Maastrichtian-Eocene): stratigraphie, environnements et evolution. J. Afr. Earth Sci. 30:183-200.

Kato N, Zapata F and H Axmann 1995. Evaluation of the agronomic effectiveness of natural and partially acidulated phosphate rocks in several soils using P-32 isotopic dilution techniques. Fert. Res. 41:235-242.

Kpomblekou K, Chien SH, Henao J and WA Hill 1991. Greenhouse evaluation of phosphate fertilizers produced from Togo phosphate rock. Comm. Soil Sci. Plant Anal. 22:63-73.

Lorenz W 1996. Togo. In: Bosse H-R, Gwosdz W, Lorenz W, Markwich, Roth W and F Wolff (eds.) Limestone and dolomite resources of Africa. Geol. Jb., D, 460-465.

Maduakor HO 1994. Unacidulated and partially acidulated Phosphate Rock as P source in an acid ultisol in the forest zone of southeastern Nigeria. Z. Pflanzenernaehrung Bodenk. 157:387-392.

Mobbs PM 1995. Togo. Minerals Yearbook, vol. III, United States of the Interior, Geological Survey, p.117.

Mokwunye AU 1995. Reactions in soils involving phosphate rocks. In: Gerner H and AU Mokwunye (eds.) Use of phosphate rock for sustainable agriculture in West Africa. IFDC, Miscellaneous Fert. Studies 11: 84-92.

Nnadi LA and I Haque 1988. Agronomic effectiveness of rock phosphate in an andept of Ethiopia. Commun. Soil Sci. Plant Anal. 19:79-90.

Palut JP 2000. Togo. Mining Annual Review. The Mining Journal Ltd. London.

Slansky M 1986. Geology of sedimentary phosphates. Elsevier Science Publ. New York, 210pp.

Slansky M 1989. The Eocene phosphate deposits of Togo. In: Notholt AJG, Sheldon RP and DF Davidson (eds.) Phosphate deposits of the world. Vol. 2. Phosphate rock resources, Cambridge University Press, Cambridge, UK: 258-261.

Truong B and C Fayard 1995. Small-scale fertilizer production units using raw and partially solubilized phosphate. In: Gerner H and AU Mokwunye (eds.) Use of phosphate rock for sustainable agriculture in West Africa. IFDC, Miscellaneous Fert. Studies 11:181-197.

Uyovbisere EO and G Lombim 1991. Efficient fertilizer use for increased crop production - the subhumid Nigeria experience. Fert. Res. 29:81-94.

Van Kauwenbergh SJ and GH McClellan 1990. Comparative geology and mineralogy of the southeastern United States and Togo phosphorites. In: Notholt AJG and I Jarvis (eds.) Phosphorite research and development. Geological Society Special Publication 52:139-155.

Uganda

Total population (July 2000 estimate): 23,318,000
Area: 236,040 km^2
Annual population growth rate (2000): 2.72 %
Life expectancy at birth (1998): 40.7 years
People not expected to survive to age 40 (1998): 45.9 % of total population
GDP per capita (1998): US $1,074

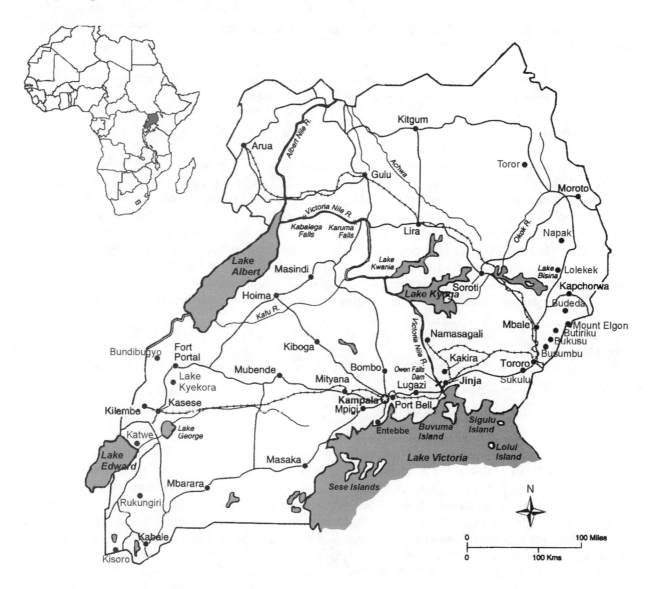

Uganda is a landlocked country in central East Africa, north and west of Lake Victoria. The landscape of central Uganda is characterized by gently undulating hills and broad valleys at elevations between 1,000 and 1,500 m above sea level. The western part of the country consists of rolling mountainous land, and the Ruwenzori Mountains, an uplifted block at the flanks of the Western Rift Valley. The south-eastern section of the country, at the border with Kenya, is dominated by the Mount Elgon strato-volcano.

Agriculture dominates the economy, contributing 44% of the GDP, and employing an estimated 80% of the working population. The main food crops of Uganda are plantains, cassava, sweet potatoes, maize and millet. The main export crops are coffee and tea. Other crops include sugarcane, potatoes, beans, tobacco, cotton and groundnuts. Non-traditional agricultural exports include cut flowers.

At present, mining plays only a minor role in the economy of the country. The Kilembe copper mine at Kasese and the copper smelter at Jinja closed in 1978. Approximately 1.1 million tonnes of cobalt-rich tailings from the Kilembe mining operation are currently being treated using bioleaching, solvent extraction and electrowinning techniques. Other small mineral related-activities include gold exploration in the south-eastern part of the country and industrial mineral development.

Geological outline

Precambrian rocks underlie two-thirds of Uganda. Archean rocks are exposed in the south-east of Uganda. They are part of the extensive granite-greenstone terrain of the Tanzania Craton. Three major Proterozoic belts underlie central and west Uganda: the Paleoproterozoic Buganda-Toro metasediments, the Mesoproterozoic Karagwe-Ankolean (Kibaran) Belt in the southwest of the country and Neoproterozoic Pan-African rocks (Gabert 1984). The Neoproterozoic includes the Bunyoro Series with tillites and argillites (Bjorlykke 1973), and the undeformed shallow water sediments of the Bukoban Supergroup. Tertiary to Recent sediments have filled parts of the down-faulted Western Rift. Tertiary carbonatites and Cenozoic volcanics are related to rift activities and occur along the eastern and western borders of the country. The distribution of carbonatites and alkaline intrusions in southeast Uganda is shown in Figure 2.20.

AGROMINERALS

Phosphates

1.   Sukulu

Extensive phosphate resources in eastern Uganda have been discovered in the Sukulu carbonatite complex, located 6 km southwest of Tororo. The Sukulu carbonatite complex is the southernmost member of the Tertiary alkaline province in eastern Uganda (Fig. 2.20). Davies (1947), Williams (1959), Bloomfield *et al.* (1971) and Reedman (1984) have carried out geological and geochemical work at the Sukulu carbonatite ring complex. This carbonatite, approximately 4 km in diameter, is mainly made up of calcium-carbonatite (soevite/alvikite) with minor amounts of dolomite and Fe-carbonates. Accessory minerals in the carbonatite are magnetite, mica (in places weathered to vermiculite), apatite, and small amounts of pyrochlore and zircon. A thick blanket of phosphate-rich 'residual soils' covers the carbonatite complex. In one of the three principal valleys the residual soil reaches a depth of 67 m (Reedman 1984).

The main constituents of the residual soils covering the carbonatite are magnetite (at places up to 50%), hematite, goethite, apatite with minor amounts of quartz, ilmenite, micas, zircon, pyrochlore and baddeleyite. Detailed studies of the residual soils have also recorded the presence of Al-phosphates, for instance crandallite. Apatites make up over 20% of the soil and in some places more than 50%. Detailed mineralogical and chemical studies of the apatite by scientists from the International Fertilizer Development Centre (IFDC) show that the neutral ammonium citrate (NAC) solubility of a concentrate of the Sukulu phosphate rock (Sukulu PR) is low, 1.6% P_2O_5. This is lower than the NAC solubility of the neighbouring Busumbu phosphates (NAC = 2.3% P_2O_5). The total reserves of the residual phosphates at Sukulu have been calculated as 230 million tonnes averaging 12.8% P_2O_5 (Van Kauwenbergh 1991).

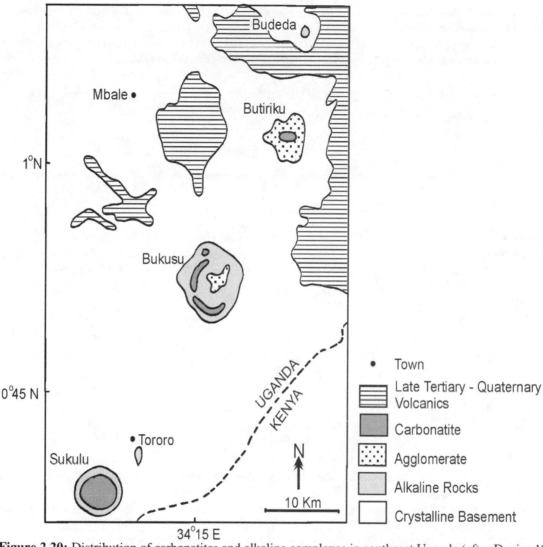

Figure 2.20: Distribution of carbonatites and alkaline complexes in southeast Uganda (after Davies 1956).

The 'ore' mined at Sukulu between 1962 and 1978 consists of residual soil, the weathering products of the Sukulu carbonatite with an average grade of 12.8% P_2O_5. Tororo Industrial Chemicals and Fertilizer Ltd. (TICAF) started out by mining the residual soils of the North Valley, which contain approximately 32% apatite, 57% magnetite and goethite, as well as 0.25% pyrochlore. The apatite from the Sukulu soils was won through grinding and magnetic separation, followed by flotation. The apatite concentrate (40-42% P_2O_5) was acidulated with sulphuric acid and converted into single superphosphate. TICAF produced approximately 160,000 tonnes of apatite concentrate (40-42% P_2O_5) from 2.16 million tonnes of ore. In 1969, TICAF produced 13,800 tonnes of apatite concentrate and 22,390 tonnes of single superphosphate.

During the 1980s, the fertilizer plant was destroyed and partly dismantled and more recently, the plant has been leveled and the remaining equipment dismantled.

The phosphate resources of Sukulu have been investigated intensively. A comprehensive economic and engineering study was carried out by Bearden-Potter Corporation of Florida (financed by the World Bank) in the early 1980s (Bearden-Potter Co. 1982). However, the 230-million tonne Sukulu phosphate deposit has yet to be developed for a number of reasons, one being the high capital investment required for the production of soluble P-fertilizers (US $121 million) (Annual Mining Review 1988). In addition, the processing techniques proposed by Bearden-Potter Co. are technically sophisticated and capital intensive.

Agronomic Testing of Sukulu Phosphate Rock

Various researchers have tested Sukulu PR on its agronomic performance, including Zake and co-workers (Zake *et al.* 1988; Nkwiine *et al.*) and Butegwa *et al.* (1996a, b). Both research groups showed that Sukulu PR used as direct application P-fertilizer was ineffective on acid soils. Better performance could be achieved by combined application with organic matter and 25-75 kg sulphur per hectare (Zake 1988). The use of partially acidulated phosphate rock (PAPR) manufactured from Sukulu PR had a lower agronomic effectiveness than Sukulu PR compacted with TSP at a total P ratio of 50:50 (Butegwa *et al.* 1996a). The effectiveness of partially acidulated phosphate rock (PAPR) was low on soils with high fixing capacities (Butegwa *et al.* 1996b).

---

2.   Busumbu:

The Busumbu phosphate rock deposit is located at Busumbu Hill, some 10 km west of the Kenyan border at $0°$ 50'12" N and $34°$ 15'55" E, approximately 30 km north of Tororo. It is a residual phosphate deposit that overlies the Busumbu carbonatite, which in turn is part of the circular, 24-26-million year old alkaline Bukusu complex, one of the largest alkaline complexes in Africa. The main carbonatite forms a partial ring, cutting ultramafic and alkaline rocks (Fig. 2.20).

The Busumbu ridge, approximately 2,000 m long and 400 m wide, is made up of a deeply weathered phosphate-enriched residual soil. The primary carbonatite underlying the residual phosphate deposit consists of a calcite-magnetite-apatite-phlogopite assemblage.

Davies discovered carbonate rocks at Busumbu in the early 1930s. A pitting and drilling program, conducted between 1942 and 1945, revealed about 5 million tonnes of phosphate rock with grades between 8 and 35% P_2O_5. The average P_2O_5 content from samples of 430 m of pitting was 11.9% (Davies 1947, 1956). After Davies, the deposit has been studied by a succession of geologists, including Taylor (1955, 1960), Baldock (1969), Bloomfield (1973), Celenk and Katto (1993) and Mathers (1994). A joint team from the Department of Geological Survey and Mines (DGSM) and the United Nations Department for Development Support and Management carried out detailed geological investigations at Busumbu. Findings indicate that proven reserves of higher grade 'hard' phosphates (average grade 28.5 % P_2O_5) are 332,000 tonnes, and lower grade 'soft' phosphates with an average grade of 13.5 % P_2O_5 account for more than 2,468,000 tonnes (Celenk and Katto 1993). These initial and preliminary reserve estimates were based on limited pit excavations to a depth of 6 m from the surface.

Subsequent work by Katto (1995, 2000) proved ore reserves of 8.5 million tonnes. This included 3 million tonnes with an average grade of 11% P_2O_5 in the soil with an average thickness of 2 m. An additional 5.5 million tonnes of phosphate ore has been delineated in the underlying 4 m of weathered material (saprolite) with an average grade of 15% P_2O_5. The calculations are based on a total thickness of soil plus weathered material of only 6 m. However, since the deposit is thicker than 6 m, the reserves are most likely higher than the 8.5 million tonnes reported by Katto (1995). Proven reserves on one of the ridge-forming hills, Hill 2, are calculated to be 8.4 million tonnes grading 12.6% P_2O_5 (Wolukawu, pers. comm. 1998).

Two types of phosphate have been identified at Busumbu: the 'hard rock' and the 'soft rock.' The 'soft rock' below the 1-2 m thick red soils consists of soft brown friable material with unaltered primary apatite in an iron-rich earthy matrix. This material is very friable and can easily be excavated by pick and shovel operation or by simple mechanical means. Apart from fluor-apatite, the ore contains mainly magnetite and other iron oxides. The 'hard rock,' which makes up approximately 13% of the deposit (Davies 1956), is a mixture of primary apatite cemented together by secondary phosphate. Davies (1947) identified the secondary phosphate mineral as carbonate-substituted francolite. A mineralogical study of Busumbu PR indicates that the francolite is a low-substituted variety (Van Kauwenbergh 1991). The neutral ammonium citrate (NAC) solubility of the total rock is reported by Van Kauwenbergh (1991) as 2.3% P_2O_5, somewhat higher than most typical igneous apatites. For example the NAC solubility of apatites from Rangwa in Kenya is 0.4% P_2O_5 and that of the Sukulu concentrate is 1.6% P_2O_5. The unit-cell a-value of the Busumbu PR is 9.362 Å.

Mineralogical studies of the soft phosphate ore including X-ray diffractometry by Katto (1995) and Scanning Electron Microscopy (SEM) studies by van Straaten (unpublished) indicate the presence of fluor-apatite, and small amounts of Al-phosphates including crandallite, as well as magnetite, goethite, and hematite.

Scanning electron microscopy of hard phosphate samples shows a clear difference between primary apatites and the secondary apatites, which surround them. The primary apatites contain 41-42% P_2O_5, have CaO/P_2O_5 ratios of 1.31-1.34, and low F-values (1.5-2.0%). The corresponding data for the secondary apatites are: 37-38% P_2O_5, CaO/P_2O_5 ratios of 1.43-1.46, and 3.7-4.4% F (van Straaten 1997).

Phosphate rocks from Busumbu were mined between 1944 and 1963 from small open pits along Busumbu ridge. Until 1956 the 'hard' phosphate rock was excavated, crushed and screened before being exported to neighbouring Kenya for the manufacture of citric-soluble soda phosphate fertilizer (using soda-ash from Lake Magadi). The undersized, fine phosphatic material was used as direct application fertilizer. From 1956 onward the customer requirement changed and 'hard' phosphate rock was replaced by a blend of soft phosphate rock with a P_2O_5 content of 15% P_2O_5 and hard phosphate with a P_2O_5 content of 30%. This phosphate blend was upgraded using magnetic separation techniques. The annual production reached 6,000 tonnes and a total of 62,000 tonnes of phosphate concentrate were produced during the lifetime of the mine. The production of this small-scale operation ceased when the large phosphate fertilizer plant at Sukulu came into operation.

Agronomic Testing of Busumbu 'Soft' Phosphate Rock

Researchers from the Kenya Agricultural Research Institute (KARI), and the International Centre for Agroforestry (ICRAF) tested the concentrates from the Busumbu soft ore (Busumbu soft PR) on acid P-deficient soils of western Kenya between 1998 and 2001. In most fields the relative agronomic effectiveness (RAE) of unmodified Busumbu soft PR is low (28-45 %). However, Busumbu soft PR blended with triple superphosphate at a rate of 30% TSP and 70% Busumbu soft PR show high yield increases, the RAE reaching 70-80% (Buresh, pers. comm. 1998). Greenhouse testing with Busumbu phosphate rock blended with TSP and mono-ammonium phosphate (MAP) at a ratio of 50:50 show RAEs of 80% and more than 90% respectively (Ngoze et al. 2000).

Initial results of Busumbu soft PR composted with various locally available organic wastes show low agronomic effectiveness in near neutral, sandy soils in eastern Uganda (Oshier, 2002).

Other phosphates

Small bodies of secondary phosphates were discovered at the western edge of the Butiriku carbonatite complex during exploration studies by Reedman (1974). The volume and grade of the Bukiribo and Bududa phosphate rocks, both within the Butiriku carbonatite complex, have not yet been established but seem to be on the order of several hundred thousand tonnes.

Scanning electron microscope studies by van Straaten (unpubl.) show that these phosphates are mainly made up of secondary phosphates, specifically francolite. Ground and directly applied Bukiribo phosphate rock were agronomically tested in western Kenya and showed very good initial and residual effects (ICRAF, unpubl. data).

The carbonatitic lavas from Western Uganda contain small amounts of apatite. The P_2O_5 content of two samples of vesicular and zeolitic carbonatitic lava from Kalyango near Fort Portal is 3.32 and 3.57 respectively (Von Knorring and du Bois 1961).

Limestone/dolomite/travertine

There are several well-investigated limestone resources in Uganda. Sedimentary limestone and travertine resources are found spatially related to the Western Rift. Metamorphosed dolomitic limestones and marbles are associated with Precambrian metasediments. The Proterozoic rock sequences of the Buganda-Toro and Karagwe Ankolean (Kibaran) belts are largely devoid of carbonates. The Ugandan carbonatites are voluminous point sources of Ca- and Ca-Mg-carbonates.

Sedimentary limestones and travertines, commonly low in magnesium content, occur in Quaternary sediments of the Western Rift valley close to Lake George in western Uganda. These deposits are mainly lacustrine, chemically precipitated tufaceous limestones and travertines deposited close to mineral springs. They are generally fine-grained with a vuggy texture (Mathers 1994). At least three limestone deposits occur in the Kasese area in western Uganda: the Hima deposit, the Dura deposit and the Muhokya deposit. The Hima limestone deposit, approximately 15 km northeast of Kasese, with measured reserves of 18 million tonnes is currently exploited for the manufacture of cement. The Hima cement factory has an installed capacity of 300,000 tonnes per annum.

The Dura limestone deposit located at the eastern side of the Western Rift, 18 km east of Kasese contains powdery marls, grey compact travertines and satin spar (Mathers 1994). The reserves of these high-grade limestones are estimated at 1.5 million tonnes (Department of Geological Survey and Mines -DGSM, written comm. Feb. 2000).

The Muhokya limestone, 13 km south of Kasese, is a sedimentary lacustrine deposit with reserves estimated at 0.25 million tonnes. The deposit has been worked intermittently since 1945 for the exclusive manufacture of lime as soil stabilizer in road construction, for sugar refining, as lime mortar and whitewash. It is not known whether some of the lime has also been used for agricultural purposes. Local companies involved in lime production include Equator Lime Ltd. This company operates continuous vertical shaft kilns and produces up to 5 tonnes of hydrated lime per day.

Other limestone/travertine resources in western Uganda include Kainanira in the Kaku Valley, 16 km from Kisoro in Kigezi District (1 million tonnes), which is currently exploited for the manufacture of lime using batch kilns. Other small limestone resources are located near Ndorwa, Kitumba, Bubale, Kigata and Kigararma (all in the vicinity of Kabale), and Kisiizi, Rubabo, and Rwonye in Rukungiri District (DGSM, written comm. Feb. 2000).

Enormous reserves of dolomitic limestone, dolomite and marble occur in eastern Uganda, along the border with Kenya and south and east of Moroto. The Neoproterozoic Karasuk metasedimentary sequence of metamorphosed limestones contains approximately 13 billion tonnes of dolomitic marble (DGSM, written comm. Feb. 2000). Unfortunately these limestone and dolomite resources occur in a semi-arid area, distant from the main markets for cement, lime consumption and from agricultural areas with acid soils.

Carbonate resources related to carbonatites in eastern Uganda are associated with the Sukulu, Tororo, Bukusu, Butiriku, and other carbonatites along the Kenya-Uganda border. The Sukulu Hills carbonatite, about 6 km southwest of Tororo, is mainly composed of soevitic limestone with possible carbonate reserves of 16.3 million tonnes. Small-scale miners are currently excavating a small portion of the Sukulu carbonatite complex and calcine the limestone in batch kilns. The Tororo Cement Industries excavate some other parts of the deposit.

The Limekiln Hill and Cave Hill phosphatic carbonates of the Tororo carbonatite complex, just outside Tororo, have been used for many years as raw material by the company Tororo Cement Industry. The P_2O_5 level in the raw material reaches up to 1.7%. Reserves are estimated at 82 million tonnes.

Carbonates are also reported from the Bukusu alkaline/carbonatite complex in Mbale District. A small portion of this large ring complex is made up of carbonates. No reserve figures are available and no mining is currently being carried out. Other carbonates, located at the Butiriku carbonatite complex in the Bukiribo area, 3 km north of Bududa in Mbale District, have probable carbonate reserves of 16.3 million tonnes. The proven reserves are 3 million tonnes. Information on the carbonate resources of other carbonatites in eastern and northeastern Uganda, such as the Budeda, Lolekek, Napak and Toror, is sparse.

Other carbonate-rich rocks include calcite-bearing tuffs from the foot of Mount Elgon in the Mbale district and in volcanic rocks from the Fort Portal and Kisoro area in western Uganda.

Carbonatitic lavas are known from the Katwe area, from Kalyango volcano near Fort Portal and from Lake Kyekora, south of Fort Portal. The groundmass of the vesicular carbonatitic lava from Kalyango is composed of minute grains of pyroxene, olivine, biotite, magnetite, apatite and calcite (Gittins 1966).

Gypsum

The best known source of natural gypsum, $CaSO_4 \cdot 2H_2O$, is at Kibuku, at the southwestern end of Lake Albert in Bundibugyo District (Kabagambe-Kaliisa 1977). The gypsum occurs as coarse selenite in 1-4 m thick clay layers with a tonnage of approximately 12 million tonnes. Currently small-scale miners of the Bundibugyo Miners Association extract the gypsum through simple manual washing and sorting techniques and sell 2,500 tonnes of final product per year to the Hima cement plant, near Kasese.

The 'waste gypsum' produced from the bioleaching process of cobalt-bearing pyrite tailings near Kasese in western Uganda reaches 300 tonnes per day. This chemical gypsum has been considered as cement retarder. This 'waste gypsum' could also be considered for agricultural applications provided the elevated trace element concentrations of nickel and copper can be reduced.

K-rich igneous rocks

Potassium in silicate rocks is found in Uganda mainly in K-rich lavas and intrusive rocks like mica-pyroxenites. The potassium occurs in the crystal structure of phlogopite and biotite mica, and in feldspar.

Samples from carbonized volcanic vent agglomerates in the Bukusu alkaline complex in eastern Uganda, contain up to 8.6% K_2O and 15% CaO (Baldock 1967). Samples from fresh pyroxenite of the same complex contain up to 6.4% K_2O. Apatite-magnetite-phlogopite bands in the pyroxenite of the Bukusu complex contain up to 3.4% K_2O and 12.4% P_2O_5 (van Straaten, unpubl.). Feldspathic agglomerates that form the large areas of the central part of the Butiriku carbonatite complex contain up to 9.8% K_2O (Reedman 1973). Bukusu and Butiriku are both areas of intensive banana cultivation, a crop known for high K requirements.

Trachytes from the Toror carbonatite complex near Moroto in eastern Uganda contain up to 13.9% K_2O (Sutherland 1965; King and Sutherland 1966). On the western side of Uganda, the volcanic fields north-northeast of Lake George, especially the Katwe-Kikorongo and Bunyanguru (Kichamba) fields, contain up to 7% K_2O (Lloyd *et al.* 1991). The very extensive (more than 2500 km^2) Virunga fields in southwest Uganda and northern Rwanda contain large lava flows with considerable amounts of potassium-silicates, mainly in the form of silica-undersaturated leucite tephrites (Lloyd *et al.* 1991). The potassium occurs in leucite, which is relatively unstable in weathering systems. Electron microprobe analyses of leucite and interstitial groundmass, reported by Lloyd *et al.* (1991), showed K_2O concentrations between 19.55 % and 27.26 %. Other rocks, like olivine leucitites (also called ugandites) may, upon weathering, provide potential valuable nutrients to the soils, especially to soils with low base saturations.

Vermiculites

A vermiculite deposit was discovered in the early 1950s near Namekara, 1 km west of the Busumbu phosphate mine in the Bukusu alkaline complex. Detailed pitting and trenching in the 1950s showed reserves of about 0.5 million tonnes of vermiculite-bearing residual soil to a depth of 15 m beneath a surface layer of magnetite rubble (Taylor 1956). In the mid 1950s, the amount of recoverable vermiculite was estimated at 350,000 tonnes. Recent exploration work to greater depth and in adjacent areas resulted in the delineation of sizeable additional vermiculite resources in the Namekara area. The average depth to the unweathered bedrock is 40-45 m. Vermiculites in the Namekara area are spatially related to mica-pyroxenites and 'glimmerites' of the pyroxenite zone of the Bukusu alkaline complex.

The quality of the Namekara vermiculite is good, the cation exchange capacity exceeds 110 cmol$^+$/kg and the exchangeable Mg^{2+} content reaches 4,390 mg/kg. The Namekara vermiculite is well suited for export but will also have a small local market in the emerging horticultural and floricultural industry of Uganda.

Natural zeolites

So far only small amounts of natural zeolites have been found in volcanic rocks, for instance in vesicles of carbonatitic lava in western Uganda (Von Knorring and du Bois 1961). There are extensive pyroclastic deposits in the volcanic areas of western Uganda, some of which could be zeolitic.

Agromineral potential

The potential for using indigenous agrogeological resources in Uganda depends largely on the agronomic effectiveness of the various agrominerals on Ugandan soils. The phosphate resources are extensive and some of these resources, specifically from Busumbu and Butiriku, have shown that they can be applied effectively on P-deficient acid soils in neighbouring Kenya. More data and agronomic tests will have to be conducted on acid P-deficient soils in Uganda to validate their usefulness as part of Uganda's agricultural modernization plans. Liming materials are present in several areas, some of them, however, in remote locations. Calcareous tuffs and K-rich volcanics occur very close to banana growing areas (Bukusu, Butiriku) of eastern Uganda, and in volcanic areas of western Uganda. These 'ultra-potassic' volcanics should be investigated regarding their potential as local K-sources. Agronomic tests should be conducted with these materials, especially on crops that require large amounts of potassium, such as starchy food crops, bananas and potatoes.

The potential for discovering substantial amounts of natural zeolites within pyroclastic and volcaniclastic sediments associated with young volcanics and Quaternary sediments in western Uganda is regarded as high (Mathers 1994).

References:

Baldock JW 1967. The geology and geochemistry of the Bukusu carbonatite complex, South-East Uganda. Unpubl. Ph.D thesis, University of Leeds, UK, 284 pp.

Baldock JW 1969. Geochemical dispersion of copper and other elements at the Bukusu carbonatite complex, Uganda. Transact. Inst. Min. Metall. (Sec. B), 78:B12-B28.

Bearden-Potter Corporation, 1982. Uganda Phosphate Engineering Project, Phase I, Technical Report, Section 1 - Geology, 34pp.

Bjorlyyke K 1973. Glacial conglomerates of later Precambrian age from the Bunyoro Series, W. Uganda. Geol. Rdsch. 62:938-947.

Bloomfield K 1973. Economic aspects of Uganda carbonatite complexes. Overseas Geol. Min. Resour. 41:139-167.

Bloomfield K, Reedman JH, and JGG Tether 1971. Geochemical exploration of carbonatite complexes in eastern Uganda. In: Geochemical exploration, Montreal, Canada, CIM Spec. Vol. 11:85-101.

Butegwa CN, Mullins GL and SH Chien 1996a. Agronomic evaluation of fertilizer products derived from Sukulu Hills phosphate rock. Fert. Res. 44:113-122.

Butegwa CN, Mullins GL and SH Chien 1996b. Induced phosphorus fixation and the effectiveness of phosphate fertilizers derived from Sukulu Hills. Fert. Res. 44:231-240.

Celenk O, and E Katto 1993. Direct application phosphate potential of Busumbu Hill prospect, East Uganda. Uganda Geol. Surv. and Mines, and United Nat. Dep. Dev. Support Managem. Serv., unpubl. report, 28pp.

Davies KA 1947. The phosphate deposits of the Eastern Province, Uganda. Econ. Geol. 42:137-146.

Davies KA 1956. The geology of part of south-east Uganda, with special reference to the alkaline complexes. Geol. Survey of Uganda, Memoir 8:62-76.

Department of Geological Survey and Mines -DGSM (2000). Written communication 14. Febr. 2000: Limestone/dolomite occurrences in Uganda. 4pp.

Gabert G 1984. Structural-lithological units of Proterozoic rocks in East Africa, their base, cover and mineralisation. In: Klerkx J and J Michot (eds.) Geologie Africaine - African Geology, Musee royale de l'Afrique centrale, Tervuren, Belgium:11-22.

Gittins J 1966. Summaries and bibliographies of carbonatite complexes. In: Tuttle OF and J Gittins (eds.) Carbonatites. Interscience Publ. New York, 417-570.

Kabagambe-Kaliisa FA 1977. A detailed geological mapping of the area covered by the Kibuyu gypsum project. Department of Geological Survey and Mines, Unpubl. Rep. FAKK/4, 19pp.

Kabagambe-Kaliisa FA 1989. The Sukulu phosphate deposit, south-eastern Uganda. In: Notholt AJG, Sheldon RP and DF Davidson (eds.) Phosphate deposits of the world. Vol 2. Phosphate rock resources, Cambridge University Press, Cambridge, UK:184-186.

Katto E 1995. Evaluation of the phosphate resource of Busumbu ridge. M.Sc. Thesis, ITC, Delft, Netherlands, 176pp.

Katto E 2000. The Busumbu phosphate resource, southeastern Uganda. Abstracts: 18th Colloquium of African Geology, Graz, Austria, J. Afr. Earth Sci. 30/4A:45.

King BC and DS Sutherland 1966. The carbonatite complexes of Eastern Uganda. In: Tuttle OF and J Gittins (eds.) Carbonatites. Interscience Publ. New York: 73-126.

Kisitu VB 1991. Fertilizer material occurrences in Uganda. Fert. Res. 30:187-189.

Lloyd FE, Huntingdon AT, Davies GR and PH Nixon 1991. Phanerozoic volcanism of southwest Uganda: A case study for regional K and LILE enrichment of the lithosphere beneath domed and rifted continental plate. In: Kampunzu AB and RT Lubala (eds.) Magmatism in extensional structural settings. Springer Verlag, Berlin, Germany:24-72.

Mathers SJ 1994. Industrial mineral potential of Uganda. In: Mathers SJ and AJG Notholt (eds). Industrial Minerals in Developing Countries. AGID Geosciences in International Development 18:144-166.

Ngoze SO, Buresh RJ, Okalebo JR, van Straaten P, Jama B and P Smithson 2000. Evaluation of fertilizer products derived from Busumbu phosphates in Eastern Uganda. Abstr. Annual meeting Am. Soc. of Agronomy, Minneapolis Nov. 5-9, 2000, p.281.

Reedman JH 1973. Potash ultra-fenites at the Butiriku carbonatite complex in south-east Uganda. Ann. Rep. Research Institute for African Geology, Univ. Leeds, No 17:78-81.

Reedman JH 1974. Residual soil geochemisty in the discovery and evaluation of the Butiriku carbonatite, southeast Uganda. Inst. Mining Metall. Transact., Section B, 83:B1-12.

Reedman JH 1984. Resources of phosphate, niobium, iron, and other elements in residual soils over the Sukulu Carbonatite Complex, Southwest Uganda. Econ. Geol. 79:716-724.

Schlueter T 1997. Geology of East Africa. Gebrueder Borntraeger Berlin-Stuttgart, 484pp.

Sutherland DS 1965. Potash-trachytes and ultra-potassic rocks associated with the carbonatite complex of Toror Hill, Uganda. Min Mag 35:363

Taylor R 1955. Ore reserves of Busumbu phosphate mine. Geol. Survey of Uganda, Unpubl. Rep. RT/13, 9pp.

Taylor R 1956. The vermiculite occurrence of Namekara. Rep. Geol. Surv. Uganda, TR/19.

Taylor R. 1960. Busumbu phosphate mine. Geol. Survey of Uganda, Unpubl. Rep. RT/35, 3pp.

Van Kauwenbergh SJ 1991. Overview of phosphate deposits in East and Southeast Africa. Fert. Res. 30:127-150.

Von Knorring O and CGB du Bois 1961. Carbonatitic lava from Fort Portal area in western Uganda. Nature 192:1064-1065.

Williams CE 1959. Sukulu Complex, eastern Uganda and the origin of the African carbonatites. Ph.D. thesis, Univ. of Cape Town, 154pp.

Zake JYK, Tenywa JT, Nkwiine C, Katwire D and V Ochwoh 1988. Research on the application of Tororo Rock Phosphate as a fertilizer in Uganda soils. United Nations Economic Commission for Africa. Regional conference on utlization of mineral resources in Africa. Kampala, June 15 1988, Proceedings 5 B6.1:100-113.

Zambia

Total population (July 2000 estimate): 9,582,000
Area: 752,614 km^2
Annual population growth rate (2000): 1.95 %
Life expectancy at birth (1998): 40.5 years
People not expected to survive to age 40 (1998): 46.2 % of total population
GDP per capita (1998): US $719

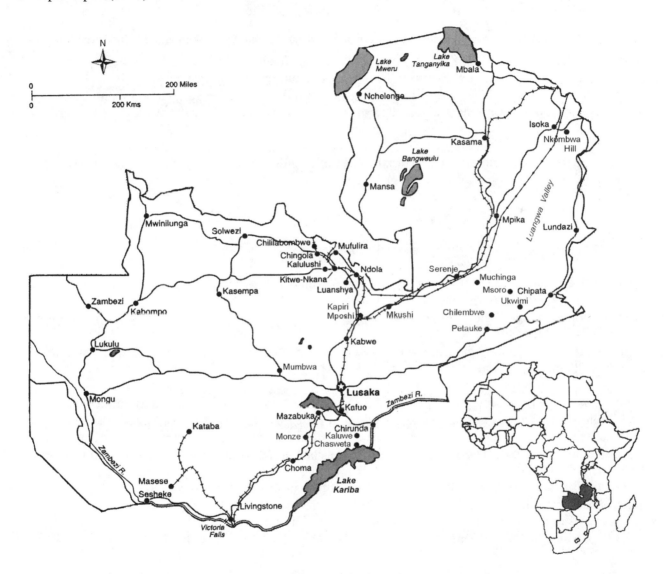

Zambia is a landlocked country in central southern Africa. The dominating landscape of Zambia is a plateau at elevations around 1,000 m, which is incised by large open rift valley-related river systems, such as the northeast-southwest Luangwa River and the Zambezi and Kafue Rivers. The alluvial plains in the south of the country, with altitudes around 300 m, form the lowest and hottest parts of the country.

Zambia is one of the most urbanized countries in sub-Saharan Africa. Urban development is restricted to the six major Copperbelt towns and along the railway via Lusaka to Livingstone at the border with Zimbabwe. Zambia's economy is historically based on the mining industry of copper and cobalt. The mineral sector contributes between 8 and 20% of the GDP, and employs approximately 15% of the wage-earning work force and accounts for about 75% of Zambia's export earnings. With declining copper prices and revenue the government diversified the economic base with a focus, among other things, on agricultural development.

Agriculture generates about 25% of the country's GDP. The livelihood of most of the rural population depends on subsistence farming. Efforts to increase agricultural production depend largely on increasing soil productivity. Hence, the government's strategy stressed the increase of soil nutrient inputs like fertilizers and manures. Currently, all fertilizers are imported, costing substantial amounts of foreign exchange.

The main food crops in Zambia are cassava, maize, millet, groundnuts and sugar cane. Cash crops for export are sugarcane, cotton, tobacco and green coffee.

Geological outline

The Precambrian geology of Zambia can be divided into several domains:

- the Paleoproterozoic (Eburnian) in the Bangweulu Block,
- the Mesoproterozoic (Kibaran) Irumide Belt,
- the Neoproterozoic Katanga Supergroup.

Phanerozoic rocks including the Karoo Supergroup, the Late Tertiary to Pleistocene Kalahari sands and Recent sediments.

In northern Zambia, the Proterozoic basement is largely made up of rocks of the Bangweulu Block, which was deformed during the Paleoproterozoic (Eburnian). Also, the northeast striking Mesoproterozoic Irumide Belt and the Neoproterozoic rocks of the Katangan Supergroup, which form the Lufilian Arc, are exposed in the northern and north-western parts of the country (Drysdall et al. 1972; Andersen and Unrug 1984). The Katangan Supergroup has been subdivided into the Roan Group (in which the copper-cobalt mineralization occurs), the Mwashia Group and the Kundelungu Group. While the Roan Group is represented by marine sediments including carbonates, the Mwashia and Kundelungu Groups consist of various types of sediments. Two fluvio-glacial (possibly tillite) deposits, the 'Grand Conglomerat' in the Roan Group and the 'Petit Conglomerat' in the Kundelungu Group, occur in the Katanga Supergroup.

Neoproterozoic to early Cambrian Pan-African granitoids and Pan-African fault zones are reported in the southeast part of the country. The Neoproterozoic Zambezi Belt, which links with the Mozambique Belt, the Lufilian Arc and the inland branch of the Neoproterozoic Damara Belt in the southeast of the country (Hanson et al. 1994).

The Karoo sedimentary succession, Carboniferous to lower Cretaceous in age, is made up of clastic sediments, coal and tillites. Karoo beds are found in the Luangwa Rift Valley and the Zambezi Rift Valley. Late Tertiary to Pleistocene Kalahari sands cover large parts of western Zambia.

Several carbonatites occur in Zambia that are spatially related to rift valley structures. The Proterozoic Nkombwa carbonatite is spatially associated with the Luangwa Rift Valley. The cluster of carbonatites in the Rufunsa Rift Valley (Kaluwe, Nachomba, Mwambuto and Chasweta) are Jurassic to Cretaceous in age, located at the triple junction of rift valley structures (Bailey 1966).

AGROMINERALS

Phosphates

The phosphate occurrences and deposits in Zambia have been described and summarized by many authors, among them Deans and McConnell (1955), Bailey (1966), Bwerinofa and Somney (1977), Davidson (1986), Turner *et al.* (1986), Tether (1987), Borsch (1988a, 1988b, 1991), Tether and Money (1991), Mulela (1991), Sliwa (1991), Simukanga *et al.* (1994) and Chileshe *et al.* (2000).

The phosphate mineralizations in Zambia are associated with two types of igneous rocks, carbonatites and syenites. While the phosphate mineralization related to carbonatites is well described from many parts of the world, the association of phosphate mineralization with syenites is not well documented as yet.

No sedimentary phosphates have been found in Zambia so far, and the chances of finding sedimentary marine phosphates in Zambia are very small. The types of sediments, ages and geological settings of sediments deposited in Zambia are unfavourable for phosphate deposition (Davidson 1986; Mulela 1991).

Phosphate accumulations associated with carbonatites have been studied in detail at Nkombwa Hill in northern Zambia and at the Kaluwe carbonatite in the south of the country. The well-studied syenite-related phosphate mineralizations are Chilembwe and Mumbwa North (Sugar Loaf). The location of the phosphate mineralizations is shown in Figure 2.21.

1. Phosphates associated with the Nkombwa Hill carbonatite

The Nkombwa Hill carbonatite occurs in northeastern Zambia, some 25 km east of Isoka ($10°09'S$; $32°51'E$). The carbonatite forms a prominent hill rising approximately 300 m above the surrounding area. The size of the carbonatite is 1.5 x 2.5 km. The age of Nkombwa Hill is 689 ± 26 million years. This carbonatite is part of the chain of Proterozoic carbonatite and alkaline complexes that intruded along an extensive structural zone from northern Zambia via western Tanzania into Burundi and the Democratic Republic of Congo (Tack *et al.* 1984).

At least four major lithologies have been identified at the Nkombwa Hill carbonatite complex (Mambwe 1993):

- fenitic phlogopite carbonatite,
- dolomitic carbonatite,
- ankeritic carbonatite,
- silicified carbonatite .

The main phosphate mineral at Nkombwa Hill is isokite ($CaMgPO_4F$), a mineral discovered in the early 1950s by Deans and McConnell (1955). The other main phosphate mineral found at Nkombwa Hill is a strontium-rich fluor-apatite. The primary reserves of the Nkombwa phosphate-bearing rocks have been estimated at more than 200 million tonnes with a grade of 4.6% P_2O_5. A selected part of the dolomitic and ankeritic carbonatite of Nkombwa Hill yields 130 million tonnes with 7.3% P_2O_5 (Sliwa 1991). Accessory minerals include Rare Earth Element (REE) bearing minerals, and to a smaller extent the niobium (Nb)-bearing mineral pyrochlore.

The foot of Nkombwa Hill is covered with weathered residual and transported iron-rich brown soils. These soils are enriched in phosphorus relative to the original carbonatite rock. The resources of these brown soils are estimated at 1 million tonnes. Analyses of the residual and transported soils at Nkombwa Hill have shown up to 10-18% P_2O_5 in the soil, 15-30% Fe, 1-2% REE and 0.5% Nb. In order to concentrate the phosphates from the residual and transported soils several methods have been tried. Coventional flotation methods have been unsuccessful mainly because of limonite coating of the phosphates. Alternative methods to concentrate and release phosphorus from the P-rich soils, such as heap leaching and biological solubilization have been tested. Some preliminary laboratory test work using acid heap leaching techniques have indicated positive results (Borsch 1988b).

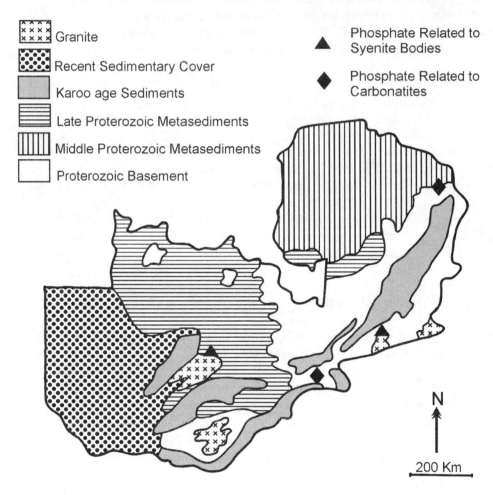

Figure 2.21: Simplified geology of Zambia with location of known phosphate deposits.

2. Phosphates associated with the Kaluwe carbonatite.

Kaluwe is the most extensive and voluminous carbonatite in Zambia. It is located at the triple junction between the middle Zambezi, lower Zambezi and Luangwa Rift Valleys in southern Zambia (15°10'S; 30°01'E). The sheet-like carbonatite, at least 250 m thick and on average of 1.5 km wide, is slightly folded into a northwest plunging syncline. The main outcrop extends for more than 10 km from east to west. The carbonatite has been studied in detail by Bailey (1960, 1966), Turner (1988), as well as geologists from the Zambian Geological Survey Department and the Mineral Development Corporation (MINDECO) and the Mineral Exploration (MINEX) department of the Zambia Industrial and Mining Corporation Ltd.

The volume of the Kaluwe carbonatite resource is 207 million tonnes at 2.5% P_2O_5 (Bwerinofa and Somney 1977). Beneficiation tests of the primary carbonatite rock have shown that the recovery of apatite from this resource is difficult because the apatite grains are intergrown with carbonates. The low grade of the primary deposit and the difficulties of beneficiation render this resource uneconomic.

Of greater practical and economic interests are the residual brown soils overlying the Kaluwe carbonatite in southwest Zambia. They have been extensively sampled, trenched, drilled and analyzed. The resource base of the Kaluwe brown soils was estimated by two different methods, indicating 6.6 million tonnes at 11% P_2O_5 or 10.8 million tonnes grading 4.14% P_2O_5 respectively (Sliwa 1991). Beneficiation tests have been conducted to evaluate the recovery of apatite and the niobium-bearing mineral pyrochlore. The results of these tests were encouraging. They indicate that a phosphate concentrate of 30.4% P_2O_5 could be produced at a recovery rate of 73.8% (Mulela 1991). Niobium is concentrated in these residual soils as pyrochlore and could form a valuable co-product to phosphate. Currently, this resource is not considered for phosphate extraction for various technical and economic reasons.

3.   The syenite-related phosphate mineralization at Chilembwe.

The syenite-related Chilembwe phosphate deposit is the most promising of all the phosphate mineralizations in Zambia. It is located approximately 40 km northeast of Petauke in the Eastern Province of Zambia (13°59'S; 31°41'E). The phosphate deposit at Chilembwe, discovered in 1978 during a regional prospecting campaign by MINEX, consists of five small massive leucocratic apatite-bearing bodies composed of mainly apatite and quartz and apatite-biotite-amphibole rocks. These bodies occur within the syenite that borders the 510 million year old Sinda Batholith (Sliwa 1991). The origin of this phosphate mineralization is unclear. Tether (1987) suggested that the phosphate accumulation as a result of late-stage injections of segregated fluids derived from the syenite intrusion.

Mulele (1991) calculated the reserves of the Chilembwe deposit and reported the tonnage of two of the four phosphate ore bodies as:

- Body No. 2 = 1.64 million tonnes at 11.8% P_2O_5 (cut-off grade = 6% P_2O_5),
- Body No. 4 = 0.22 million tonnes at 9.9% P_2O_5.

Although the Chilembwe phosphate deposit is relatively small, the ease of extraction and processing makes it currently the most attractive phosphate resource in Zambia.

The solubility of the Chilembwe phosphate concentrate is low, having a neutral ammonium citrate solubility (NAC-AOAC method) of only 1.0% P_2O_5 (Frederick 1991, referencing an IFDC characterization study of an ore sample from Chilembwe). This low solubility renders the Chilembwe phosphates unsuitable as direct application P fertilizer. Modification is required to make this phosphate more agronomically effective. Several modification techniques were tested by Zambian researchers, including partial acidulation (Nkonde et al. 1991; Zambezi and Chipola 1991; Borsch 1993; Simukanga et al. 1994; Chileshe et al. 2000) and fusion with magnesium sources (Mulela 1991). Innovative low-cost technologies for the partial acidulation process were developed at the University of Zambia and at MINEX (Nkonde et al. 1991; Zambezi and Chipola 1991; Borsch 1993; Nkonde and Simukanga 1993; Chileshe 2000). One of the innovative pieces of equipment tested for this process is a low-tech, modified concrete mixer (Borsch 1993).

In addition to technical studies, a financial evaluation (Simukanga et al. 1993), an economic assessment of partially acidulated Chilembwe PR (Frederick 1991) and an environmental impact assessment for the proposed Chilembwe mining project were conducted (Phiri 1993). In addition, Mukuka (1993) carried out a preliminary study on the social impact of producing PAPR fertilizers in rural Zambia, near Chilembwe.

Agronomic Testing of Chilembwe Phosphate Rock

The Chilembwe phosphate concentrate was agronomically tested on various soils as a directly applied P-source, as partially acidulated phosphate rock (PAPR) and as phosphate fused with magnesium sources (Fused Magnesium Phosphate, FMP). The direct application of Chilembwe PR was generally unsuccessful in producing short-term response and yield increases. However, testing of PAPR from Chilembwe using millet and maize as test crops on various soils showed agronomic effectiveness comparable to that of the soluble P-fertilizer TSP (Damaseke *et al.* 1993; Phiri *et al.* 1993; Simukanga *et al.* 1994; Chileshe *et al.* 2000). Also the use of a fused magnesium phosphate (FMP) with Chilembwe PR showed encouraging agronomic effects (Goma *et al.* 1991). The processing of FMP but was constrained by technical and economic problems.

---

4.   The syenite-related phosphate mineralization at Mumbwa North.

The Mumbwa North phosphate mineralization was discovered by MINEX in 1984 in the course of a systematic survey of syenite bodies peripheral to large granite batholiths. The syenite-hosted phosphate mineralization is located at latitude 14°45'S, longitude 26°50'E, approximately 50 km northwest of Mumbwa in the Central Province.

Mulela (1991) differentiates between three types of phosphate mineralization at Mumbwa North:

Type 1.   apatite associated with primary copper and iron mineralization (at Sugar Loaf),

Type 2.   copper-phosphate mineralization in the supergene environment, such as turquoise-chalcosiderite,

Type 3.   'apatite pegmatite' bodies.

The apatite in the Type 1 mineralization occurs as fractured prismatic crystals in a ferruginous breccia of altered syenite fragments (Sliwa 1991). Mulela (1991) interpreted this body as fractionated cumulate that was subsequently brecciated and subjected to hydrothermal alteration. Resource estimates of this mineralization indicate 0.5 million tonnes of ore with grades between 8 and 12% P_2O_5 (Sliwa 1991).

The phosphate mineralization of some interest for agricultural purposes is the apatite in pegmatites (Type 3). The apatite pegmatite bodies occur as irregular veins with sharp contacts to the surrounding country rock. The rocks are almost monomineralic apatite with occasional K-feldspar and crack-filling iron oxides. The apatite near the contact is fine to medium-grained and in the central part of the pegmatite the apatite is coarse grained with crystals up to 10 cm in diameter (Sliwa 1991). According to Mulela (1991), the mineralogical composition is that of a hydroxy-apatite with elevated levels of rare earth elements (REE) and radionuclides. The largest of the pegmatite bodies is estimated to contain 0.22 million tonnes of ore with an average grade of 16% P_2O_5 (Mulela 1991).

Other phosphate occurrences

Tether and Money (1991) describe two other small phosphate occurrences, one at Chikombwe within a veined stockwork in gabbros, the other in an amphibolite near Chakanga, north and northeast of Petauke. Both have irregular phosphate mineralization with generally low grades. These occurrences seem to be of small volume and low grades, and thus are of no economic interest.

Other agrominerals

Liming material

Large parts of Zambia are covered by acid and strongly depleted soils especially the strongly leached soils developed from felsic rocks under high rainfall regimes in the north of the country. The nature of these strongly acid soils, with pH levels $(CaCl_2)$ below 4.5, and corresponding high aluminum (Al^{3+}) saturation, are major constraints to crop production (Singh 1989; Goma 1994). Experiments carried out on these soils by the Ministry of Agriculture and various organizations have shown the effectiveness of finely ground 'liming materials' including dolomitic limestones.

In Zambia, carbonate rocks have been classified into three groups:

- crystalline limestones and dolomitic limestones of the Precambrian,
- chemically formed limestone-travertine deposits, deposited from spring water,
- plug and sheet-like carbonatite bodies.

Most of the limestone and dolomite resources of Zambia are found in central Zambia, occurring in an area from Lusaka via Kapiri Mposhi and Kitwe to the Solwezi area in the Northwestern Province. The volume of these deposits is very large. Some of these resources are used for the Zambian cement industry, for example the carbonate resources at Chilanga (20 km south of Lusaka) and Ndola. Others are used for aggregate production. Small, relatively undeveloped resources are described from north of Mkushi (Rao 1986; Bosse 1996).

In the west of Zambia only few sizeable carbonate resources have been delineated. Dolomitic limestone resources are located 16 km northwest of Kabompo (1.4 million tonnes). Other liming resources occur 43 km north of Zambezi town (dolomitic limestone: 3 million tonnes; marble: 1 million tonnes). The neutralizing value of the dolomitic limestones and marbles is high, ranging from 97-112% (Rao 1986).

In eastern Zambia, carbonate rocks are known in the Lundazi, Chipata and Petauke areas. A quarry south of Lundazi supplies eastern Zambia with hard rock aggregates. Several more dolomitic limestones are reported in this area, south and southwest of Lundazi. Near Msoro Mission, lenses with dolomitic marble were used in the past for lime production. Near Ukwimi, coarse-grained, white calcitic marbles with accessory phlogopite, apatite and graphite were extracted and processed into lime until 1960 (Bosse 1996). North and west of Petauke, there are several extensive dolomitic marbles. Some of these carbonate deposits were previously processed into agricultural lime, for example the marble from Muchinga, east of Serenje. In the 1980s, annual production from this source was 3,000 tonnes.

Only a few, small occurrences of carbonate rocks are known from Northern, Luapula and Eastern Central Provinces where liming material is most needed. The limestones in Luapula Province occur in the Kundelungu Group near Matanda and Bukanda (approximately 70 km west of Mansa). The reserves of the Matanda deposit alone are in the range of 5 million tonnes. The neutralizing values of these limestones are high, ranging from 89-104 % (Rao 1986).

The main carbonate resource in the Northern Province is Nkombwa Hill, a large carbonatite complex, some 25 km east of Isoka. The volume of easily extractable dolomitic carbonatite is in excess of 700,000 tonnes (Nalluri 1984). Tests by Singh (1989) and Tveitnes and Svads (1989) on local soils indicate low initial response to liming, but good response to liming in combination with P application.
 In addition to the sedimentary limestone and dolomite resources, the carbonatites in the Rufunsa area, specifically Kaluwe and Chasweta, contain significant volumes of carbonate rock.

The need for liming materials, especially for the acid soils of the northern part of Zambia prompted some investigations on appropriate crushing and grinding equipment. Rao (1986) collected equipment quotes for a 10,000 tonne per year capacity crushing and grinding plant. The equipment including drilling equipment, primary crusher, a hammer mill and tertiary crushers is quoted at US $121,932 (Rao 1986).

The British Geological Survey in co-operation with the Geological Survey of Zambia, the University of Zambia, and the Ministry of Agriculture is currently developing a demonstration lime production facility. They plan to test various limestones (and phosphates) in cooperation with small-scale farmers.

Guano

Several guano deposits are reported by Tether and Money (1991) in the northwest of the country and near Lusaka. However, no details on location, chemical composition and tonnage have been provided.

Potassium-rich minerals

There are no known evaporite-type potash deposits in Zambia. In the search for alternative K-bearing materials, Borsch (1990) and Tether and Money (1991) describe some initial tests on potassium-containing silicates. Extraction tests on clays and K-feldspar-bearing rocks from Zambia showed low available potassium, although treatment with various acids improved potassium release. The experiments carried out by Borsch (1990) showed that shales and argillites from the Copperbelt mining area contained 1.5-7.4% total K_2O, but that only 0.01-1% K_2O was available. After acid treatment the available K_2O content reached 3.9% using nitric acid and 5.7% using sulphuric acid. Micas from pegmatites with a total K_2O content of 7-14% released only 0.8% K_2O in water. Nitric acid treatment increased the available K_2O content to 2-4%, and sulphuric acid treated biotites released 9.6% K_2O (Borsch 1990).

Tether and Money (1991) report on tests on metasomatized mudstone and feldspathic breccia surrounding the Mwambuto and Nachomba carbonatites (between Kaluwe and Chasweta). The total K_2O levels reached 16%. However, very little K is readily soluble in HCl. They concluded that the recovery of K from K-feldspars is unlikely to be economic.

Sulphides/sulphates

Zambia's sulphur resources occur in the form of sulphides. Primary pyrite is extracted from the 20 m thick lode of the Nampundwe pyrite mine (48 km west of Lusaka). Reserves are approximately 10 million tonnes averaging 16.8% S (Tether and Money 1991). Other sulphide mineralizations are associated with base metal ores. However, in recent years, Zambia's copper industry has imported large volumes of sulphuric acid from neighbouring Zimbabwe.

Other sulphur-resources in Zambia include gypsiferous clays (gypsite). They occur in surficial environments of the Kafue Flats and the Siloana Plain, close to hot springs (Tether and Money 1991). The gypsiferous clays of Lochinvar, some 38 km from Monze, occur in layers up to 2 m thick under a thin layer of clay on the edges of the alluvial plain of the Kafue River (Sikombe 1982). The gypsum content in these clays reaches 40% with crystals up to 4 cm in size. Detailed exploration revealed 320,000 tonnes of recoverable gypsum from an area of 200 ha (Sikombe 1982). The extraction of gypsum, required by the cement industry as retarder, ran into problems at Lochinvar, and economic and technical problems (removal of gypsum from clay) forced the Chilanga cement factory to withdraw from the project. Consequently, the Lochinvar gypsum resource was not developed and the Chilanga cement factory found its own gypsum supplies from 'waste gypsum,' a material produced from neutralization of acid effluents from electrolytic copper refineries.

Agromineral potential

Zambia is well endowed with igneous phosphate resources. The phosphate resources in carbonatites are large but generally of low grade and low reactivity. The very low-grade residual soils at Kaluwe are relatively easy to extract and concentrate. However, the best potential for development of an indigenous phosphorus source is the syenite-related phosphate resources at Chilembwe, and to a smaller extent, at Mumbwa North. The resource base is relatively small and classical, large-scale industrial acidulation techniques of P-fertilizer production seem to be uneconomic. Because direct application of phosphate rock (PR) of unreactive composition is largely ineffective in the short term, teams at the University of Zambia and MINEX have tested alternative innovative processing techniques (for example partial acidulation). These efforts have been successful and require continued support. Additional low input techniques, such as biological modification, blending and compaction/pelletizing techniques should also be included in the processing and testing program.

The potential of slow release of potassium from micas, specifically biotites and phlogopites, should be investigated. The studies should focus on potential K-resources in close proximity to K-deficient soils, and on areas where high K-demanding crops such as potatoes, sunflowers and bananas are grown.

The limestone and dolomite resources of Zambia are extensive. However, the distribution of these resources is concentrated in the southern, northwestern and central areas. The highest demand for liming materials is in the northern areas of Zambia where only few limestone and dolomite resources are located. Efforts should be made to use the carbonate resources of the Nkombwa Hill carbonatite complex in the Northern Province, the resources in the Luapula Province, for instance, Matanda, and the occurrences in the Mkushi area.

References:

Andersen LS, Fabian J, Kasolo PC, Misra GB and NJ Vibetti 1981. Agricultural lime potential of calcareous rocks in Northern and Luapula Provinces, Zambia. School of Mines, University of Zambia, unpubl. rep. 76pp.

Andersen LS and R Unrug 1984. Geodynamic evolution of the Bangweulu Block, northern Zambia. Precambr. Res. 25:187-212.

Bailey DK 1960. Carbonatites of the Rufunsa valley, Feira District. Bull. Geol. Surv. Northern Rhodesia, 5.

Bailey DK 1966. Carbonatite volcanoes and shallow intrusions in Zambia. In: Tuttle OF and J Gittins (eds.) Carbonatites. Interscience Publishers, New York, 127-154.

Borsch L 1988a. The separation of phosphate from brown soils from the Kaluwe and Nkombwa carbonatites. Internal MINEX report, 15pp.

Borsch L 1988b. The beneficiation of the Kaluwe and Nkombwa Hill brown soils - some preliminary laboratory test results on the extraction of phosphate. Internal MINEX report, 28pp.

Borsch L 1990. Potential of potash-rich rocks and minerals in agriculture: some preliminary tests. AGID 61/62, p2.

Borsch L 1991. Stream sediments and soils as a geochemical guide to apatite mineralization in eastern Zambia. Fert. Res. 30:225-238.

Borsch L 1993. Exploration and development studies of phosphate resources in Zambia - a case study. In: Pride C and P van Straaten (eds.) Agrogeology and small-scale mining. Bull 5-6, Small Mining International:15-16.

Bosse HR 1996. Zambia. In: Bosse H-R, Gwosdz W, Lorenz W, Markwich, Roth W and F Wolff (eds.). Limestone and dolomite resources of Africa. Geol. Jb., D, 102:495-512.

Bwerinofa K and KY Somney 1977. Kaluwe carbonatite P.L. 136. Final report, MINDECO Ltd. Unpublished report, Lusaka, Zambia.

Chileshe F, Nkonde GK and S Simukanga 2000. Zambian phosphate resources: Local benefits. Phosphorus and Potassium 226:9-18.

Damaseke MI, Sakala GM and K Munyinda 1993. Agronomic effectiveness of partially acidulated phosphate rock in southern Zambia. In: The Zambia Fertiliser Technology Development Committee – ZFTDC. Proceedings of an international workshop: Phosphate rock - derivates and their use. 49-56.

Davidson DF 1986. Phosphate resource of Zambia based on available geologic data. Final Report to UN/DTCD INT/80-R45. United Nations, New York, 21pp.

Deans T, and JDC McConnell 1955. Isokite, CaMgPO$_4$F, a new mineral from the North of Rhodesia. J. Min. Soc. 681-690.

Drysdall AR, Johnson RL, Moore TA and JG Theime 1972. Outline of the geology of Zambia. Geol. Mijnbouw 51:265-276.

Frederick MT 1991. Production and economics of partially acidulated phosphate rock - implications for Zambia. In: Zambia Fertiliser Technology Development Committee (ZFTDC) Utilization of local phosphate deposits for the benefits of the Zambian farmer: 163-182.

Goma HC 1994. Managing agriculture in fragile soils of the high rainfall areas of Zambia: A review. Paper presented at refresher course for Alumni from Tropical Africa of the International Training Centre for Postgraduate soil scientists of the University of Ghent, Belgium. Unpub. Report.

Goma HC, Phiri S, Mapiki A and BR Singh 1991. Evaluation of fused magnesium phosphate in acid soils of the high rainfall zone of Zambia. In: Zambia Fertiliser Technology Development Committee (ZFTDC) Utilization of local phosphate deposits for the benefits of the Zambian farmer: 138-149.

Hanson RE, Wilson TJ and H Munyanyanyiwa 1994. Geologic evolution of the Neoproterozoic Zambezi Orogenic Belt in Zambia. J. Afr. Earth Sci 18:135-150.

Lungu OI, Temba J, Chirwa B and C Lungu 1993. Effects of lime and farmyard manure on soil acidity and maize growth on an acid Alfisoil from Zambia. Trop. Agric. (Trinidad) 70:309-314.

Mambwe SH 1987. Nkombwa Hill PL 382. Quarterly report No 1, MINEX Dept. Unpubl. Report, Lusaka, Zambia.

Mambwe SH 1993. The complexity of the Nkombwa Hill Carbonatite phosphate ore, Isoka District, Zambia. In: The Zambia Fertiliser Technology Development Committee – ZFTDC. Proceedings of an international workshop: Phosphate rock - derivates and their use:1-18.

Mukuka L 1993. The social impact of a partially acidulated phosphate rock (PAPR) rural-based plant on the community. In: The Zambia Fertiliser Technology Development Committee – ZFTDC. Proceedings of an international workshop: Phosphate rock - derivates and their use:118-122.

Mulela D 1991. Igneous phosphate occurrences in Zambia. In: Zambia Fertiliser Technology Development Committee (ZFTDC). Utilization of local phosphate deposits for the benefits of the Zambian farmer: 15-25.

Nalluri GK 1984. Agriculture lime survey, Nkombwa Hill, Isoka District. Internal MINEX report, 16pp.

Nkonde GK and S Simukanga 1993. Determination of process variables in the production of partially acidulated phosphate rock. In: The Zambia Fertiliser Technology Development Committee – ZFTDC. Proceedings of an international workshop: Phosphate rock - derivates and their use: 35-40.

Nkonde GK, Simukanga S and LK Witika 1991. Production of partially acidulated phosphate rock (PAPR) from Chilembwe phosphate ore. In: Zambia Fertiliser Technology Development Committee (ZFTDC) Utilization of local phosphate deposits for the benefits of the Zambian farmer: 63-73.

Phiri JK 1993. Environmental impact assessment (EIA) for proposed Chilembwe Phosphate Development Project. In: The Zambia Fertiliser Technology Development Committee - ZFTDC: Proceedings of an international workshop: Phosphate rock - derivates and their use: 92-100.

Phiri S, Mapiki A, Goma HC and BR Singh 1993. Agronomic evaluation of partially acidulated phosphate rock in Northern Zambia. In: The Zambia Fertiliser Technology Development Committee - ZFTDC: Proceedings of an international workshop: Phosphate rock - derivates and their use: 41-48.

Rao LP 1986. Occasional report on the agricultural lime potential in Zambia. Unpubl. Report, MINEX, 33pp.

Reeve WH and T Deans 1954. An occurrence of carbonatite in the Isoka District of Northern Rhodesia. Colon. Geol. Miner. Res. 4:271-281.

Sikombe WB 1982. Lochinvar gypsum mine, Zambia: A case study in production of an industrial mineral. In: JM Neilson (editor) Strategies for small-scale mining and mineral industries, AGID report 8:121-129.

Simukanga S, Lombe WC and GK Nkonde 1991. Chemical and mineralogical study of Chilembwe phosphate ore. In: Zambia Fertiliser Technology Development Committee (ZFTDC). Utilization of local phosphate deposits for the benefits of the Zambian farmer:26-38.

Simukanga S, Nkonde GK and ECK Chanda 1993. A preliminary financial evaluation for production of PAPR at Chilembwe, Eastern Province. In: The Zambia Fertiliser Technology Development Committee - ZFTDC: Proceedings of an international workshop: Phosphate rock - derivates and their use:75-82.

Simukanga S, Nkonde GK and V Shitumbanuma 1994. Status of phosphate rock in Zambia - resources and use. In: Mathers SJ and AJG Notholt (eds.) Industrial minerals in developing countries. AGID Report Series Geosciences in International Development 18:257-264.

Singh BR 1989. Evaluation of liming materials as ameliorants of acid soils in high rainfall -areas of Zambia. Norw. J. Agric. Sci. 3:13-21.

Sliwa AS 1991. Phosphate resources of Zambia and progress in their exploration. Fert. Res. 30:203-212.

Tack L, De Paepe P, Deutsch S and J-P Liegois 1984. The alkaline plutonic complex of the upper Ruvubu (Burundi): Geology, age, isotopic geochemistry and implications for the regional geology of the Western Rift. In: Klerkx J and J Michot (eds.) Geologie Africaine - African Geology, Musee royale de l'Afrique centrale, Tervuren, Belgium:91-114.

Tether J 1987. Phosphate resources of Zambia. In: Wachira JK and AJG Notholt (eds.) Agrogeology in Africa. Commonwealth Sci. Council, Technical Publ. Series 226:100-105.

Tether J and NJ Money 1991. A review of agricultural minerals in Zambia. Fert. Res. 30:193-202.

Turner DC 1988. Volcanic carbonatites of the Kaluwe complex, Zambia. J. Geol. Soc. London, 145:95-106.

Turner DC, Andersen SN, Punukollu SN, Sliwa A and F Tembo 1986. Igneous phosphate resources in Zambia. In: Notholt AJG, Sheldon RP and DF Davidson (eds.) Phosphate deposits of the world. Vol. 2. Phosphate rock resources, Cambridge University Press, Cambridge, UK:247-257.

Tveitnes S and H Svads 1989. The effect of lime on maize and groundnut yields in the high rainfall areas of Zambia. Norw. J. Agric. Sci. 3:173-180.

Zambezi P and P Chipola 1991. Production of partially acidulated phosphate rock (PAPR) at Minex. In: Zambia Fertiliser Technology Development Committee (ZFTDC). Utilization of local phosphate deposits for the benefits of the Zambian farmer: 57-62.

Zimbabwe

Total population (July 2000 estimate): 11,343,000
Area: 390,580 km^2
Annual population growth rate (2000): 0.26%
Life expectancy at birth (1998): 43.5 years
People not expected to survive to age 40 (1998): 41% of the total population
GDP per capita (1998): US $2,669

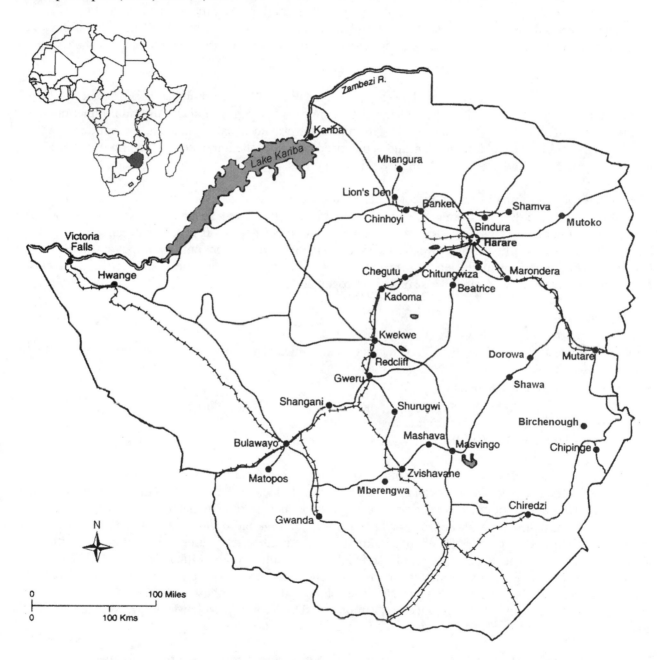

Zimbabwe is a landlocked country in central southern Africa, located between the Zambezi River and the Limpopo River. The landscape in the centre of the country is a gently rolling highland. Hot and dry lowlands occupy the southeast of Zimbabwe, as well as the Zambezi valley in the north. An extensive flat area covered with aeolian sands of the Kalahari marks the landscape in the west of the country. A series of mountain ranges straddle along the border with Mozambique.

Modern mining and farming activities are important to the economy of Zimbabwe. Over 40 minerals are mined in Zimbabwe, some of which are processed in the country to provide added value. Mineral production is dominated by gold, followed by asbestos, nickel, chromium and coal. The dimension stone industry, especially the extraction of 'black granite' is expanding rapidly. Trans-national companies operate many of the major mines while nationals largely run small mines. Small-scale artisanal gold mining has attracted many people, especially during times of economic hardship. The International Labour Organization (1999) estimated that between 50,000 and 350,000 persons are involved in small-scale mining in Zimbabwe.

The agricultural sector, which accounted for 20% of the GDP in 1999 and employed approximately 27% of the working population, is divided into large-scale commercial farming and agricultural production in so-called 'communal areas.' The commercial farming sector produces maize, tobacco, and cotton, as well as livestock. Small-scale subsistence farming is practised mainly in the impoverished 'communal areas' with maize, sorghum and vegetables being the principal crops.

Most of the soils in Zimbabwe are nutrient deficient and are degrading at a rapid rate. Large portions of Zimbabwe's soils are derived from granitic parent materials with nutrient-deficient sandy soils and low organic matter contents (Nyamapfene 1991). The soils with 'greenstones,' as parent material have a much higher inherent soil fertility. Zimbabwe's soils are continuously cropped but nutrient removal through harvesting without sufficient nutrient replenishment leads to a continuing decline in soil fertility. The two main limiting nutrients on Zimbabwe's soils are nitrogen and phosphorus.

Geological outline

Zimbabwe consists predominantly of Precambrian rocks, which can be divided into several units:

- the Archean granite/greenstones,
- the Archean Limpopo mobile belt,
- the Paleoproterozoic Umkondo and Lomagundi Group,
- the Neoproterozoic Makuti, Rushinga and Sijarira Groups.

Archean granites and greenstones of the Zimbabwe Craton cover about half of Zimbabwe and form the central part of the country. The Archean Limpopo mobile belt, located between the Zimbabwe and Kapvaal Cratons in the south, is characterized by high-grade metamorphic rocks that have undergone poly-phase deformation. The linear Great Dyke, one of the longest mafic and ultramafic layered intrusion in the world, crosses the country for about 550 km in a north-northeasterly direction. It varies in width from 4 km to 12 km. The age of the Great Dyke is 2,586 ±16 million years (Mukasa et al. 1998). The Paleoproterozoic low-grade metasediments of the Umkondo Group are exposed in the east-southeast of Zimbabwe along the border with Mozambique. The folded and metamorphosed Lomagundi Group covers extensive areas northwest of Harare in central Zimbabwe. The Neoproterozoic Makuti, Rushinga and Sijarira Groups are metasedimentary successions in the northwest of the country.

Non-marine Carboniferous to Triassic sediments of the Karoo Supergroup unconformably overlie Precambrian rocks in two separate basins, in the northwest and southeast. Tillites, sandstones, mudstones and coal beds are part of the Karoo sequence. Extensive basalts in the northwest and southern parts of the country overlie these sediments. Aeolian sands cover large parts of western Zimbabwe.

Several Mesozoic and Precambrian alkali ring complexes and carbonatites have intruded the Precambrian and the Karoo.

AGROMINERALS

Phosphates

Zimbabwe has a well-developed indigenous phosphate industry. All of the known phosphate resources are either of igneous provenance, associated with carbonatites, or guano. There are no known sedimentary phosphates in the country. The distribution of carbonatites and bat guano occurrences is shown in Figure 2.22.

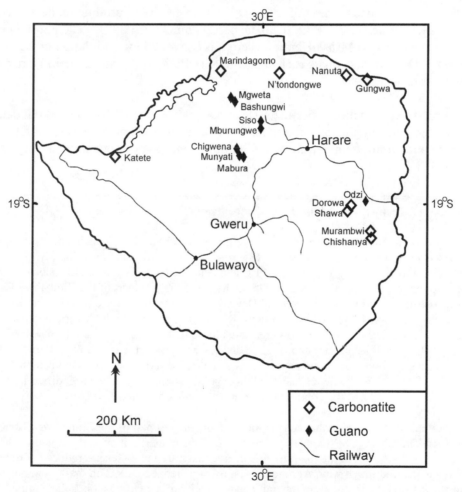

Figure 2.22: Location of known carbonatites and cave deposits of bat guano in Zimbabwe (after Barber 1991).

Barber (1991) reports 12 structures with lithologies that are considered to be carbonatites. Four of these structures are Mesozoic carbonatites and two of the 'probable' carbonatites are Precambrian in age. Little information is available from the other six recently discovered 'carbonatites' (Barber 1991). From the four Mesozoic carbonatites (Dorowa, Shawa, Chishanya, and Katete), only the Dorowa deposit is mined for phosphates at present.

1.   The Dorowa carbonatite:

The Dorowa phosphate mine is located in the Buhera District along the tarmac road from Nyazura to Murambinda at 19°04'S; 31°46'E. Dorowa is a carbonatite with associated foyaite, ijolite and pulaskite rocks surrounding it (Barber 1991). The actual calcium carbonate plug forms only a very small portion of the complex with larger parts of the carbonatite likely occurring beneath the present surface level. The central nepheline-rich foyaites and ijolites have been extensively mineralized with phlogopite/vermiculite and apatite.

According to the phosphate mining company Dorowa Minerals Ltd., the total measured resources are 72-78 million tons at 6.56% P_2O_5 (Barber 1991). At present, the northern ore body is mined. Ore excavation and processing rates are 3,000-3,500 tonnes per day. The ore is upgraded from 6.5% to 35-36% P_2O_5 at the mine site through crushing, sieving, magnetic separation and flotation. Over the last ten years, the Dorowa phosphate mine has produced an annual average of 1,128,300 tonnes of ore (Fernandes 1995), yielding 132,000 tonnes of concentrate at 35.2% P_2O_5. In the year 2000, production decreased slightly to 125,000 tonnes of concentrate at 37% P_2O_5 (Chitata, pers. comm. April 2001). The phosphate concentrate is transported by road and rail to Msasa/Harare, where it is converted by acidulation processes to SSP and TSP. The price of the Dorowa phosphate rock concentrate (DPRC) at the mine site in Dorowa is US $37.26 per tonne (Fernandes 1995).

Fernandes (1978) and the International Fertilizer Development Center (IFDC) carried out detailed mineralogical investigations on phosphate samples from Dorowa. The apatite was identified as hydroxy-fluor-apatite. The neutral ammonium citrate solubility of the phosphate concentrate is very low, 0.8% P_2O_5.

Agronomic Testing of Dorowa Phosphate Rock Concentrate

Several agronomic experiments have been conducted using Dorowa Phosphate Rock Concentrate (DPRC). As predicted, the DPRC in its unmodified form has little agronomic effect when applied directly to the soil due to its low reactivity. However, partially acidulated DPRC and pelletized and compacted phosphate blends have shown good agronomic response (Govere et al. 1995; Dhliwayo 1999). As part of the Zimbabwe-Canada agrogeology project, supported by the International Development Research Centre (IDRC), the DPRC was pelletized in a locally developed, low-cost disc pelletizer, as well as compacted with various organic and inorganic materials. The materials used for the phosphate blends include various amounts of DPRC and triple superphosphate (TSP), as well as manure and an agricultural waste product, castor cake (Dhliwayo 1999). Research results from greenhouse and field experiments using maize and pigeon peas indicate that compacted phosphate blends performed slightly better than the less expensive pelletized blends. Modified DPRCs performed considerably better than the control and the directly applied unmodified DPRC.

Farm research with phosphorus rock-enhanced manures are ongoing as part of the Zimbabwe-Canada agrogeology project. The DPRC-TSP-blended pellets added to the manure act not only as source of phosphorus but also lower the pH in the manures to a degree that nitrogen losses are reduced. Farmers then apply the manures in the traditional way. Agronomic testing of pelletized DPRC on maize and other crops continues on farms in the Buhera region, in the immediate vicinity of the Dorowa phosphate mine.

---

2.   The Shawa alkaline complex:

The Shawa alkaline ring complex, located in the Buhera District in east-central Zimbabwe (19° 31'S; 31° 43'E), is a 209 ±16 million year old, circular alkaline complex, approximately 5 km in diameter. Serpentinite and olivine-bearing dunite form the central part of the alkali ring structure. These rocks are in turn intruded by carbonatite.

The thick residual soils in the centre of complex are phosphate rich, derived from weathering of the carbonatite. Phosphate resources of the residual soils were calculated to be 20.3 million tonnes grading 10.8% P_2O_5, plus a further 2.7 million tonnes at 16% P_2O_5. Resources with low carbonate content, suitable for the existing flotation process at Dorowa, are estimated 16.3 million tonnes at 10.4% P_2O_5, 32.5% Fe_2O_3 and 0.8% CO_2 (Barber 1991). No detailed mineralogical characterization and agronomic testing of these phosphate resources have been carried out as yet.

3.   The Chishanya carbonatite:

The Chishanya carbonatite complex in eastern Zimbabwe, at 19° 45'S; 32° 18'E, is a lower Cretaceous, 127 million-year old carbonatite complex with an approximate width of 1.5 km and a length of 5 km. The carbonatite is largely made up of coarse crystalline Ca-carbonatite (soevite). The surrounding hills contain lenses of late-stage dark brown Fe-carbonatite, rich in magnetite and apatite. The northern part of this complex was estimated to contain 1,600 tonnes of ore per metre depth with an average grade of 8% P_2O_5. Selective mining of the 2-3 m wide apatite-rich dikes at Baradanga Hill has been considered (Barber 1991).

No detailed characterization of the phosphate-rich ore has been carried out. Also, no agronomic testing has been conducted with this phosphate resource.

4.   The Katete carbonatite:

The Katete carbonatite, 50 km northeast of Hwange (18° 09'S; 26° 53'E) in the northwest of the country, intruded into sediments of the Karoo Supergroup. Phosphates at Katete occur in the form of monazite, not apatite. The phosphorus content in the primary and secondary environment is low, ranging from 0.1 to 1.19% P_2O_5.

Guano

In Zimbabwe, bat guano is not classified as a mineral under the Mines and Minerals Act. The title of ownership of the bat guano is with the landowner. However, the marketing is controlled by the Fertilizer Act, which states that bat guano shall contain at least 2.5% N and at least 8% of N and P_2O_5 combined (Barber 1991). There are several caves with bat guano in Zimbabwe and the majority of the deposits lie in or adjacent to areas of subsistence farming or small-scale commercial farms. Barber (1991) considered them as 'potential sources of possibly inferior, although still highly beneficial, phosphate-rich fertilizers suitable for direct application.' Potential health problems related to the mining of bat guano are associated with the respiratory fungal disease of *Histoplasmosis* (inhalation of spores from *Histoplasma capsulatum*).

Most of the bat guano caves in Zimbabwe are found in the Lomagundi dolomitic marbles and limestones:

- near Bashungwi in the Rengwe Communal Land, Hurungwe District (Bashungwi guano caves),
- north of Chemvuri River on Murison Ranch (Chigwena guano caves),
- in the Zhombe Communal Land in Kwekwe District (Mabura-Vusa Emtoto caves),
- near the Chitomborgwizi small-scale farming area of the Makonde District (Mburungwe guano caves),
- on the northern bank of the Musuki River in the Hurungwe Communal Land, Hurungwe District (Mgweta guano caves),
- on the Munyati River in the Gokwe Communal Land in Gokwe District (Munyati River guano caves).

The only bat guano caves outside the Lomagundi dolomites are the caves in the Odzi area, in Bulawayan marble along the Odzi Greenstone Belt (Barber 1991).

Reserves of bat guano are difficult to establish due to the irregular nature of the cave floor and the presence of concealed blocks. The Mabura guano caves for example supposedly contain 2 million tonnes, but the figure is disputed by Barber (1991). The Mgweta Hill guano reserves are conservatively estimated at over 2,700 tonnes. As a general rule, the surface layers are richer in nitrogen and the underlying layers are richer in phosphate. For example, the Mabura guano deposit contains 9.26% N and 7.53% P_2O_5 near the surface and 0.49% N and 14.99% P_2O_5 at a depth of 3.7-5.0 m (Barber 1991).

In total, the resource base of these non-mineralic fertilizer materials is low and limited. Only small tonnages of cave guano can be excavated. Persons extracting cave guano should have their health monitored regularly to avoid contamination with *histoplasmosis*.

Liming material

Barber (1991) provides a detailed account of 248 limestone and dolomite occurrences in Zimbabwe. Numerous marble occurrences are reported from the Archean greenstone belts, especially from the Bulawayan Group (Barber 1991; Gwosdz 1996). They are clustered around Harare, Gwanda, and Gweru. Some of these large marble deposits are mined and processed for the cement industry (for instance Sternblick quarry for the cement industry in Harare, and Colleen Bawn, south of Gwanda for the cement industry in Bulawayo). Dolomite deposits in the Paleoproterozoic Lomagundi Group are extensive in the Kadoma and Chinhoyi areas. Some of the dolomitic marbles, for instance at Tengwe, 100 km northwest of Chinhoyi, are used for road construction and for agricultural purposes ('agricultural lime'), specifically in tobacco and maize growing areas. The volume of these dolomites is enormous, the 180 m thick dolomites at Tengwe cover an area of more than 130 km^2.

Smaller amounts of impure limestones are reported from Karoo sediments in the Hwange area and 80 km west of Kadoma.

Calcium and calcium-magnesium carbonates are part of the Chishanya and Shawa carbonatites. The carbonates in the Dorowa carbonatite are negligible.

Calcrete hardpans have been reported from the Hwange area and around Gwanda. Some of this calcrete has been used for road construction (near Hwange) and the production of quicklime.

Travertine deposits occur east of Shamwa, near Birchenough and Tengwe and some of these deposits have been used for the production of quicklime (Gwosdz 1996).

In Zimbabwe, carbonate rocks are used for many industrial and agricultural purposes, including the cement, metallurgical and construction industry. Production of agricultural liming materials, made up of ground, uncalcined limestone and dolomite, as well as slaked lime is high. According to the Central Statistical Office, the total consumption of agricultural liming agents was 55,000 tonnes in 1981, and 43,000 tonnes in 1983 (Barber 1991).

Preliminary figures of recent production indicate that the production of uncalcined limestone is in the range of a several tens of thousands of tonnes, and calcined lime is in the range of 10-20,000 tonnes. Some of the lime is produced as a co-product by the cement industry. In other operations it is recovered for the sole purpose of agricultural lime production, for example the Early Worm operation. Production data from Circle Cement indicate 1998 sales of approximately 17,800 tonnes uncalcined limestone. Their 1999 production was approximately 25,000 tonnes. Another company, G&W Minerals (which includes the Early Worm and Chegutu Stone operations) produced 39,000 tonnes 'ag-lime' in 1999. Approximately 40% of this production was calcined (G&W, pers. comm. March 2000).

Amending acid soils with limestone/dolomite or agricultural lime is common on many farms in Zimbabwe. Application rates vary between 1 tonne and several tonnes per hectare.

Sulphur/sulphides

There are considerable sulphide deposits in Zimbabwe, mainly associated with base metal and gold deposits. The only sulphide source mined for the sole purpose of providing sulphur for sulphuric acid production is the Iron Duke pyrite mine, 45 km north of Harare. This underground mine produces pyrite ore containing 35.5% S (Barber and Muchenje 1991). General annual production rates of pyrite over the last 40 years have ranged between 50,000 and 70,000 tonnes with 71,026 tonnes produced in 1994 and 70,760 tonnes in 1995. Approximately 85% of the pyrite is supplied to ZIMPHOS Ltd. at the phosphate fertilizer plant in Msasa/Harare to produce sulphuric acid for the acidulation of phosphate rock from Dorowa (Barber and Muchenje 1991). In 2001, the Zimbabwe fertilizer company ZIMPHOS will export 51,000 tonnes of sulphuric acid to the Zambian copper industry (Sunday Mail, April 4, 2001).

Investigations of the hydrochemistry of the tailings and tailings effluents at the Iron Duke mine showed extremely low pH levels (down to pH = 0.52) and toxic concentrations of Al, Cd, Zn, Cu, Cr, Ni, V and As in the drainage waters (Williams and Smith 2000).

Vermiculite

Two vermiculite mining companies (Samrec Vermiculite, and Dinidza Vermiculite Mining Co.) operate at the Shawa alkaline complex in Buhera District (see section on phosphates). The vermiculite ore is formed as a weathering product of the underlying phlogopite and biotite-rich mica pyroxenite. Production of vermiculite from both mines for the mainly international market was 14,841 tonnes in 1997 (according to the British Geological Survey World Mineral Statistics). Samrec Vermiculite (Zimbabwe) (Pvt) Ltd. will increase production to approximately 40,000 tonnes per year in 2001/2002 (Industrial Minerals, Sept., 2001).

The coarse vermiculite is exported overseas for use in the construction and horticultural industries. Approximately 30 tonnes of fines, smaller than 250 microns in size, are discarded every day as 'waste' although some of these fines are collected by Zimbabwean and South African customers for use as animal feed additives (Nyamuswa, pers. comm. April 2001).

Rock and mineral wastes

Phospho-gypsum, a waste product from the phosphate fertilizer industry in Msasa near Harare, is currently stockpiled. In 1999, the total volume of the phospho-gypsum tailings exceeded 920,000 tonnes (Mashingaidze, ZIMPHOS Ltd., pers. comm. May 2000). Part of the phospo-gypsum 'waste' is used by the local wallboard industry, part is exported to Malawi for use in the cement industry and for agricultural use, specifically for fertilizing groundnuts.

During investigations of the phosphate tailings at Dorowa, eight million tonnes of 'waste' vermiculite were 'discovered' by the Zimbabwe-Canada agrogeology project. Detailed studies on these waste resources and their potential use are ongoing.

Several million tonnes of rock waste of basaltic composition are currently discarded in the Mutoko area near Nyamazuwa, where 'black granite' is extracted from Mashonaland gabbro/dolerite deposits. In 1999, Zimbabwe produced 143,000 tonnes of black granite (Maponga and Munyanduri, in press). During extraction of the black granite blocks, some 80-90% of the rock goes to 'waste.' Early agricultural trials with heavy applications (5-40 tons per acre) of ground basaltic rock on Kalahari sand in Zimbabwe showed increased crop yield (Roschnik *et al.* 1968).

Until recently, Dorowa Minerals Ltd. discarded approximately 8 tonnes of phosphate fines daily from its drying operation. Some of this wasted 'dust' was used in compacted and phosphate-TSP blends by the Zimababwe-Canada agrogeology project.

Agromineral potential

The potential for development of the agromineral resources of Zimbabwe is good. The indigenous fertilizer industry of Zimbabwe already provides most of the raw materials for modern farming practices, but the potential to develop alternative low-cost phosphate fertilizers is also good. With an operational phosphate mine that already produces inexpensive PR concentrates, developing low-cost and agronomically effective phosphate blends for communal and small-scale farmers is a practical proposition. Experiences from the Zimbabwe-Canada agrogeology project indicate that Dorowa phosphate concentrate and phosphate fines currently disposed of as 'wastes,' can be pelletized or compacted with already existing superphosphates or with other nutrients and nutrient-containing 'waste products' to form low-cost alternative fertilizers and soil amendments. Finely ground dolerite/gabbro 'wastes' from the numerous 'black granite' operations should be tested on nearby soils to assess their potential to improve the soil fertility in local community gardens and fields, especially for perennial crops and trees.

Locally available agricultural lime needs to be tested by communal and small-scale farmers on acid soils. Phospho-gypsum from the phosphate plant near Harare should increasingly be used in groundnut production by all farmers. Alternative uses of phospo-gypsum in agriculture (Mays and Mortveldt 1986) and alternative further processing of this 'waste,' for instance, by the Merseburg process (Burnett *et al.* 1996) should be envisaged.

References:

Barber B 1989. Phosphate in Zimbabwe. - Zimbabwe Geol. Surv., Min. Res. Series 24, 31pp.

Barber B 1990. Calcium carbonate in Zimbabwe. - Zimbabwe Geol. Surv., Min. Res. Series 21, 183pp.

Barber B 1991. Phosphate resources of Zimbabwe. Fert. Res. 30:247-278.

Barber B and J Muchenje 1991. Sulfuric acid production in Zimbabwe. Fert. Res. 30:243-244.

Burnett WC, Schultz MK and DH Carter 1996. Radionuclide flow during the conversion of phosphogypsum to ammonium sulfate. J. Environm. Radioactivity 32:1-2, 33-51.

Dhliwayo D 1999. Evaluation of the agronomic potential and effectiveness of Zimbabwe (Dorowa) Phosphate Rock - based phosphate fertilizer materials. Ph. D. Thesis, University of Zimbabwe, 248pp.

Fernandes TRC 1978. Electron microscopy applied to the beneficiation of apatite ores of igneous origin. Trans. Geol. Soc. S. Afr. 81:249-253.

Fernandes TRC 1989a. Dorowa and Shawa: Late Paleozoic to Mesozoic carbonatite complexes in Zimbabwe. In: Notholt AJG, Sheldon RP and DF Davidson (eds.) Phosphate deposits of the world. Vol. 2. Phosphate rock resources, Cambridge University Press, Cambridge, UK:171-175.

Fernandes TRC 1989b. The phosphate industry in Zimbabwe. Industrial Minerals Nov. 1989:71-77.

Fernandes TRC 1995. Case study of the cost and benefit of applying rock phosphate as a capital investment in Zimbabwe: geologist's contribution. Harare, Zimbabwe (In: Johnsen *et al.* 1997).

Govere EM, Chien SH and RH Fox 1995. Effects of compacting phosphate rock with nitrogen, phosphorus, and potassium fertilisers. E. Afr. Agric. For. J. 60:123-130.

Gwosdz W 1996. Zimbabwe. In: Bosse H-R, Gwosdz W, Lorenz W, Markwich, Roth W and F Wolff (eds.) Limestone and dolomite resources of Africa. Geol. Jb., D, 102:513-532.

Holloway and Associates 1994. Zimbabwe. Mining Annual Review 1994, Mining Journal Ltd. London, 133-134.

Industrial Minerals 2001. Samrec vermiculite doubles capacity. Ind. Min. 408: p. 18.

International Labour Organization 1999. Social and labour issues in small-scale mines. TMSSM/1999, 99pp.

Johnsen FH, Fernandes R, Mukurumbira L, Sukume C and J Rusike 1997. Phosphate rock initiative - country case study for Zimbabwe. In: World Bank study: PR initiative case studies: Synthesis report. An assessment of phosphate rock as a capital investment: Evidence from Burkina Faso, Madagascar, and Zimbabwe, 1997.

Maponga O and N Munyanduri (in press). Sustainability of the dimension stone industry in Zimbabwe - challenges and opportunities. Nat. Res. Forum.

Mays DA and JJ Mortveldt 1986. Crop response to soil applications of phosphogypsum. J. Env. Qual. 15:78-81.

Mukasa SB, Wilson AH and RW Carlson 1998. A multielement geochronologic study of the Great Dyke, Zimbabwe: significance of the robust and reset ages. Earth Planet. Sci. Lett. 164:353-369.

Nyamapfene K 1991. Soils of Zimbabwe. Nehanda Publishers, Harare, Zimbabwe, 179pp.

Roschnik RK, Grant PM and WK Nduku 1968. The effect of incorporating crushed basalt rock into an infertile acid sand. Rhod. Zamb. Mal. J. Agric. Res.5(1967), 6pp.

van Straaten P. and TRC Fernandes 1995. Agrogeology in Eastern and Southern Africa: a survey with particular reference to developments in phosphate utilization in Zimbabwe. In: Blenkinsop TG and PL Tromp (eds.) Sub-Saharan Economic Geology. Geol. Soc. Zimbabwe Spec. Publ. 3, Balkema Publishers, Netherlands, 103-118.

Williams TM and B Smith 2000. Hydrochemical charcterization of acute acid mine drainage at iron Duke Mine, Mazowe, Zimbabwe. Env. Geol. 39:272-278.

Index

Notes:

Notes:

Notes:

Notes: